EPIDEMICS

EPIDEMICS

BY

Geoffrey Marks

AND

William K. Beatty

ILLUSTRATED WITH PHOTOGRAPHS

CHARLES SCRIBNER'S SONS ⋅ NEW YORK

Copyright © 1976 Geoffrey Marks and William K. Beatty

Library of Congress Cataloging in Publication Data

Marks, Geoffrey.
  Epidemics.

  Bibliography: p. 305
  Includes index.
  1. Epidemics—History. I. Beatty, William K.,
1926–   joint author. II. Title. [DNLM: 1. Disease
outbreaks—History. 2. Socioeconomic factors. WC11.1
M346e]
  RA649.M37   614.4'9   76-2584
  ISBN 0-684-14568-5

1 3 5 7 9 11 13 15 17 19 V|C 20 18 16 14 12 10 8 6 4 2

PRINTED IN THE UNITED STATES OF AMERICA

for Margaret, William, Carol,
WITH LOVE

Contents

Illustrations

Preface

EPIDEMIC diseases have provided some of the most mystifying, exciting, and devastating chapters in the history of mankind. *Epidemics* tells this story for the layman by carefully selected incidents which are often described by eyewitnesses to those epidemics. The treatment is generally chronological, but where required the organization is shifted to a geographical approach or to a historical account of a specific disease. Where pertinent, reference is made to the social, economic, political, and religious effects. Emphasis is on the growth and development of the epidemics; treatment is discussed infrequently.

Many definitions of an epidemic exist. We have chosen a fairly loose one: an epidemic is generally a communicable disease that affects many persons at one time. Two major exceptions to this are dealt with in the book: a noncommunicable disease that affects a large number of individuals in a locality because they are all exposed to the same cause (for example, the dancing mania), and a disease that is remarkable for some specially noticeable or frightening feature but which only affects a relatively small number of people (for example, poliomyelitis). We have not tried to be encyclopedic; several diseases, such as tuberculosis (although it has been a great killer), were omitted because they did not fit our plan and space.

Diseases are often hard to identify from written accounts; this is particularly true of the "plagues" and "pestilences" that occurred in ancient times. Even in modern times there is still much that we do not know about the causes, spread, and decline of many epidemic diseases. Powerful new methods of treatment have sometimes complicated the pictures by stimulating the development of resistant microorganisms. Unexplainable appearances of new or mutated strains can burst unexpectedly on an unsuspecting population. Man can even, unfortunately, create an epidemic where none existed before.

The three words that make up the "demic" family can be thought of, and kept separate, in the following terms. An endemic (from the Greek *en* meaning "on" and *demos*, "the people") disease is one that is a part of everyday life in a region. An endemic disease can be likened to the large living room rug that everyone accepts and doesn't bother to think about until its loose edge trips up occasional visitors. An epidemic (*epi* means "in") disease can be thought of as being an explosion that affects a large number of people or creates a strikingly noticeable impact. A pandemic (*pan* means "all") disease is essentially an enlarged epidemic that affects a greater number of people over a broader area. Pandemics may be thought of as chain-reaction explosions.

EPIDEMICS

From Ancient to Classical Times

EPIDEMICS and mankind have shared an uneasy partnership ever since the first time a group of cave dwellers was wiped out by an epidemic. However, the first recorded epidemic did not occur until 3180 B.C. Manetho, Egyptian priest-historian of the third century B.C., in listing the pharaohs of the First Dynasty stated, "Mempses, for eighteen years. In his reign many portents and a great pestilence occurred." [1]

British Egyptologist Arthur Weigall (1880–1934) has, however, cast doubt on the validity of Manetho's claim. Of the new pharaoh Weigall wrote that "his name was Shemsu, or more probably Shememsu, which Manetho renders as Semempse(s). As Hawk of Hieraconpolis he was called Merkhet, . . . Manetho states that in this reign a terrible pestilence afflicted Egypt, but there is no evidence to confirm this statement, and it may have had its origin in a very likely misreading of the Pharaoh's Hawk-name Merkhet as *Smerkhet*, which could mean 'causing sickness in the body.' The chronicles of the reign, as seen on the Cairo fragment of the Annals, are too much damaged to give us much information; . . ." [2]

Whether the "pestilence" reported by Manetho, or the "plague" in Canaan in 1921 B.C.,[3] or the "pestilence" in the Greek islands of Rhodes, Tenedos, Cos, Chios, Samos, and Lesbos following the Deucalion deluge sent by Zeus in the sixteenth century B.C.[4] (all of which are open to question) was the first epidemic, there seems to be no question about an epidemic that occurred early in the fifteenth century B.C.

Before proceeding further, it is to be noted that the words pestilence and plague have, historically, been used interchangeably to describe virulent and devastating epidemic diseases. In addition, the words are used without qualification to cover such disasters as an onslaught of locusts. As a result, original sources have often left scholars in every age doubtful of what precisely was involved in any given event. Even as differentiation between diseases became more exact, looseness of language persisted.

THE PLAGUES OF PHARAOH [5]

It is recorded that in the month of Adar,—answering, according to our computation of time, to the period between the middle of February and March, the end of the Jewish year,—during the reign of Pharaoh IV., king of Egypt, in the year of the world 2509 (anno 1495 before the Christian era), and in the 80th year of the life of Moses, the sacred historian and great captain of the hosts of Israel, many awful prodigies in the natural world commenced, especially in commotions of the elements, which were succeeded by a pestilence destructive both to men and beasts in the low lands of Egypt.[6]

If the suggestion that "the LORD spake unto Moses" is set aside, the "plagues" can be regarded as a series of natural catastrophes that might well occur during a particularly dry season in a climate such as that of Egypt. Since these disasters coincided with attempts by Moses and Aaron to free the Israelites from their captivity, it was convenient to introduce into the Jewish oral tradition the idea of the plagues as a series of levers to force Pharaoh to relent.

The first misfortune to hit the Egyptians was drought. How better to describe an almost dried riverbed than to say that "the waters that *were* in the river were turned to blood"? Of course, "the fish that *was* in the river died; and the river stank, and the Egyptians could not drink of the [polluted] water of the river; . . ."[7] Then came frogs, no doubt in search of water. After the frogs died,[8] there were dust storms that brought lice, and so on through a plague of flies, a murrain among cattle, boils erupting in man and beast—both by now in a less than healthy condition—hail that beat down whatever was growing, followed by crop failure, and then locusts that consumed anything that was left.

After this series of calamities, the door was wide open for an epidemic disease, and the physically weakened Egyptians were hit by the death of the firstborn. But why were the Israelites spared? It is possible, of course, that they had developed immunity to the particular disease through exposure to it in an epidemic at another time and place. Or their strict adherence to dietary laws might have brought them through the series of natural disasters in better health, and therefore with greater resistance to disease than the less careful Egyptians.

For Pharaoh, the epidemic was a last straw. Either because he believed that it had indeed been sent by the god of Israel or because his army was depleted by the epidemic to a point where it could no longer hold the captives, "he called for Moses and Aaron by night, and said, Rise up, *and* get you forth from among my people, both ye and the children of Israel; and go, serve the LORD, as ye have said. Also take your flocks and your herds, as ye have said, and be gone; and bless me also." [9] And this was not the only benefit that the epidemic conferred on the Israelites, for "the Egyptians were urgent upon the people, that they might send them out of the land in haste"; and "the children of Israel . . . borrowed of the Egyptians jewels of silver, and jewels of gold, and raiment: And the LORD gave the people favour in the sight of the Egyptians, so that they lent unto them such things as they required." [10]

IN THE WILDERNESS

Under the leadership of Moses the children of Israel wandered in the wilderness for forty years during which time they appear to have suffered three epidemics, two occurring about 1480 B.C. The first at a place named Taberah involved "fire" sent by the Lord (allegedly because the people were complaining) that "burnt among them, and consumed *them that were* in the uttermost parts of the camp." [11] Then at Kibroth-hattaavah an immense flight of quail fell by the camp. "And the people stood up all that day, and all *that* night, and all the next day, and they gathered the quails: . . . And while the flesh *was* yet between their teeth, ere it was chewed, the wrath of the LORD was kindled against the people, and the LORD smote the people with a very great plague." [12]

At Kadesh in 1471 B.C., Korah, Dathan, and Abiram rebelled against Moses and Aaron, accusing them of taking too much power upon themselves. By way of proving that he led by divine appointment, Moses called for the earth to open up and swallow them.

> And it came to pass, as he had made an end of speaking all these words, that the ground clave asunder that *was* under them:
> And the earth opened her mouth and swallowed them up, and their houses, and all the men that *appertained* to Korah, and all *their* goods.
> They, and all that *appertained* to them, went down alive into the pit, and the earth closed upon them: and they perished from among the congregation.

The congregation fled from the site rather than be swallowed up also but returned the next day and "murmured against Moses and against Aaron, saying, Ye killed the people of the LORD." By way of retaliation the Lord sent a plague which, before Aaron could pass between the living and the dead wielding a censer containing burning incense, took 14,700 lives. [13]

This account of what occurred at Kadesh involves two points of singular interest. Belief in earthquakes, or other natural phenomena, as precursors of bubonic plague persisted as late as the fourteenth century A.D. The burning of aromatic herbs or woods was long regarded as a protection against plague.

BUBONIC PLAGUE?

Plague is an acute or chronic disease of wild rodents, particularly the *Rattus rattus* of great antiquity. (The association of the rat with a disease bubonic in nature is indicated in the cuneiform writings of Babylonia.) The plague bacillus, *Pasteurella pestis*, is transmitted from rodent to rodent by the *Xenopsylla cheopis*, a flea that inhabits the hair of rodents and whose favorite food is the blood of rodents. The blood of man is at best a second choice, and epidemics of plague ordinarily involve a mass movement of wild rodents into the environs of man, with the fleas attacking man as their rat hosts drop dead.

True plague occurs in man in two forms. Bubonic plague, resulting from the bite of the vector, is characterized by swelling of the lymph nodes, causing buboes (from the Greek word boubōn, meaning groin or swelling in the groin). Pneumonic plague can spring from droplet infection or can arise as a complication of bubonic plague. The role of the rat and the flea in epidemic plague was not established until toward the close of the nineteenth century. Then why this discussion of plague when events that occurred two thousand years earlier are under review?

There is reason to believe that true plague may have existed from time immemorial, having originated in the central Asiatic plateau. If this is so, there can be little doubt that there were epidemics of bubonic plague prior to the Christian era. Therefore, in order to evaluate "plagues" occurring in biblical and classical times, it is necessary to recognize the significance of the presence or absence of rats and buboes.

In 1190 B.C., the final year of the Trojan War, the Greek army was hit by an epidemic. The cause, as recounted in the *Iliad* of Homer, was the refusal of King Agamemnon (in opposition to his fellow Greeks) to free the captured daughter of the Trojan priest Chryses, who had come begging for her release. Chryses understandably prayed to his particular god, Apollo, urging him to revenge this slight. Apollo obliged with a flight of arrows that produced a sickness lasting nine days.

Achilles called the Greeks together to seek an end to the epidemic, but all that resulted was an argument between Agamemnon and Achilles that sent the latter sulking to his tents, an incident that came close to costing the Greeks their victory at Troy. In fact, Achilles began his address to the assembly:

Why leave we not this fatal Trojan Shore,
And measure back the Seas we crost before?
The Plague destroying whom the Sword would spare,
'Tis time to save the few Remains of War. [14]

While there is no hint of the presence of buboes, two factors suggest bubonic plague.

Chryses, in evoking Apollo, employed the epithet *Smintheus*, a name supposedly deriving from a Cretan word for "rat" or "mouse." In the region around Troy there was an Apollonian cult based on the belief that Apollo Smintheus protected the fields against destructive incursions of rats.

In describing the epidemic, Homer employed the Greek word *loimos*, meaning a plague or pestilence, a word that does not appear elsewhere in either the *Iliad* or the *Odyssey*.

In 1141 B.C. the Philistines seized the ark of God and took it to the city of Ashdod where "the hand of the LORD was heavy" and he smote the citizens with "emerods." The ark was sent on to Gath where the Lord "smote the men of the city, both small and great, and they had emerods in their secret parts." There were like experiences when the ark was moved to Ekron. After the epidemic (attributable in the minds of the Philistines to illicit possession of the ark of God) had persisted for seven months, the Philistines had had enough and they decided to return the ark to Israel. As part of the accompanying "trespass offering" they included golden images of the "mice that mar the land." [15]

Some authorities prefer to believe that the emerods were hemorrhoids brought on by an epidemic of bacillary dysentery,[16] but William P. MacArthur (1884–1964), clinical lecturer in tropical medicine at the University of Oxford, was convinced that they were the buboes of plague:

> I cannot follow the reasoning that has led to the identification of the biblical epidemic as dysentery and piles. Old descriptive names for a disease were always based on some sign or symptom which is both common and striking. Names of this character given to bacillary dysentery in the past have been coined from such conspicuous

features as the bloody stools, the violent diarrhoea, and the griping pains, and are to be found in Anglo-Saxon, Latin, Celtic and other chronicles and texts. The disease does not cause piles, people do not die of piles, and an epidemic of piles in any circumstances is to my mind incredible; rectal prolapse is an occasional complication but it is not common enough to colour the general picture of the disease.

In early times the whole concept of plague was centered on the inflammatory swellings, especially those in the groin. The Greeks called the disease "pestilential groins", whence our word "bubo", and the Romans the *pestis inguinaria* [of the groin]. The Norman-French word "botch", meaning a swelling, was that in most general use in England, and was still current in 1665. "Swellings" dominate the biblical story; there was "great slaughter" and "deadly destruction", and through horror and despair "the cry of the city went up to heaven." Such a story is recorded of countless outbreaks of plague, but I have not yet found it told of epidemic dysentery alone. Further, the disease in the minds of the people was intimately bound up with "mice", and the swellings and the "mice" were linked together in votive offerings, and as parts of "one plague." *Akbar*, the [Hebrew] word translated by mouse, might equally well stand for rat.[17] Even if it has this latter specific meaning, it would still have appeared in the Greek Septuagint and the Latin Vulgate as "mouse", for in all Aryan languages, except the Germanic group, the same word was used for both mouse and rat: passages can be found in Greek and Latin where the context shows clearly that "mice" means "rats", as when Strabo, writing in the 1st Century B.C., says that from the multitudes of "mice" pestilential diseases often arise, and that in spite of the exertions of "mouse-catchers" who were paid graded bounties proportionate to the number of "mice" they destroyed, the Romans in Cantabria (Spain) barely came through the pestilence with their lives.[18]

MacArthur subsequently added: "I am informed that Professor HAAS, Professor of Comparative Anatomy, Hebrew University, Jerusalem, in a recent excavation of a neolithic site in the Abu Uba cave, Mt. Carmel, discovered the skeleton of a rat, indistinguishable from *Rattus rattus*. In other excavations of a palaeolithic site in the desert of Judea, he found another rat skeleton: the species is uncertain, but the genus is certainly *Rattus*. This puts the great antiquity of the rat in Palestine beyond question."[19]

To rid themselves of the ark of God, the Philistines, instructed by their priests, placed it in a new cart, together with a trespass offering of five golden emerods and five golden mice *"according to* the number of lords of the Philistines: for one plague *was* on you all and on your lords." The cart was hitched to two "milch kine" (whose calves were shut up at home) and "the kine took the straight way to" the border town nearest Ekron—Beth-shemesh.[20] Thus the "plague of the Philistines" resulted in the return of the ark to its rightful owners.

But the story does not end there. When the ark arrived, *"they of* Beth-shemesh *were* reaping their wheat harvest in the valley: and they lifted up their eyes, and saw the ark, and rejoiced to see it. . . . and they claved the wood of the cart, and offered the kine as a burnt offering unto the LORD." [21]

> And [the Lord] smote the men of Beth-shemesh, because they had looked into the ark of the LORD, even he smote of the people fifty thousand and threescore and ten men: and the people lamented, because the LORD had smitten *many* of the people with a great slaughter.[22]

Authorities have generally assumed that the epidemic that smote the Beth-shemeshians was a carry-over of the Philistine epidemic, that is, bubonic plague, but S. H. Blondheim of the Hadassah Medical School at the Hebrew University in Jerusalem held the view that this was pneumonic plague. He has pointed out that, while the biblical text gives details of the presence of buboes and rodents in recounting an occurrence in a hostile foreign land, there is no reference to either in relationship to the Beth-shemesh epidemic. "This omission . . . is presumptive evidence that buboes and the presence of rodents were not characteristic of the disease among the Israelites." Secondly: "From the curt description of the Israelite epidemic it may be inferred that it was of short duration and that the victims died rapidly without noteworthy symptoms." (In this connection he noted: "While the mortality of bubonic plague varies from 60–90 per cent [untreated], pneumonic plague is almost invariably fatal, so that recovery casts doubt on the diagnosis. Although bubonic plague lasts 4–7 days, the duration of pneumonic plague is only 1–3 days, death frequently occurring as early as 16 hours after the onset of the symptoms.") [23]

While discussion on this point is academic, some significance attaches to it, for, if Blondheim's interpretation is valid, chapter six of the first book of Samuel contains what is almost certainly the first record of an epidemic of pneumonic plague.

DAVID CHOOSES PESTILENCE

In 1017 B.C. in Israel a "pestilence" lasting three days is said to have killed 70,000 people. There is an account of this event in both the second book of Samuel and the first book of Chronicles. In each instance the taking of a census is involved, but with one striking difference. In Samuel, "the anger of the LORD was kindled against Israel, and he moved David against them to say, Go, number Israel and Judah"; [24] in Chronicles: "And Satan stood up against Israel, and provoked David to number Israel." [25] The second incident seems the more likely because, if the Lord moved the king to initiate the census, why would David tell the Lord that he had sinned greatly in taking it? [26] In any event, by way of punishment God offered David a choice among three years [27] of famine, three months of flight before the swords of his enemies, or three days of pestilence. David chose the last, which may well have been spread by the census takers.

THE ARMY OF SENNACHERIB

The Assyrian came down like a wolf on the fold,
And his cohorts were gleaming in purple and gold;
And the sheen of their spears was like stars on the sea,
When the blue wave rolls nightly on deep Galilee. [28]

It was in 710 B.C. that the army of Sennacherib, king of Assyria, laid siege to the cities of Judah, including Jerusalem. Called upon by Judah's king, Hezekiah, the Lord sent his angels who "smote in the camp of the Assyrians a hundred and fourscore and five thousand: and when they arose early in the morning, behold, they *were* all dead corpses." [29]

There is nothing in the biblical accounts to suggest the nature of the epidemic that so depleted Sennacherib's army that "he returned with shame of face to his own land," [30] but a description of the destruction of the army (at roughly the same time but in a *different* place) clearly suggests bubonic plague. Its author was the fifth century B.C. Greek historian Herodotus

> The next king, I was told, was a priest of Hephaestus, called Sethos.[31] This monarch despised and neglected the warrior class of the Egyptians, as though he did not need their services. Among other indignities which he offered them, he took from them the lands which they had possessed under all the previous kings, consisting of twelve acres of choice land for each warrior. Afterwards, therefore, when Sanacharib, king of the Arabians and Assyrians, marched his vast army into Egypt, the warriors one and all refused to come to his aid. On this the monarch, greatly distressed, entered into the inner sanctuary, and before the image of the god, bewailed the fate which impended over him. As he wept he fell asleep, and dreamt that the god came and stood at his side, bidding him be of good cheer, and go boldly forth and meet the Arabian host, which would do him no hurt, as he himself would send those who should help him. Sethos, then, relying on the dream, collected such of the Egyptians as were willing to follow him, who were none of them warriors, but traders, artisans, and market-people; and with these marched to Pelusium, which commands the entrance into Egypt, and there pitched his camp. As the two armies lay here opposite one another, there came in the night a multitude of field-mice, which devoured all the quivers and bow-strings of the enemy, and ate the thongs by which they managed their shields. Next morning they commenced their flight, and great multitudes fell, as they had no arms with which to defend themselves. There stands to this day in the temple of Hephaestus, a stone statue of Sethos, with a mouse in his hand, and an inscription to this effect, "Look on me, and learn to reverence the gods." [32]

The suggestion that, overnight, field mice could devour the quivers, bowstrings, and thongs of a vast army smacks of fable, but the presence of mice (rats) raised the strong possibility of an epidemic of plague as a destructive source. Of possibly even greater significance is the fact that the outbreak occurred at Pelusium. According to the Byzantine historian Procopius of Caesarea (sixth century A.D.), an eyewitness, the Plague of Justinian, the first of the three most devastating epidemics ever to hit mankind, originated in Pelusium, evidently a hotbed of bubonic plague.

ROME

In the year 790 B.C. "plague" that broke out in Rome was

so fatal, that the people died of it without any previous sickness; . . . It rained blood, too, in the city; so that their unavoidable sufferings were increased with the terrors of superstition: and when the destruction spread itself to Laurentum, then all agreed, it was for neglecting to do justice on the murderers of the ambassadors and of Tatius [Sabine leader who subsequently shared authority over Rome with Romulus], that the divine vengeance pursued both cities. Indeed, when those murderers were given up and punished by both parties, their calamities visibly abated; and Romulus purified the city with lustrations, which, they tell us, are yet celebrated at the Ferentine gate. Before the pestilence ceased, the people of Cameria [a town which Romulus had subdued earlier] attacked the Romans, and over-ran the country, thinking them incapable of resistance by reason of the sickness. But Romulus soon met them in the field, gave them battle, in which he killed six thousand of them, took their city, and transplanted half its remaining inhabitants to Rome; . . .[33]

Then in 710 B.C.,

In the eighth year of Numa's reign a pestilence prevailed in Italy; Rome also felt its ravages. While the people were greatly dejected, we are told that a brazen buckler [shield] fell from heaven into the hands of Numa. Of this he gave a very wonderful account, received from Egeria and the muses: That the buckler was sent down for the preservation of the city, and should be kept with great care: That eleven others should be made as like it as possible in size and fashion, in order, if any person were disposed to steal it, he might not be able to distinguish that which fell from heaven from the rest. He farther declared, that the place, and the meadows about it, where he frequently conversed with the muses, should be consecrated to those divinities; and that the spring which watered the ground should be sacred to the use of the vestal virgins, daily to sprinkle and purify their temple. The immediate cessation of the pestilence is said to have confirmed the truth of this account.[34]

About 640 B.C.,

Rome was afflicted with a pestilence. This caused a reluctance to bear arms, yet no respite from service was allowed by the warlike king [Tullus] (who believed, besides, that the young men were healthier in the field than at home) until he himself contracted a lingering illness. Then that haughty spirit was so broken, with the breaking of his health, that he who had hitherto thought nothing less worthy of a king than to devote his mind to sacred rites, suddenly became a prey to all sorts of superstitions great and small, and filled even the minds of the people with religious scruples. Men were now agreed in wishing to recall the conditions that had obtained under King Numa, believing that the only remedy left for their ailing bodies was to procure peace and forgiveness from the gods. The king himself, so tradition tells, in turning over the commentaries of Numa discovered there certain occult sacrifices performed in honour of Jupiter Elicius, and devoted himself in secret to those rites; but the ceremony was improperly undertaken or performed, and not only was no divine manifestation vouchsafed him, but in consequence of the wrath of Jupiter, who was provoked by his faulty observance, he was struck by a thunderbolt and consumed in the flames of his house.[35]

In 472 B.C. an epidemic disorder "rolled over the city like a torrent or a lava-stream," attacking everyone, regardless of age or sex. It "would have swept all before it had it made a longer stay." This epidemic spread throughout Italy. There was a like outbreak nine years later.[36]

The Greek scholar and historian Dionysius of Halicarnassus (d. c.7 B.C.) offered a detailed account of a pestilence, "more severe than any of those recorded from past time," that hit Rome in 452 B.C.:

> Almost all the slaves were carried off by it and about one half of the citizens, as neither the physicians were able any longer to alleviate their sufferings nor did their servants and friends supply them with the necessaries. For those who were willing to relieve the calamities of others, by touching the bodies of the diseased and continuing with them, contracted the same diseases, with the result that many entire households perished for want of people to attend the sick. Not the least of the evils the city suffered, and the reason why the pestilence did not quickly abate, was the way in which they cast out the dead bodies. For though at first, both from a sense of shame and because of the plenty they had of everything necessary for burials, they burned the bodies and committed them to the earth, at the last, either through a disregard of decency or from a lack of the necessary equipment, they threw many of the dead into the sewers under the streets and cast far more of them into the river; and from these they received the most harm. For when the bodies were cast up by the waves upon the banks and beaches, a grievous and terrible stench, carried by the wind, smote those who were still in health and produced a quick change in their bodies; and the water brought from the river was no longer fit to drink, partly because of its vile odour and partly by causing indigestion. These calamities occurred not only in the city, but in the country as well; in particular, the husbandmen were infected with the contagion, since they were constantly with their sheep and the other animals. As long as most people had any hopes that Heaven would assist them, they all had recourse to sacrifices and expiations; and many innovations were then made by the Romans and unseemly practices not customary with them were introduced into the worship of the gods. But when they found that the gods showed no regard or compassion for them, they abandoned even the observance of religious rites. During this calamity Sextus Quintilius, one of the consuls, died; also Spurius Furius, who had been appointed to succeed him, and likewise four of the tribunes and many worthy senators. While the city was af-

flicted by the pestilence, the Aequians undertook to lead out an
army against the Romans; and they sent envoys to all the other nations that were hostile to the Romans, urging them to make war. But
they did not have time to lead their forces out of their cities; for
while they were still making their preparations, the same pestilence
fell upon their cities. It spread not only over the country of the
Aequians, but also over those of the Volscians and the Sabines, and
grievously afflicted the inhabitants. In consequence, the land was
left uncultivated and famine was added to the plague. Under these
consuls, then, by reason of the pestilence nothing was done by the
Romans, either in war or at home, worthy of being recorded in history.[37]

Livy (59 B.C.–A.D. 17), the Roman historian, in a brief reference
to this epidemic, stressed the fact that "many distinguished families
were in mourning. The flamen of Quirinus, Servius Cornelius,
died, and the augur Gaius Horatius Pulvillus, in whose place the
augurs elected Gaius Veturius, the more eagerly because of his
condemnation of the plebs." He went on to note, as did Dionysius,
that death "took the consul Quinctilius, and four tribunes of the
plebs." Livy's final comment that, during the "gloomy year . . .
Rome's enemies did not molest her," seems to ignore the fact that
the Aequians' determination to act was thwarted by the spreading
of the epidemic.[38]

These several outbreaks in the fifth century B.C. inevitably reduced the population of a greater part of Italy. "But," commented
the German classical historian, Barthold G. Niebuhr (1776–1831),

depopulation is everywhere soon repaired by an increase of births
and a diminution of deaths, except where the vital energy of a people is checkt by the influence of deeprooted general distress. Thus at
Rome it was not so lasting as the effects which the mortality had on
the proportion between the two orders [nobles and common people].
It affected the close body far more sensibly than that which was
open to fresh supplies; and thus it necessarily weakened the [great]
houses in comparison with the commonalty. Many of them must
have become utterly extinct at this time, . . . Thus the patricians
more and more lost the character of a body of citizens, and shrank
up into an oligarchy, whose pretensions to the privileges of their

forefathers were as groundless as their strength was inadequate to maintain them. The clientry of the extinct houses were releast from their independence: and only a few individuals, who entered into new connexions, would be preserved to the order. Most of those who had thus become free inhabitants, would seek admission into the commonalty.

Another inevitable consequence of the calamity was a degeneracy of manners, . . . Pestilences, like inhuman military devastations, corrupt those whom they ruin. . . . Very calamitous times however serve to awaken a sense of the defects of existing institutions: many cheer themselves with the belief that the correction of these would restore their lost prosperity: and this motive unquestionably seconded the proposals made at Rome, after the pestilence and the military reverses, for the reformation of the laws.[39]

According to Herodotus, another epidemic of note occurred during the period under review.

After the defeat of the Persian navy at the battle of Salamis in 480 B.C., King Xerxes and his army retreated northward into Thessaly, where his general, Mardonius, thought the troops should winter before renewing attacks on the Greeks. The king himself decided to push on toward the Hellespont and home, leaving Mardonius in Thessaly with a picked army of three hundred thousand men. Xerxes

> marched . . . at his best speed, toward the Hellespont. In forty-five days he reached the place of passage, where he arrived with scarce a fraction, so to speak, of his former army. All along their line of march, in every country where they chanced to be, his soldiers seized and devoured whatever corn they could find belonging to the inhabitants; while, if no corn was to be found, they gathered the grass that grew in the fields, and stripped the trees, whether cultivated or wild, alike of their bark and of their leaves. They left nothing anywhere, so hard were they pressed by hunger. Plague too and dysentery attacked the troops while still upon their march, and greatly thinned their ranks. Many died; others fell sick and were left behind in the different cities that lay upon the route, the inhabitants being strictly charged by Xerxes to tend and feed them. Of these some remained in Thessaly, others in Macedon, and others again in Siris of Paeonia. . . .

The Persians, having journeyed through Thrace and reached the passage, entered their ships hastily and crossed the Hellespont to Abydos. The bridges were not found stretched across the strait; since a storm had broken and dispersed them. At Abydos the troops halted, and obtaining more abundant provision than they had yet got upon their march, they fed without stint; from which cause, added to the change in their water, great numbers of those who had hitherto escaped perished. The remainder, together with Xerxes himself, came safe to Sardis.[40]

The Plague of Thucydides
and the Epidemics of Hippocrates

THE year 431 B.C. found Athens mistress of land and sea and the envy of her Peloponnesian neighbors who banded together to dethrone her. The Peloponnesian War, which resulted, was to continue for twenty-one years.

> Thucydides, an Athenian, wrote the history of the war. . . . He began to write when they first took up arms, believing that it would be great and memorable above any previous war. For he argued that both states were then at full height of their military power, and he saw the rest of the Hellenes either siding or intending to side with one or other of them. No movement ever stirred Hellas more deeply than this; it was shared by many of the Barbarians, and might be said even to affect the world at large.[1]

Thus Thucydides (460?–?400 B.C.) began his contemporary account of a war which did dwarf all conflicts that had preceded it.

> The greatest achievement of former times was the Persian War; yet even this was speedily decided in two battles by sea and two by land. But the Peloponnesian War was a protracted struggle, and attended by calamities such as Hellas had never known in a like period of time. Never were so many cities captured and depopulated— some by barbarians, others by Hellenes themselves fighting against one another; several of them after their capture were repeopled by

strangers. Never was exile and slaughter more frequent, whether in the war or brought about by civil strife. And rumours, of which the like had often been current before, but rarely verified by fact, now appeared to be well grounded. There are earthquakes unparalleled in their extent and fury, and eclipses of the sun more numerous than are recorded to have happened in any former age; there were also in some places great droughts causing famines, and lastly the plague did immense harm and destroyed numbers of the people.[2]

The "plague" Thucydides referred to (which, incidentally, was to bear his name) broke out early in the second year of the war, not long after the Peloponnesian army, under the command of the Lacedaemonian king Archidamus, had invaded and established itself in Attica where it ravaged the country. (It is to be recalled that in classical times campaigns were limited to the summer months.) While a similar disorder was said to have occurred previously in a number of places, according to Thucydides "there is no record of such a pestilence occurring elsewhere, or of so great destruction of human life."

Precisely what disease was involved has remained a mystery, notwithstanding the many theories advanced. More than likely it was a mixed epidemic comprising several different diseases brought together by the forced wartime migration of peoples who did not ordinarily mingle. Attempts by the Athenian physicians to apply remedies were fruitless because they did not know the nature of the disease. In fact, the doctors themselves "were among the first victims, because they oftenest came into contact with it."

> The disease is said to have begun south of Egypt in Aethiopia; thence it descended into Egypt and Libya, and after spreading over the greater part of the Persian empire, suddenly fell upon Athens. It first attacked the inhabitants of the Piraeus, and it was supposed that the Peloponnesians had poisoned the cisterns, no conduits having as yet been made there. It afterwards reached the upper city, and then the mortality became far greater.

Not only did Thucydides witness the sufferings of others, but he also was himself one of the victims. He nevertheless refused to speculate as to the causes of the epidemic, believing that "every man, whether physician or not, will give his own opinion." However, so that the disorder might be recognized should it ever reappear, he undertook to describe its symptoms fully and its actual course:

The season was admitted to have been remarkably free from ordinary sickness; and if anybody was already ill of any other disease, it was absorbed in this. Many who were in perfect health, all in a moment, and without apparent reason, were seized with violent heats in the head and with redness and inflammation of the eyes. Internally the throat and the tongue were quickly suffused with blood, and the breath became unnatural and fetid. There followed sneezing and a hoarseness; in a short time the disorder, accompanied by a violent cough, reached the chest; then fastening lower down, it would move the stomach and bring on all the vomits of bile to which physicians have ever given names; and they were very distressing. An ineffectual retching producing violent convulsions attacked most of the sufferers; some as soon as the previous symptoms had abated, others not until long afterwards. The body externally was not so very hot to the touch, nor yet pale; it was of a livid colour inclining to red, and breaking out in pustules and ulcers. But the internal fever was intense; the sufferers could not bear to have on them even the finest linen garment; they insisted on being naked, and there was nothing which they longed for more eagerly than to throw themselves into cold water. And many of those who had no one to look after them actually plunged into the cisterns, for they were tormented by unceasing thirst, which was not in the least assuaged whether they drank little or much. They could not sleep; a restlessness which was intolerable never left them. While the disease was at its height the body, instead of wasting away, held out amid these sufferings in a marvellous manner, and either they died on the seventh or ninth day, not of weakness, for their strength was not exhausted, but of internal fever, which was the end of most; or, if they survived, then the disease descended into the bowels and there produced violent ulceration; severe diarrhoea at the same time set in, and at a later stage caused exhaustion, which finally with few exceptions carried them off. For the disorder which had originally settled in the head passed gradually through the whole body, and, if a person got over the worst, would often seize the extremities and leave its mark, attacking the genitals and the fingers and the toes; and some escaped with the loss of these, some with the loss of their eyes. Some again had no sooner recovered than they were seized with a forgetfulness of all things and knew neither themselves nor their friends.

The malady took a form not to be described, and the fury with which it fastened upon each sufferer was too much for human nature to endure. There was one circumstance in particular which distinguished it from ordinary diseases. The birds and animals which feed on human flesh, although so many bodies were lying unburied, either never came near them, or died if they touched them. This was proved by a remarkable disappearance of birds of prey, who were not to be seen either about the bodies or anywhere else; while in the case of the dogs the fact was even more obvious, because they live with man.

Such was the general nature of the disease: I omit many strange peculiarities which characterised individual cases. None of the ordinary sicknesses attacked anyone while it lasted, or, if they did, they ended in the plague. Some of the sufferers died from want of care, others equally who were receiving the greatest attention. No single remedy could be deemed a specific; for that which did good to one did harm to another. No constitution was of itself strong enough to resist or weak enough to escape the attacks; the disease carried off all alike and defied every mode of treatment. Most appalling was the despondency which seized upon any one who felt himself sickening; for he instantly abandoned his mind to despair and, instead of holding out, absolutely threw away his chance of life. Appalling too was the rapidity with which men caught the infection; dying like sheep if they attended on one another; and this was the principal cause of mortality. When they were afraid to visit one another, the sufferers died in their solitude, so that many houses were empty because there had been no one left to take care of the sick; or if they ventured they perished, especially those who aspired to heroism. For they went to see their friends without thought of themselves and were ashamed to leave them, even at a time when the very relations of the dying were at last growing weary and ceased to make lamentations, overwhelmed by the vastness of the calamity. But whatever instances there may have been of such devotion, more often the sick and dying were tended by the pitying care of those who had recovered, because they knew the course of the disease and were them-

selves free from apprehension. For no one was ever attacked a second time, or not with a fatal result. All men congratulated them,
and they themselves, in the excess of their joy at the moment, had
an innocent fancy that they could not die of any other sickness.

A complicating factor was the migration of the inhabitants of
Athenian territories that had been ravaged by war, especially the
country folk, into the city. In a sense

the newly arrived suffered most. For, having no houses of their
own, but inhabiting in the height of summer stifling huts, the mortality among them was dreadful, and they perished in wild disorder.
The dead lay as they had died, one upon another, while others
hardly alive wallowed in the streets and crawled about every fountain craving for water. The temples in which they lodged were full
of corpses of those who died in them; for the violence of the calamity
was such that men, not knowing where to turn, grew reckless of all
law, human and divine. The customs which had hitherto been observed at funerals were universally violated, and they buried their
dead each one as best he could. Many, having no proper appliances,
because the deaths in their household had been so frequent, made no
scruple of using the burial-place of others. When one man had raised
a funeral pile, others would come, and throwing on their dead first,
set fire to it; or when some other corpse was already burning, before
they could be stopped, would throw their own dead bodies upon it
and depart.

To the Plague of Thucydides must be attributed two adverse
side effects—a breakdown in religious belief and practice and an
abandonment of moral principles that bordered on lawlessness.
When the physicians failed to produce a counteractant to the
malady, many Athenians turned to "supplications in temples, en-
quiries of oracles, and the like," but when these proved "utterly
useless . . . men were overpowered by the calamity and gave them
all up."
As for moral disintegration,

Men who had hitherto concealed their indulgence in pleasure now
grew bolder. For, seeing the sudden change, how the rich died in a

moment, and those who had nothing immediately inherited their property, they reflected that life and riches were alike transitory, and they resolved to enjoy themselves while they could, and to think only of pleasure. Who would be willing to sacrifice himself to the law of honour when he knew not whether he would ever live to be held in honour? The pleasure of the moment and any sort of thing which conduced to it took the place both of honour and expediency. No fear of God nor law of man deterred a criminal. Those who saw all perishing alike, thought that the worship or neglect of the gods made no difference. For offenses against human law no punishment was to be feared; no one would live long enough to be called to account. Already a far heavier sentence had been passed and was hanging over a man's head; before that fell, why should he not take a little pleasure? [3]

The Plague of Thucydides raged in Athens for two years. Then, after abating for a time, it flared up again at the end of 427 B.C., lasting on this occasion for a year. In the opinion of Thucydides, "To the power of Athens certainly nothing was more ruinous." [4]

TYPHUS VERSUS MEASLES

It has already been mentioned that the precise nature of the disease(s) involved in the Plague of Thucydides has remained a mystery. Attempts to solve that mystery have led to some warm debates between William P. MacArthur and Denys Lionel Page, Regius Professor of Greek at the University of Cambridge.

Page, in his 1953 article, "Thucydides' Description of the Great Plague at Athens," devoted the first dozen pages to establishing Thucydides as "a keen observer, a clear thinker, and an accurate writer" whose "conception of historical method and principles is closely related to the doctrine of [the contemporary Hippocratic] school," with which he was more than probably familiar. After individual analysis of the Greek medical terms employed by Thucydides in his description of the disorder, Page could conclude (a) that seventy-seven out of ninety-four nouns, adjectives, and verbs employed "recur as standard terms, apparently for the most part with the same meanings, in medical writings of the fifth and fourth centuries B.C."; (b) that all but a half-dozen of the terms were in use among doctors and that several of the exceptions "are closely related to the standard terminology"; (c) that some of Thucydides' terms are seldom (a few never) to be found outside medical and scientific treatises and "others, though found elsewhere, are especially characteristic of medical writers"; (d) that none of Thucydides' technical terms (and only two of his general terms) were in conflict with medical usage.[5]

Having established the essential accuracy of Thucydides' reporting, Page proceeded to make a point that, he said, had constantly been overlooked—*"that obviously significant phenomena, which could have been observed, but which are not mentioned by Thucydides, did not occur"* [italics in original]. The most "conspicuous absentees" were physical prostration at an early stage, dysentery, and mental disorder. On the positive side, there was no period of incubation—"the patient passed from health to sickness in a moment," a period of seven or nine days during which the disorder ran its (usually) fatal course, a period thereafter in which survivors suffered lesions of the intestines, diarrhea, and weakness, and then, for those who still survived, gangrene of the extremities, loss of sight, and, in some cases, loss of memory. Thucydides went further in establishing that the Athenians were facing a "new" infectious disease, unrecognized by their physicians, that "did not attack the same person twice, at least not with fatal effect," adding, for whatever diagnostic worth it might offer, "that carrion-birds and beasts abstained from infected corpses."[6]

At this point Page turned for guidance to an article by J. F. D. Shrewsbury of the University of Birmingham,[7] and presented this writer's arguments against smallpox, typhus fever, bubonic plague, and typhoid fever, all of which had been favored by "modern medical writers." Shrewsbury's personal conclusion was that the epidemic disease was measles. In support of this contention, Page proceeded to list the Thucydidean symptoms that fitted the "descriptions of measles in respectable modern works of reference":

Feverishness, inflammation and redness of the eyes, redness of tongue and throat; sneezing, hoarseness, coughing, vomiting, convulsions (rare except in children); the skin-eruption; thirst, restlessness, sleeplessness; diarrhoea. As complications: ulceration and other affections of the intestines; loss of eyesight; gangrene, especially *noma* of the tissues about the mouth, but also of other parts of the body, including the pudenda [external genitalia]. All state that the disease is highly infectious. None mentions physical prostration at an early stage, and none associates delirium or stools of blood with it. The following Thucydidean symptoms are mentioned by at least one of the five [authorities]: dark purple colour of the skin during the exanthematous [eruption] period; sensation of great internal heat; general distress and mental depression; unproductive retching.

Finally, Page "borrows" from Shrewsbury "a most interesting part of his exposition." The desire to immerse the body in cold water spoken of by Thucydides was paralleled in 1875 when measles was introduced into the Fiji Islands and the natives employed every conceivable means of exposing their bodies to cold water.[8]

Within a matter of weeks, MacArthur was challenging the conclusion that the Plague of Thucydides was measles of a virulent type. "I believe that only typhus could account for all that Thucydides here relates, and I can find nothing that has not been experienced in outbreaks of typhus since his day."

He picked up Shrewsbury's assertion (as quoted by Page) that "before typhus fever can even be considered . . . we need some historical evidence, or at least a strong presumption, that the Athenians were familiar with the black rat," indicating that this was immaterial because "*epidemic typhus* is transmitted by infected faeces of the louse of man and does not originate from the black rat; nor are rats concerned in its transmission. It must not be confused with the distinct disease known as *murine typhus* which originates from rodents, but is not epidemic."

He took exception to Page's observation that Thucydides said nothing of the mental derangement that would be expected in typhus, pointing out that " 'violent convulsions' (whatever their cause) cannot occur if the brain is normal; and their occurrence is incompatible with mental lucidity. Nor would amnesia develop in undamaged brains."

As for the Fijians who immersed themselves in cold water, Mac-

Arthur cited several authorities to the effect that these islanders took to the water when they felt "feverish from any cause." By way of example, during the influenza epidemic of 1918, "they went into the sea in crowds." Furthermore, MacArthur regarded intense thirst as typical of typhus, pointing out that "in the Black Assize of Oxford [1577] . . . some of the typhus victims 'would leap headlong into deep waters.' " [9]

Page restricted his rebuttal to disputing MacArthur's deduction of "mental derangement," stating that "wild delirium and hallucinations, followed by coma or restless coma-vigil," characteristic of typhus, were not mentioned by Thucydides, and for Thucydides to fail to mention anything he had observed was atypical. [10]

There the matter might have rested had not P. Salway and W. Dell entered the lists. "Professor Page rightly rejects typhus, but I think, for the wrong reason," Salway wrote of the Page-MacArthur exchange in an addendum to an article he and Miss Dell had already prepared. MacArthur, he felt, made out so strong a case for mental disturbance that the symptoms "taken together can hardly represent anything else." On the other hand, the Mac-Arthur claim that, because "typhus has broken out with unfailing regularity in time of war, especially in stationary armies and crowded cities," Athens was unlikely to have escaped, was untenable. "If in fact typhus broke out 'with unfailing regularity' in Greek wars it is very odd that Thucydides treats the plague as something very extraordinary . . . But while [he] mentions that the Plague *was said* to have occurred in many places around Lesbos and elsewhere and that the present outbreak *was said* to have originated in the Persian Empire (he does not commit himself to accepting these statements), he specifically states that no epidemic on such a scale with such mortality was remembered anywhere."

The Salway-Dell conclusion was that the Plague of Thucydides was neither measles, typhus, smallpox, bubonic plague, typhoid, nor any other disease that might be suggested, but ergotism resulting from the ingestion of flour (a popular staple in Athenian diet) derived from the careless milling of neglected crops to which the parasitical fungus *Claviceps purpurea* had attached itself. [11]

A basic objection to ergotism as the culprit was that *Claviceps purpurea* ordinarily grows on rye and rye was not used for bread in the Mediterranean region throughout antiquity, but conceding that the fungus may attack other grains, Page, who saw the Salway-Dell article in typescript, raised two other objections: "(1) we should have to suppose that Thuc. was mistaken in thinking that the Plague was *infectious:* a very bad blunder, if it was one; (2) delirium and similar mental disturbances are said to be characteristic of ergotism." [12] (The second of these objections Salway was firmly to dispute in the addendum to the article.)

Perhaps it would be the better part of wisdom to rest on Professor Page's admission "that a number of medical authorities have declared identification to be impossible." [13]

THE *EPIDEMICS* OF HIPPOCRATES

The work that bears this name has been described by the English physician, translator, and editor, W. H. S. Jones (1876–1963), as "the most remarkable product of Greek Science." [14]

Two books, the first and the third of seven, are usually attributed to Hippocrates (c. 470–c. 400 B.C.) himself. As to the balance, Francis Clifton (d. 1736), physician to the Prince of Wales and an active classicist, has offered the suggestion that, after Hippocrates' death, "his sons, or those who succeeded him," finding loose papers, some of which had served as bases for his major writings and a great many of which were "curious observations (some of 'em taken by himself, others by those of his pupils who were dispers'd for that purpose all over *Greece*, and many parts of *Thrace* . . .) [being] unwilling to burn or destroy any, . . . jumbled 'em together with very little method or design," thereby producing, *inter alia*, the other five books. [15]

The title *Epidemics* is to some degree misleading since the Greek word at the time of Hippocrates offered several connotations only one of which was the modern "epidemic." Hippocrates may well have had in mind such meanings as common and prevalent, which more exactly describe much of his text. The discussion here will concentrate on Hippocrates' accounts of prevalent disease and will omit the unrelated case histories that form much of the remainder of the two books.

The epidemics described in the first book took place on the northern Aegean island of Thasus (Thasos) in three successive years. In each instance Hippocrates related the diseases to weather conditions, opening each account with a careful review of them. Here, by way of example, is the initial paragraph of the first book:

> In *Thasus* in the *Autumn*, about the *Æquinox*, and under the *Pleiades*, the *Rains* were great, continual, and soft, as when the Wind is southerly. The *Winter* mild, with southerly Winds, and very little northerly. With these were *greater droughts than ordinary*, so that the whole *Winter* was, in effect, like the *Spring*. The *Spring* was also affected with southerly Winds, but yet was cold, and a little wet. The *Summer* was for the most part cloudy and dry. The [regular northerly] *Etesiæ* [winds] blew but little, faintly, and irregularly.

Hippocrates then introduced the diseases of the spring in this manner:

> The whole year being thus affected with *southerly Winds*, and *greater Droughts than ordinary*, early in the *Spring* (from the former year's being different, and affected with *northerly Winds*) some few were attack'd with *Burning-Fevers* of a kind good sort, and a few others with *Hæmorrhages*, neither of which prov'd mortal. . . .[16]

Rudolph E. Siegel of Buffalo General Hospital (New York), supported by MacArthur, believed that the "burning fever" may have been the modern Mediterranean-type relapsing fever.[17] In any event, it was followed by an epidemical outbreak that included among its symptoms swellings behind the ears. It attacked children and young persons, as well as adults—"especially those who frequented the publick places of exercise." This was almost certainly mumps.

In the early summer, "and from that time till the *Winter*, many of those who had been for a long while somewhat consumptive, were laid up with *Consumptions;* and others, who were doubtful, were then fatally convinc'd." [18] In Hippocrates' day, pulmonary consumption (phthisis) was regarded as epidemic.

The next year the winter winds were out of the north and there was considerable rain mixed with snow. Conditions were not unseasonable until about the middle of February when the wind and the snow increased and there was an "abundance of Rain without ceasing. . . . The *Spring* was cold, northerly, watery, and cloudy. The *Summer* not very scorching. . . . The whole year being thus damp and cold, . . . in the beginning of the *Spring* many persons (not to say a great many) were taken ill."

The problem they faced was inflammation of the eyes (what Hippocrates called "humid Ophthalmies") "with weepings, pain, and indigestion," that continued until fall. Summer brought dysenteries (almost certainly not the intestinal disease as it is known today) and severe diarrheas. But the year's most serious epidemic involved what Hippocrates described as "continual" fever, which he differentiated from semitertian, tertian, quartan, quintan, septan, and nonan fevers as being "the acutist, the strongest, the most dangerous, and the most fatal" of fevers. (It may have been typhoid.) Striking in the fall, in most cases the fever ran a long course, and in some cases there were complications, such as abscesses and eruptions. "It prov'd fatal to persons of every age, but chiefly to children just wean'd, and to those of eight or ten years old, and those under the age of puberty." Relief came through dysenteries, diarrheas, and sometimes dropsies, but, Hippocrates observed, cure could be counted as almost certain when strangury (painful and interrupted urination in drops) intervened.

At this point in his account—Clifton was of the opinion that the remarks "were not intended to come in here . . . but were added by some of his successors to fill up the page"—Hippocrates defined "the duty of a Physician [as] being to relate what is past, to understand what is present, and to foretel what is to come. He is also to take special care of two things, *viz. to do good in his office, or at least no harm.*" [19]

In the third year, the winter was stormy, the spring wet and cold yet drier than usual, and the summer so hot and scorching that it led to widespread drought. "During this state of the weather, in the *Winter Paraplegia's* began and attack'd many, some of whom dy'd in a short time: for the disease was very *epidemical.*" Through the rest of the year the dominant diseases were burning fever and phrenitis (fever with delirium).

Most patients who went down with fever in the spring or summer survived, but "when the *Autumn* and wet weather sett in, [fever] prov'd mortal to many." However, the attacks were not invariably fatal:

> These Fevers were of such a nature, that when any one *bled freely and plentifully from the nose,* he was sav'd by it more than by any thing else; and not one of those who were taken thus dy'd this Season, so far as I know. . . . Others again were attack'd with a *Jaundice*, or a *disorder of their belly*, or a *Dysentery*, . . . In the *Summer*, *Dysenteries* were *epidemical*; . . .
>
> But about the *Æquinox*, to the setting of the *Pleiades*, and even in the *Winter* . . . a great many became *phrenitick*, and went off [died]; . . . These *Burning-Fevers* pointed out the *Prognosticks* from the beginning, where the case was desperate. For immediately an acute fever came on from the first, with gentle *Shiverings*, *Watchings* [sleeplessness], *Ramblings*, *Thirst*, *Nausea's* and *Anxiety*. They *sweated* a little about the forehead and collar-bone, but no-body all over. Great *Deliriums* attended with fears and dejectedness; the *Extremities* were coldish, the toes and fingers especially. . . . The *Extremities* did not recover their warmth, but were livid and cold; . . . The *Urine* was black, little, and thin; . . . No *Hæmorrhage* from the nose, . . . [they] dy'd on the sixth day in a sweat. As to the *Phrenitics* . . . the *crisis* came on generally the *eleventh* day, and in some the *twentieth*. . . .[20]

Siegel has advanced the opinion this epidemic was typhus. "Modern accounts of Typhus match fairly well the Hippocratic description and permit a tentative diagnosis." [21] His conclusion is of particular interest both because of MacArthur's strong contention that the Plague of Thucydides was typhus and because there have been numerous attempts to link that epidemic with the *Epidemics* of Hippocrates. Other suggestions have included bubonic plague, perhaps because in Book III, Hippocrates refers to dis-

EPIDEMICS

orders being "most dangerous . . . when they fell upon the *pubes* or *private parts*" and to "*swellings in the groin.*" Thucydides, on the other hand, offered no more than this: "For this disorder which had originally settled in the head passed gradually through the whole body, and, if a person got over the worst, would often seize the extremities and leave its mark, attacking the genitals and the fingers and the toes; and some escaped with the loss of these, some with the loss of their eyes." Thus no one can deny that bubonic plague may have been among the diseases that beset Athens.[22]

From Athens to Constantinople

REPORTS of epidemics occurring in the millennium following the Peloponnesian War are often fragmentary but it is possible to piece together some representative occurrences.

Toward the close of the fifth century B.C. a Carthaginian army under the command of Himilco laid siege to a number of cities on the south coast of Sicily. Moving eastward from Agrigentum, after the fall of Gela and Camerino the only remaining major city was Syracuse. The question arises why, rather than march on Syracuse, Himilco sent envoys to treat for peace. The likely answer is that an epidemic disease that had hit his troops a year earlier broke out again, for when he returned to Carthage, sickness had reduced his army to half its former strength. While the passage is incomplete, the fact of this epidemic as a basis for peace-feelers seems to be confirmed by the first century B.C. Greek historian, Diodorus Siculus.[1] Niebuhr has expressed the opinion that the epidemic was measles.[2] In any event, the campaign that had begun so successfully ended in disaster. The returning army brought the epidemic into Carthage and its environs and multitudes perished. In 397 B.C., as Himilco was preparing to do battle with a menacing Syracusan fleet, epidemic disease struck his men a third time and the Carthaginians suffered a severe defeat both at sea and on land.[3]

The church historian Paulus Orosius (fl. A.D. 414–417) has offered this account of a pestilence that afflicted Rome in 365–364 B.C.:

In the three hundred and eighty-fourth year after the founding of
the City, in the consulship of Lucius Genucius and Quintus Servi-
lius, a great pestilence seized all Rome; not as usual a more or less
than customary disturbed temperature of the seasons, that is, either
untimely dryness in winter or sudden heat in spring or unseasonable
moisture in summer or the confused allurement of a fruitful autumn,
over and above all this, a devastating breeze blown in from the pas-
ture land of Calabria brought in sudden flashes of violent epidemics;
moreover it was severe and long-lasting, without regard for sex and
age for two continuous years it crushed all with wasting disease, so
that even those whom it did not drive to death, it left wasted and
afflicted with horrible emaciation. The detractors of the Christian
period would complain at this point, as I think, if by chance I passed
over in silence the ceremonies with which at that time the Romans
tried to placate the gods and allay the diseases. When the pestilence
increased day by day, the pontifices persuaded the writers to put on
dramatic performances for the gods who coveted them. Thus, to
dispel a temporal plague of their bodies, an eternal disease of their
souls was summoned. . . .[4]

AESCULAPIUS COMES TO ROME

Strolling along the Tiber in the course of a visit to Rome, we pass
the Ponte Garibaldi; and then, a few steps further on, in the direction of the Aventine, we suddenly come into view of the site whence
the influence of the Greek god of medicine spread through the whole
Roman empire. From the Lungotevere dei Cenci we look across to
the Tiber Island where the church of San Bartolomeo stands amid a
group of hospital buildings. Thus disposed, church and hospital are
heirs to an ancient Asklepieion, a cult site unique in form. On closer
investigation we discover, on the southern tip of the island, the
remains of an old containing wall, built of travertine. This wall gave
the island the form of a ship, commemorating Asklepios' voyage
from his native Epidauros to Rome. A fragment of relief representing Asklepios—or Aesculapius, as the Romans called him—and a
snake is still visible on the wall. The snake is coiled around a staff.
Inside the church we find columns from an ancient temple. . . .[5]

The events leading up to the erection of a temple honoring Aesculapius on an island in the Tiber began in 292 B.C. Livy offers a
succinct account:

The year had been one of many blessings, which yet were hardly a consolation for one misfortune—a pestilence which ravaged both city and countryside. Its devastation was now grown portentous, and the Books were consulted to discover what end or what remedy the gods proposed for this misfortune. It was discovered in the Books that Aesculapius must be summoned to Rome from Epidaurus; but nothing could be done about it that year, because the consuls were occupied with the war, except for one day a supplication to that god was held.

But at length

envoys dispatched to bring over the image of Aesculapius from Epidaurus to Rome fetched away a serpent, which had crawled into their ship and in which it was generally believed the god himself was present. On the serpent's going ashore on the island of the Tiber, a temple was erected there to Aesculapius.[6]

The Augustan poet Ovid (43 B.C.–?A.D. 17) devoted about 125 lines of his *Metamorphoses* to the incident. He began by asking "whence did the island bathed by the deep Tiber bring Coronis' son [Aesculapius] and set him midst the deities of Rome" and proceeded to answer himself.

In olden time a deadly pestilence had corrupted Latium's air, and men's bodies lay wasting and pale with a ghastly disease. When, weary with caring for the dead, men saw that their human efforts were as nothing, and that the healers' arts were of no avail, they sought the aid of heaven, and, coming to Delphi, situate in the earth's central spot, the sacred oracle of Phoebus, they begged that the god would vouchsafe with his health-bringing lots to succour them in their wretchedness and end the woes of their great city.

The oracle told them that the help they sought was to be had from Apollo's son (Aesculapius) and an embassy led by Quintus Ogulnius was forthwith sent to his temple at Epidaurus in southern Greece. Appearing in a dream, Aesculapius told Ogulnius that he would come to Rome in the form of the serpent entwined about his staff, but that he would "be larger and . . . seem as great as celestial beings should be when they change." The next morning "the

golden god, in the form of a serpent with a high crest, uttered hiss-
ing warnings of his presence," and, after being worshipped by both
the Epidaurians and the Romans, he "glided down the polished
steps . . . wound his way along the ground covered with scattered
flowers . . . proceeded through the city's midst to the harbour"
and took his place within the Roman ship.

The journey, as recounted by Ovid, was not without incident,
but Rome was reached in due course and the

> serpent raised himself aloft and, resting his head upon the mast's
> top, moved it from side to side, viewing the places fit for his abode.
> The river, flowing around, separates at this point into two parts,
> forming the place called the Island; on each side of it stretches out
> two equal arms with the land between. On this spot the serpent-son
> of Phoebus disembarked from the Latin ship and, resuming his
> heavenly form, put an end to the people's woes and came to them as
> health-bringer to their city.[7]

The arrival of the Aesculapian serpent was commemorated by a
coin commissioned by the emperor Antonius Pius who, born in
A.D. 86, reigned from 138 to 161. The coin showed the galley
approaching two arches of the Pons Fabricus (now the Ponte Quat-
tro Capi) with the Aventine Hill in the background. The serpent,
erect on the prow, overshadowed the god of the Tiber reclining
comfortably and making welcoming gestures.[8]

EPIDEMICS IN THE SECOND AND THIRD CENTURIES

It is unfortunate that contemporary authors had little to say about
the severe epidemic, possibly smallpox, that decimated the Roman
army under Avidius Cassius toward the end of the Parthian War
(161–166) and was, over the next few years, spread throughout the
empire by soldiers returning from the east, because there is every
reason to regard the outbreak as a turning point in Roman history.
The lack of an eyewitness account becomes more regrettable when

it is realized that the Greek physician Galen (130–c. 200) was in Rome when the disease hit the capital in 166. (J. F. Gilliam of the University of Oregon has suggested that Galen's departure from Rome shortly thereafter may have been to escape the epidemic.[9]) The epidemic caused so many deaths that Rome was left largely defenseless.

> Before the eastern situation [the Parthian War] had reached a satis-factory settlement, a much more serious condition had developed in the Danubian frontier. There, apparently in consequence of the pressure exerted upon them by migratory people further to the north, the Marcomanni, Quadi, Iazyges, and some lesser tribes united in an attempt to force their way into the Roman provinces. The army of the Danube, weakened by the withdrawal of strong de-tachments for service in the East, was unable to check their assaults; Noricum and Pannonia were overrun, and the barbarians reached Aquileia at the head of the Adriatic. Conditions were really critical, owing to the lack of adequate troops, the disorganization caused in army camps by the plague, and the depletion of the treasury through the expenses involved in the Parthian War, and Marcus Aurelius [emperor, 161–180] was forced to adopt heroic measures to cope with them. He raised money by auctioning off the treasures of the imperial household; he drafted slaves and gladiators into the army and even hired mercenaries among the Germans and Scyth-ians.[10]

By 173 Marcus Aurelius had crossed the Danube and defeated the invaders, but the extent to which the empire had become depopulated is spoken to by the fact that he not only required thousands of the conquered peoples to serve in his armies, but he also settled them within the empire as landholders, apparently fac-ing no problem in finding vacant land for them to occupy.

The high point in the population of the empire seems to have been reached between 150 and 160. The decline from the apogee began with this epidemic during the reign of Marcus Aurelius. It was not limited to the deaths the epidemic caused. The then tax structure was such that the survivors were required to meet the full preexisting assessment. This meant financial ruin if they remained

in their communities, so many simply deserted. Furthermore, before the lost ground could be regained, the empire was hit by
another equally severe epidemic.

According to Arthur E. R. Boak (1888–1962), writing when he
was Richard Hudson Professor of Ancient History at the University of Michigan,

> It is hardly possible to exaggerate the effects of the great epidemic
> which began in 251 A.D. and raged until 266 A.D., equalling in dura-
> tion the pestilence of the time of Marcus Aurelius. Since the Em-
> peror Claudius Gothicus fell a victim to plague in 270 A.D., it is
> probable that it lingered on in some districts even after it had sub-
> sided in general. Beginning in Ethiopia and striking Egypt with par-
> ticular severity, it extended its ravages to the extreme western parts
> of the Empire. Hardly a city escaped, and some of them experienced
> two visitations of the disease, which seems to have been of the char-
> acter of bubonic plague. According to a contemporary writer, the
> population of Alexandria, the second city of the Roman world,
> shrank to such a degree that the total surviving population between
> the ages of fourteen and seventy was only equal to the former
> number of those between forty and seventy, that is to say, a loss of
> about two thirds of the inhabitants.[11]

The "contemporary writer" to whom Boak referred was Bishop
Dionysius (190?–265) of Alexandria, and the parallel passage from
one of his letters, as quoted by church historian Eusebius of Caesarea (260?–?339), reads as follows:

> Yet men wonder and are at a loss whence the continuous pestilence,
> whence the severe diseases, whence the different forms of death,
> whence the widespread and varied destruction of human beings,
> why this great city no longer contains within itself so great a multi-
> tude of inhabitants, from tender infants up to those of extreme old
> age, as it used to support those whom it called hearty old men. But
> those of forty years of age to seventy were so much more numerous
> at that time that their number is not to be matched today, even
> when those of fourteen to eighty years have been registered and
> reckoned together . . .[12]

This epidemic, covering as it did most of the then known world, had far-reaching effects on agriculture, the military, the economy, and even literature and art within the empire.

Large stretches of farmland lay neglected, not merely because the work force had been depleted by disease but because the reduced population of towns required less food and to produce more was unprofitable. Depopulation left the imperial armies chronically short of recruits. As for the economy, the decline in production at the silver mines led to debasement of the currency. Under Gallienus (emperor, 253–268) the silver content of the standard silver coin was reduced to 2 percent, the balance being copper. The result was inflation, with prices rising, in Egypt, for example, to between fourteen and twenty times their former level.

Furthermore, faced with diminishing revenues because of general depopulation and impoverishment, the government became even more exacting than before in its demand for services and extraordinary contributions from those who survived. The associations of businessmen and tradesmen were forced more and more into the public service and put under stricter control, while the municipal obligations pressed more and more heavily on the propertied townspeople who formed the middle class of the Empire. From the ruin of the third century this class as a whole never recovered.[13]

Amidst this disorder few writers had the inclination to write. Architecture was limited by the prevailing poverty to imperial commissions to construct such public buildings as amphitheaters, triumphal arches, baths, and temples. Sculpture was sustained to a degree in busts of the emperors, in portraits in relief on sarcophagi, and in imperial effigies on coins. In short, Rome and her provinces in the last half of the third century were bolstered by the type of make-work projects that helped the United States through the 1930s.

GOD DISPOSES

Maximinus (d. 313), who ruled Syria and Egypt from 305 under the emperor Galerius (reigned, 305–311), first as Caesar and then, from 308, as Augustus (emperor), was a persistent persecutor of Christians and was consequently referred to by Eusebius as "the tyrant." Maximinus "boldly bragged that because of his zeal for the idols and his attack upon us neither famine nor pestilence nor even war had taken place within his time." But around 310 all this changed when

> the customary rains and showers of the winter season which then prevailed were withholding their usual downpour upon the earth, and an unexpected famine came upon us, and besides these a plague [that] crept over the whole body and caused the sufferers serious danger, but especially against the eyes did it direct its greatest attack, and it deprived countless men, together with women and children, of their sight.
>
>   In addition to this there was forced upon the tyrant the war against the Armenians, men from of old friends and allies of the Romans, whom also, since they were Christians and zealous in the exercise of piety toward the Deity, he tried to force to sacrifice to idols and demons; and he thereby made them foes instead of friends, enemies instead of allies.[14]

The outcome was again inflation. Maximinus,

> together with his commanders, was worn out over the war with the Armenians, and famine as well as pestilence so exhausted the rest of the inhabitants of the cities under him that 2,500 Attic drachmas was the cost of a single measure of wheat. Countless were those who then died in the cities, and more numerous than these in the country and villages, so that the registers which formerly showed an extensive rural population suffered almost complete reduction, almost all being suddenly destroyed by lack of nourishment and pestilential disease. And some resolved to sell their dearest possessions to those better provided for the slightest bit of nourishment; others, selling off their goods little by little, were soon reduced to the last extremity of need; and some by chewing small wisps of hay and recklessly

eating certain noxious herbs ruined their body constitutions and perished. And some of the women, the well-born ladies in cities, were driven by their want to shameless necessity and went out into the market places to beg, displaying evidence of their past cultural training by their shamefacedness and by the decency of their apparel. And some, wasted away like ghostly corpses, at their last gasp, shaking and slipping here and there, because of their inability to stand fell down, and stretched out prone in the middle of the streets, earnestly begging that a small piece of bread be handed to them, and clinging to life with their last breath they shouted that they were hungry, having strength for this most distressing cry alone. Others, such as were regarded to be of the wealthier classes, astounded at the multitude of beggars, after giving out immeasurable amounts, resorted henceforth to a hard and relentless disposition of mind, expecting that they themselves, also, before very long would be suffering the same as the beggars, so that in the middle of the market places and alleys corpses and naked bodies, scattered here and there and unburied for many days, furnished a most pitiful sight to those who looked upon them. Then, too, some became food for dogs; and for this reason, chiefly, the living turned to killing dogs lest these become mad and commence to devour men. And not the least serious was the pestilence which devoured entire houses, especially those whom hunger had not been able to bring low because they were well provided with food. Thus did men living in plenty, rulers and governors and countless officials, as if expressly left behind by the famine for the pestilence disease, suffer a quick and very speedy death. Thus all places were full of lamentations; in all alleys and market places and streets there was nothing to hear but funeral dirges, together with flutes and noises usually accompanying them. Waging war, then, in this manner, with the two aforesaid weapons of pestilence and famine, death in a short time wasted away entire families, so that one could see the bodies of two or three dead being carried out in one funeral procession.

Such were the rewards of the proud boasting of Maximin and of the decrees in cities against us, when the testimonies of the zeal and of the piety of the Christians in all things became quite clear to all the heathen. For example, they alone in such evil surroundings exhibited their sympathy and humanity by actual deeds: all during the day some persevered diligently with the last rites and the burial of the dead (for there were countless who had no one to care for them); others gathered in one assemblage the multitude of those who throughout the entire city were wasting away from famine, and distributed bread to all of them, so that the matter became noised about among men, and they glorified the God of the Christians, and, convinced by the facts themselves, they confessed that these were truly pious and religious.[15]

In this case, "the great and heavenly defender of the Christians, God," intervened, first to punish, then to reward. In Britain about 150 years later he was less generous. As reported by the English scholar, historian, and theologian, the Venerable Bede (673–735), the barbarians ("Irish robbers" and "Picts") had been plundering the country for about twenty years when the Britons, spurred by the resultant famine, drove the invaders out of their territory.

When, however, the ravages of the enemy at length ceased [in 446–447], the island began to abound with such plenty of grain as had never been known in any age before; with plenty, luxury increased, and this was immediately attended with all sorts of crimes; in particular, cruelty, hatred of truth, and love of falsehood; insomuch, that if any one among them happened to be milder than the rest, and inclined to truth, all the rest abhorred and persecuted him, as if he had been the enemy of his country. Nor were the laity only guilty of these things, but even our Lord's own flock, and his pastors also, addicting themselves to drunkenness, animosity, litigiousness, contention, envy, and other such crimes, and casting off the light yoke of Christ. In the meantime, on a sudden, a severe plague fell upon that corrupt generation, which soon destroyed such numbers of them, that the living were scarcely sufficient to bury the dead: yet, those that survived, could not be withdrawn from the spiritual death, which their sins had incurred, either by the death of their friends, or the fear of their own.[16]

Five years later (in 452) smallpox was epidemic throughout the south of France. Nicaise, bishop of Rheims, who would later be canonized as the patron saint of smallpox, contracted the disease but recovered from the attack "because, according to his own statement, he had anointed himself with holy oil."

The following year he was martyred by barbarian invaders. According to one legend, after the barbarians laid siege to Rheims, "he went forth attended by his clergy to meet the enemy, singing hymns: one of the barbarian soldiers, however, struck off the upper half of his head, but the saint, nevertheless, continued to sing his stave until, after a few steps, he fell dead." Shrewsbury has commented that "this legend is not so unreasonable as it may sound, because there are many authenticated records from modern wars of individuals continuing to perform active movements for considerable periods after severe head injuries," but he was more skeptical about another version that had the bishop, carrying his skull in his hand, return to the cathedral after the assassination, only falling dead when he reached the altar. Shrewsbury wondered what the barbarians were doing while Nicaise "was perambulating with his head in his hand." [17]

The Plague of Justinian

THE year 541 must have looked good to the Byzantine emperor
Justinian (ruled, 527–565). Nine years earlier he had signed a peace
treaty with his chief enemy, Persia. Other enemies were weak,
scattered, and disunited. He had recaptured North Africa from the
Vandals and much of Italy from the Ostrogoths. The Mediterranean countries from Italy to Spain could be expected to welcome
the imperial armies. The treasury was full. Manpower was adequate. It seemed that Justinian's ambition to reestablish the former
Roman Empire was about to be fulfilled. Then came the first of the
three most devastating epidemics to hit mankind.

The disease "alternatively languished and revived; but it was not
until the end of a calamitous period of fifty-two years that mankind
recovered their health." [1]

Procopius of Caesarea has provided a singular eyewitness account of the coming of the plague to Constantinople (Byzantium)
and the havoc it caused:

> During these times there was a pestilence, by which the whole
> human race came near to being annihilated. . . . For it did not come
> in a part of the world nor upon certain men, nor did it confine itself
> to any season of the year, so that from such circumstances it might
> be possible to find subtle explanations of a cause, but it embraced
> the entire world, and blighted the lives of all men, though differing
> from one another in a most marked degree, respecting neither sex nor
> age. . . .
>   It started from the Aegyptians who dwell in Pelusium. Then it

divided and moved in one direction towards Alexandria and the rest of Aegypt, and in the other it came to Palestine on the borders of Aegypt; and from there it spread over the whole world, always moving forward and travelling at times favourable to it. For it seemed to move by fixed arrangement, and to tarry for a specified time in each country, casting its blight slightingly upon none, but spreading in either direction right out to the ends of the world, as if fearing lest some corner of the earth might escape it. For it left neither island nor cave nor mountain ridge which had human inhabitants; and if it had passed by any land, either not affecting the men there or touching them in indifferent fashion, still at a later time it came back; then those who dwelt round about this land, whom formerly it had afflicted most sorely, it did not touch at all, . . . And this disease always took its start from the coast, and from there went up to the interior. And in the second year it reached Byzantium in the middle of spring, where it happened that I was staying at the time.

Procopius went on to report that many persons, as a prelude to the disease, saw supernatural beings either in a waking vision or a dream. When these apparitions would not be exorcised "by uttering the holiest of names," most fled to the sanctuaries, but they died anyway. As a next step, others shut themselves up in their homes, refusing to admit any friend who called on them because he might be "one of the demons."

But with the majority it came about that they were seized by the disease without becoming aware of what was coming either through a waking vision or a dream. And they were taken in the following manner. They had a sudden fever, some when they just roused from sleep, others while walking about, and others while otherwise engaged, without any regard to what they were doing. And the body showed no change from its previous colour, nor was it hot as might be expected when attacked by a fever, nor indeed did any inflammation set in, but the fever was of such a languid sort from its commencement and up till evening that neither to the sick themselves nor to a physician who touched them would it afford any suspicion of danger. It was natural, therefore, that not one of those who had contracted the disease expected to die from it.

Procopius now turned to what has been hailed as the first detailed description of bubonic plague:

> But on the same day in some cases, in others on the following day, and in the rest not many days later, a bubonic swelling developed; and this took place not only in the particular part of the body which is called "boubon" [groin], that is below the abdomen, but also inside the armpit, and in some cases also behind the ears, and at different points on the thighs.
>
> Up to this point, everything went in about the same way with all who had taken the disease. But from then on very marked differences developed; . . . For there ensued with some a deep coma, with others a violent delirium, and in either case they suffered the characteristic symptoms of the disease. For those who were under the spell of the coma forgot all those who were familiar to them and seemed to be sleeping constantly. And if anyone cared for them, they would eat without waking, but some also were neglected, and these would die directly through lack of sustenance. But those who were seized with delirium suffered from insomnia and were victims of a distorted imagination; for they suspected that men were coming upon them to destroy them, and they would become excited and rush off in flight, crying out at the top of their voices. And those who were attending them were in a state of constant exhaustion and had a most difficult time of it throughout. For this reason everybody pitied them no less than the sufferers, not because they were threatened by the pestilence in going near it * (for neither physicians nor other persons were found to contract this malady through contact with the sick or with the dead, for many who were constantly engaged either in burying or in attending those in no way connected with them held out in the performance of this service beyond all expectation, while with many others the disease came on without warning and they died straightway); but they pitied them because of the great hardships which they were undergoing. . . .

(The "great hardships" involved preventing patients from falling out of bed, rushing out of their houses, attempting to immerse

* Evidence that the epidemic was bubonic plague with pneumonic plague seldom if ever present.

themselves in the sea, starving to death, or throwing themselves
from a height.)

> And in those cases where neither coma nor delirium came on, the
> bubonic swelling became mortified and the sufferer, no longer able
> to endure the pain, died. As one would suppose that in all cases the
> same thing would have been true, but since they were not at all in
> their senses, some were quite unable to feel the pain; for owing to
> the troubled condition of their minds they lost all sense of feeling.
>   Now some of the physicians who were at a loss because the symp-
> toms were not understood, supposing that the disease centered in
> the bubonic swellings, decided to investigate the bodies of the dead.
> And upon opening some of the swellings, they found a strange sort
> of carbuncle that had grown inside them.
>   Death came in some cases immediately, in others after many days;
> and with some the body broke out with black pustules about as large
> as a lentil and those did not survive even one day, but all succumbed
> immediately. With many also a vomiting of blood ensued without
> visible cause and straightway brought death. Moreover I am able to
> declare this, that the most illustrious physicians predicted that many
> would die, who unexpectedly escaped entirely from suffering
> shortly afterwards, and that they declared that many would be
> saved, who were destined to be carried off almost immediately. . . .
> Indeed the whole matter may be stated thus, that no device was dis-
> covered by man to save himself, so that either by taking precautions
> he should not suffer, or that when the malady had assailed him he
> should get the better of it; but suffering came without warning and
> recovery was due to no external cause. . . .
>   Now in those cases where the swelling rose to an unusual size and
> a discharge of pus had set in, it came about that they escaped from
> the disease and survived, for clearly the acute condition of the car-
> buncle had found relief in this direction, and this proved to be in
> general an indication of returning health; but in cases where the
> swelling preserved its former appearance there ensued those troubles
> which I have just mentioned.[2]

The Plague of Justinian did not run its course in Constantinople,
and the English historian Edward Gibbon (1737–1794) has given
some account of its progress: "The fatal disease which depopulated

the earth in the time of Justinian and his successors, first appeared in the neighbourhood of Pelusium, between the Serbonian bog and the eastern channel of the Nile. From thence, tracing as it were a double path, it spread to the East, over Syria, Persia, and the Indies, and penetrated to the West, along the coast of Africa, and over the continent of Europe. . . . No restraints were imposed on the free and frequent intercourse of the Roman provinces: from Persia to France, the nations were mingled and infected by wars and emigrations; and the pestilential odour which lurks for years in a bale of cotton, was imported, by the abuse of trade, into the most distant regions." [3] Had Gibbon lived for another century he might have come to realize that it was the rat, the flea, and the bacillus (rather than the "pestilential odour") that followed the trade routes.

PLAGUE IN ITALY

The eighth-century historian Paulus Diaconus (or Paul the Deacon), member of a noble Lombard family, while not an eyewitness to the Plague of Justinian, has left an account of bubonic plague in Italy that bears out the assertion that the disease "alternatively languished and revived." The first outbreak to which he drew attention occurred "particularly" in the province of Liguria (of which the principal city is Genoa) in 566–567. Paulus began with a description of a somewhat quaint event which only the imagination of a superstitious era could associate with the epidemic that was to follow: "For suddenly there appeared certain marks among the dwellings, doors, utensils, and clothes, which, if any one wished to wash away, became more and more apparent." He then continued:

> After the lapse of a year indeed there began to appear in the groins of men and in other delicate places, a swelling of the glands, after the manner of a nut or a date, presently followed by an unbearable fever, so that upon the third day the man died. But if any one should pass over the third day he had a hope of living. Everywhere there was grief and everywhere tears. For as common report had it that those who fled would avoid the plague, the dwellings were left

deserted by their inhabitants, and the dogs only kept house. The
flocks remained alone in the pastures with no shepherd at hand. You
might see villas or fortified places lately filled with crowds of men,
and on the next day, all had departed and everything was in utter
silence. Sons fled, leaving the corpses of their parents unburied;
parents forgetful of their duty abandoned their children in raging
fever. If by chance long-standing affection constrained any one to
bury his near relative, he remained himself unburied, and while he
was performing the funeral rites he perished; while he offered obsequies to the dead, his own corpse remained without obsequies.
You might see the world brought back to its ancient silence: no voice
in the field; no whistling of shepherds; no lying in wait of wild
beasts among the cattle; no harm to domestic fowls. The crops,
outliving the time of the harvest, awaited the reaper untouched; the
vineyard with its fallen leaves and its shining grapes remained undisturbed while winter came on; a trumpet as of warriors resounded
through the hours of the night and day; something like the murmur
of an army was heard by many; there were no footsteps of passers
by, no murderer was seen, yet the corpses of the dead were more
than the eye could discern; pastoral places had been turned into a
sepulchre for men, and human habitations had become places of refuge for wild beasts. And these evils happened to the Romans alone
and within Italy alone, up to the boundaries of the nations of the
Alamanni and the Bavarians. Meanwhile, the emperor Justinian departed from life and Justin the younger undertook the rule of the
state at Constantinople.

The next episode, occurring in 589, also had its mystical portents. There was "a deluge of water in the territories of Venetia
and Liguria, and in other regions of Italy such as is believed not to
have existed since the time of Noah. Ruins were made of estates
and country seats, and at the same time a great destruction of men
and animals. The paths were obliterated, the highway demolished, and . . . the walls of the city of Verona itself were partly
demolished by the same inundation. . . . In this outpouring of the
flood the river Tiber at the city of Rome rose so much that its
waters flowed in over the walls of the city and filled great regions
in it. Then through the bed of the same stream a great multitude of
serpents, and a dragon also of astonishing size passed by the city

and descended to the sea." The stage was now set for the upcoming epidemic:

> Straightway a very grievous pestilence called inguinal followed this inundation, and it wasted the people with such great destruction of life that out of a countless multitude barely a few remained. First it struck Pope Pelagius, a venerable man, and quickly killed him. Then when their pastor was taken away it spread among the people. In this great tribulation the most blessed Gregory, who was then a deacon, was elected Pope by the common consent of all. He ordained that a seven-fold litany should be offered, but while they were imploring God, eighty of them within the space of one hour fell suddenly to earth and gave up the ghost. The seven-fold litany was thus called because all the people of the city were divided by the blessed Gregory into seven parts to intercede with the Lord. . . .

Also in 589 "a very severe plague again devastated Ravenna [northeast of Florence] and those places which were around the shores of the sea [and] in the following year great mortality wasted the people of Verona."

Finally in 617–618 (beyond the accepted terminal date of the Plague of Justinian but surely part of the continuing pattern) Rome was hit by "a scab disease of such a kind that no one could recognize his own dead on account of the great swellings and inflammation." [4]

IN FRANCE

Gregory (538?–593), bishop of Tours, has left a contemporary, if not always an eyewitness, account of bubonic plague in France.

What may well have been the first recorded appearance of the pestilence in Western Europe seems to have occurred in 543, only a year after the Plague of Justinian fell upon Constantinople and therefore well in advance of the first outbreak in Italy. The date is inferred from a passage in Gregory's *The History of the Franks* in which he spoke of "the pestilence known as the plague of the groin" that raged during the episcopate (c. 527–551) of Gall, bishop of

Clermont, "in divers regions, but especially in the province of Arles." In response to entreatments by the bishop that "he might not live to see his people devastated," the Lord sent an angel who told him that as long as he lived "no man in this region shall perish of this plague." Then the angel volunteered that Gall would live another eight years. Since he died in 551, the angel evidently delivered his message in 543 and, according to Gregory, while the plague "consumed other regions, through the intercession of the holy Gall it did not reach Clermont."

Gregory next described a disastrous outbreak that occurred in Auvergne in 571. At its coming,

> there was made such slaughter of the people through all that region, that the legions of men who fell there might not even be numbered. When coffins and planks failed, ten men or more were buried in a common pit. In the single church of Saint Peter there were counted on a certain Sunday three hundred corpses. For death came suddenly. There appeared in the groin or armpit a wound like that from a snakebite, and those who had it were swiftly destroyed by the poison, that on the second or third day they breathed their last: the strength of the poison robbed men of their senses. It was at this time that the priest Cato died. Many had fled from this pestilence; but he never left that place, burying the people, and courageously saying his masses. This priest was a man of great humanity and devoted to the poor; and if his character inclined somewhat to pride, this charity tempered it. Bishop Cautinus, after going from place to place in fear of the pest returned to the city and, taking the infection, died upon Good Friday, the very hour that Tetradius his cousin perished. Lyons, Bourges, Chalon, and Dijon lost much people through this sickness.

In 588 "Marseilles was ravaged by a plague affecting the groin, which had rapidly spread to a village called Octavus near Lyons." It was a ship from Spain that "unhappily" brought "the tinder which kindled this disease" (undoubtedly flea-bearing rats).

> Many citizens purchased various objects from the cargo, and soon a house inhabited by eight people was left empty, every one of them being carried off by the contagion. The fire of this plague did not

spread immediately through all the houses in the place; but there
was a certain interval, and then the whole city blazed with the pest,
like a cornfield set aflame. Nevertheless the bishop [Theodore] came
back [from a visit to the king], and abode within the walls of the
church of the holy Victor with the few that remained beside him;
there throughout the whole calamity he gave himself up to prayers
and vigils, imploring God's mercy, that at last the destruction might
have end, and peace and quiet be granted to the people. After two
months the affliction ceased, and the people returned, thinking the
danger overpast. But the plague began once more, and all who had
returned perished. On several occasions Marseilles was afflicted by
this death.

Meanwhile, as the epidemic spread, Childebert II (ruled
575–595), king of the Franks, "like some good bishop" was doing
what he could "to heal the scars of a people that had sinned." His
remedy involved continual prayer and "nothing . . . to be taken
by way of nourishment but barley bread and pure water." Gregory
repeated the tale, "commonly told by the faithful," of a woman,
whose son was abed with a four-day fever, who "tore off by stealth
some particles of the fringe upon [the king's] royal mantle,"
steeped it in water, and gave the drink to her son who was
promptly cured. This episode is of interest because Gregory concluded: "I cannot doubt the story, since I myself have often heard
evil spirits in the hour of their possession invoking the king's name,
and confessing their crimes, compelled by his miraculous power."

In 590 bubonic plague ravaged the city of Avignon, northwest of
Marseilles, and moved on to Viviers farther up the river Rhone.
The following year Marseilles was hit again. Then in April, "a terrible pestilence destroyed the people of the territory of Tours and
in that of Nantes; the attack in each case was followed by a slight
headache, soon after which the patient died." Gregory did not
make clear whether this pestilence was bubonic plague. He died
two years later.[5]

While the empire survived, it was an empire with wings clipped,
its territories limited, and its structure changed. With a population
loss of up to 50 percent by the end of the century—according to
Procopius, in Byzantium "the tale of the dead reached five thou-

sand each day, and again it even came to ten thousand and still more than that" [6]—and with many landowners unable to pay their taxes, the imperial government fell heir to a considerable amount of land which it distributed to organizations of free peasant-soldiers, leading to the replacement of great estates by small freeholders. Thus the "plague by its sheer power molded sixth- and seventh-century society into a new demographic and social pattern—the pattern which was to persist throughout the rest of the medieval period and which, in modified form, remains today." [7] With Greco-Roman culture eclipsed, Europe moved under the cloud of the Middle Ages. If the Plague of Justinian had never occurred and the empire had been reestablished in all its glory, would the Dark Ages have evolved? The question is moot.

The Middle Ages

JUST as bubonic plague was not identified until the age of Justinian, other epidemic diseases were not adequately described until the Middle Ages.

SMALLPOX AND MEASLES

It is unthinkable in the twentieth century that smallpox should be confused with measles, but such a confusion existed in early times and persisted well into the Middle Ages. In fact, as late as the mid-eighteenth century the prominent and successful Richard Mead (1673–1754), physician to George II, wrote *A Discourse on the Small Pox and Measles* in which he said:

> The measles have great affinity with the small pox; being originally bred in the same country, propagated in the same manner, by infection, into distant parts of the world; and never seizing any person more than once.[1]

While smallpox was vaguely described by some of the church fathers as early as the sixth century A.D. and by the seventh-century chronicler credited with having written thirty books of physic, Aaron of Alexandria, it was not until around 910 that the Arabian physician Rhazes (860–932) drew the distinction between smallpox and measles. Since "the account of Rhazes is so vivid and complete that it is almost modern," [2] it will be of value to review what he had to say before looking at the historic emergence of smallpox and measles. In Rhazes' view,

> the body of man, from the time of his nativity, till he arrives at old age, continually tends to dryness; . . . therefore the blood of infants and children, and, in proportion, the blood of young men, abounds much more with humidity, than the blood of old men, and is also hotter. . . .
>
> Therefore, the blood of children may be compared to new wine, in which the fermentation leading to ripeness is not yet begun: and the blood of young men to the same, fermenting and emitting steams, till it is quiet and ripe. And lastly, the blood of old men is like to wine, whose strength is gone, so that it becomes vapid, and begins to grow sour.
>
> Now, the small pox arises, when the blood putrifies and ferments, and the fermenting particles are thrown out of it; the blood of children, like the new wine, being changed to that of young men, which is a wine perfectly ripened. And this fermentation is the disease.
>
> And this is the reason, why children, especially males, rarely escape being seized with it. . . .

Still, not everyone was susceptible and Rhazes distinguished between "bodies disposed to" smallpox and measles and those that were not. Vulnerable bodies, he said,

> are generally such as are moist, pale, and fleshy; the well coloured also, especially if they are ruddy and tending to brown, are disposed to it, if they are loaded with flesh. So are likewise those, which are frequently liable to acute and continual fevers, to running of the eyes, red pimples, and boils, proceeding from the eating of sweet things; as dates, honey, figs, grapes, and all those sweets, in which there is a gross humor; particularly, thick gruels, food made of unground wheat with honey and water, or a great quantity of wine and milk.
>
> Lean, bilious, hot, and dry bodies are more inclinable to the measles, than to the small pox. But if they happen to be taken with the small pox, the pustules are either few, distinct, and favourable; or, on the contrary very bad, irregular, deceitful, dry, with putrefaction, and no maturation.

Lastly, thin and dry bodies, of a cold temperament, are neither subject to the small pox, nor to the measles. And if they happen to catch the small pox, they have but few, in a moderate way, and without danger, with a very slight fever; because such constitutions extinguish the disease at its very beginning.

The seasons of the year, in which the small pox are most frequent, are various: they rage most at the latter end of the autumn, and the beginning of the spring; and when in the summer there are great and frequent rains, with continual south winds; and lastly, when the winter is warm and the winds southerly.

When the summer is exceedingly hot and dry, and succeeded by a hot autumn, in which rains come on very late; then the measles quickly seize those, who are disposed to them, that is, those who are lean, hot, and of bilious constitutions.

But all these things admit of great differences, by reason of the diversity of countries and places, and occult dispositions in the air, which bring on those distempers, and render bodies subject to them. . . .

How were these diseases to be recognized and how could one distinguish between them?

The eruption of the small pox is preceded by a continual fever, a pain in the back, itching in the nose, and terrors in sleep. These are the proper signs of the approaching small pox, especially the pain in the back, with a fever; and also a pricking, which the patient feels all over his body; together with a fullness and redness of the face, which at times goes and comes; a redness of the eyes, a heaviness of the whole body; frequent yawnings, a pain in the throat and breast, with a difficulty in breathing, and streightness in the gullet; then a dryness of the mouth, thick spittle, a hoarsness of the voice; head ach, anxiety of mind, inquietude; sick qualms and heaviness of heart, with this difference, that anxiety of mind, sick qualms and heaviness of heart, oppress more in the measles, than in the small pox, unless the small pox be of a bad sort; for the measles are from a very bilious blood. And, on the other hand, the pain in the back, the heat and inflammation of the whole body, especially in the throat, with a shining redness, are more proper to the small pox than to the measles.

Wherefore, upon the appearance of these signs, or some of the worst of them, you may be assured, that one or the other of these diseases is nigh at hand.

Rhazes then dealt with methods of prevention and treatment, including such topics as refining and drying the pustules, taking away the dry scabs, and destroying the pockmarks. Finally he distinguished between curable and incurable smallpox and measles.[3]

While it is accepted that smallpox has afflicted man since ancient times, its point of origin remains uncertain. However, it is clear that it was in India and China at a very early date. The Hindu society is one of the oldest from which decipherable records exist, and the Sanskrit language included several names for smallpox. The disease was present in China in the dynasty of Tcheou (c. 1122 B.C.) and was known as *Venom from the Mother's breast*. It involved "the eruption of pustules, their increase, suppuration, flattening and crusting." [4] Strange as it may seem, smallpox did not reach Japan from China until the thirtieth year of the reign of King Siomu (A.D. 737). The *Ishinho*, the oldest Japanese medical text in existence, written in 982 by Yasuhori Tamhu, referred to isolation hospitals for smallpox victims.

James Moore (1763–1834), English surgeon and director of the National Vaccine Establishment, writing in 1815, asked how it was that smallpox did not move from India into Persia, and thence into Greece, long before the age of Hippocrates, and offered this answer:

> The dread of the Small Pox, and the strong measures adopted in the East to controul it, may be considered as causes which contributed to prevent this infection from extending westward. But, undoubtedly, the principal cause was the peculiar situation of the regions through which this infection was diffused, separated from the rest of the world by deserts and by the ocean. Yet neither these barriers formed by nature, nor any defences fabricated by man, have preserved any country from foreign hostile intrusion. . . .

This defenselessness proved true enough in India's case. She was invaded in the fifth century B.C. by Darius son of Hystaspes and

late in the fourth century B.C. by Alexander, but neither appears to
have carried smallpox back to Persia. This, in Moore's view, may
have been because a disease is more likely to be carried into a
country by an invading army than brought home by the remnants
of a retreating army that has been smitten in the field. He then
pointed out that

> the industrious Chinese, and the unambitious East Indians never
> thought of quitting their homes, to break into territories of their
> neighbors.
>   The rapacious invaders who went from Persia, would of course be
> attacked by the diseases which prevailed in the countries they laid
> waste: but the numbers which perished, the time which was spent in
> so distant warfare, and the extent of the deserts which were re-
> crossed, appear to have secured their native country from being con-
> taminated by the few survivors of the expeditions.[5]

Moore based his conclusion that Alexander's army was hit by
smallpox on an assertion by Quintus Curtius Rufus, the first century A.D. Roman historian renowned for his history of Alexander
the Great, that, when encamped at the mouth of the river Indus, "a
scab attacked the bodies of the soldiers, and spread by contagion."
Curtius Rufus, Moore reported,

> dwells with eloquence on the miseries which the army endured from
> famine, diseases, and pestilences, in a march of sixty days, through a
> horrid country, part of which resembled a wilderness. As no food
> was to be found even for the beasts of burden, they all perished; the
> sick, unable to proceed, in spite of their entreaties, were left to
> starve; while the remaining troops hurried forward to reach a cul-
> tivated country. Certainly there is little likelihood that those affected
> with the Small Pox could survive such hardships.[6]

So much for invasion, but what of commerce? China and India
offered trade goods tempting to their Western neighbors. Why was
smallpox not communicated by commercial intercourse? Moore
recognized two barriers to the early spread of smallpox.

Because the Eastern countries were separated "in so remarkable a manner from the rest of the habitable world," trade was carried on either overland or by ships "that crept timidly along the coast." (Navigation was in its infancy, the mariner's compass unknown.)

> Commerce with those nations by land, was only practicable by means of the camel, whose powers of enduring heat and thirst, without drinking for ten days, enabled the merchants to convey their goods across the sandy deserts. But we may safely conjecture, that no person known to be inflicted with Small Pox, would be suffered to join a caravan. And if from accident, that ever occurred, there can be little doubt, that the infected would be abandoned to their destiny.
>
> The horror entertained of the Small Pox would also excite attention not to admit the infected into ships, which in the early ages were small in size, requiring but a few mariners to navigate them; while the tediousness of the coasting voyage gave ample time for the extinction of the infection.[7]

The delay in the spread of smallpox into what would come to be known as the Middle East was augmented by the fact that the Persians "entertained an insuperable superstitious aversion to the sea," but at the beginning of the sixth centiry A.D., when a demand for muslins, silks, spices, pearls, and diamonds from India, Siam (Thailand), and China developed in the Roman Empire, Persians overcame this aversion and their harbors were filled with trading vessels en route to convenient ports from which the luxuries of the East could be conveyed to Alexandria and thence to Europe. This, said Moore,

> augmented the danger of transporting the variolous [smallpox] contagion . . . and as ships coming from India, both in their passage to the Persian Gulph, and to the Red Sea, frequently touched at the Arabian ports, that country was peculiarly exposed, and there accordingly it was first observed.[8]

In the year 568 the idolatrous inhabitants of Mecca defiled a church that the Christian Abyssinian prince Abrahah had built with a view to converting the Arabians to Christianity. Abrahah was so angered that he assembled a large army and, mounted on an elephant, led it to Mecca. When he attempted to enter the city, "his elephant knelt down, then turned round, and could not be forced to advance; while he was disconcerted by this incident, a large flock of supernatural birds . . . came flying from the sea. . . . All of them were armed, each carrying a small stone the size of a pea in its bill, and two in its talons. These stones were inscribed with the name of the person they were intended to strike, and were thrown down at once on the army. The stones pierced through the helmets and bodies of the Abyssinian soldiers: none escaped, except Abrahah, who fled to Ethiopia." As he was describing the catastrophe to the emperor of Abyssinia, a bird "which had pursued him during his flight, and which still hovered over his head . . . launched a stone at him, and laid him dead at the Emperor's feet."

It seemed clear to Moore that, since Mecca was being defended by "a handful of frightened citizens," it would have taken more than "miraculous birds" to deter the Ethiopian forces. The birds were allegorical and what smote the army was smallpox and measles. He backed up this assertion by reference to a manuscript account of the siege of Mecca by an Abyssinian writer, El Hameesy, according to whom smallpox and measles broke out in Arabia at this time and "almost totally destroyed the army of Abrahah." He also referred to a Latin dissertation written in 1746 by John James Reiske (1716–1774) of Leyden, a German authority on Arabian antiquities, in which he spoke of smallpox and measles being carried into Arabia by the Ethiopians in 569.[9]

Just when smallpox reached Egypt is open to question. The mummified head of Ramses V suggests that he may have died (1160 B.C.) of smallpox. Setting this possibility aside, A.D. 572 is a favored date. But, said Moore, if smallpox and measles had not reached Alexandria, "that emporium of trade," by 616, it must have arrived then, when Khosrau, a Persian tyrant, after massacring thousands of Christians in Jerusalem, overran Egypt. Six years later "Mahomet began to collect the wandering tribes, whom he led forth inflamed with fanatic fury, and contaminated with disease, against the surrounding nations." Then in 647 the Moslems carried smallpox to Tripoli and by the end of the century it had spread the length of the African coast of the Mediterranean. In 718, the Saracens, "inflamed with the desire of possessing Europe," attempted to take Constantinople, but the Roman inhabitants "by surpassing the Arabians in art, . . . burnt their fleet with Greek fire, and compelled them to raise the siege. Thus, the Mahometan Empire was bounded by the Hellespont, and the entrance for Small Pox into Europe was barred up." [10]

Smallpox entered Spain in 710 as the consequence of the rape by King Roderick of an attendant upon the queen named Cava whose father, Count Julian, by way of revenge, betrayed his country to the Miramolin of Africa. "An army of Moors, conducted by Julian, landed at Gibraltar; the Goths were routed, Roderick perished, and the Mahometans were established in Spain. . . . By this invasion the Small Pox must have been brought into Spain, and the victorious Saracens soon reached the Pyrenees."

In 731 the Saracens poured across the mountains into southern France. "They were opposed, under the walls of Tours, by Charles Martel" and were ultimately driven back into Spain, "but the Small Pox and Measles remained in France." [11]

A powerful agent in carrying smallpox from the East to the West was the Crusades in the eleventh, twelfth, and thirteenth centuries.

The first mention of smallpox by an English historian was that of Raphael Holinshed (d. c. 1580) who, in describing a plague that occurred in England in 1366, said, "Also manie died of the Small Pocks, both men, women, and children." However, a tenth-century Anglo-Saxon manuscript had offered an "Exorcismus contra Variolas" (exorcism against smallpox).

"Hispaniola, or St. Domingo, was the first settlement founded by Columbus [in the New World]: after he was gone, numbers of adventurers flocked thither, whose hearts were hardened by avarice and fanaticism. The safety of the Indians never entered the thoughts of these men; and it is ascertained that the Small Pox and Measles were carried to that island in the year 1517; . . ." [12]

The word "measles" was first introduced in the earliest English treatise on medicine, the *Rosa Anglica* of John of Gaddesden (1280–1364).

DYSENTERY

"Various forms of painful infectious diarrhea, commonly called dysentery, have accompanied all armies as a fifth column, and have often decided the outcome of wars." [13]

References to this disease date back to Hippocrates and beyond. It seems clear that the disaster described by Herodotus that overcame the retreating army of Xerxes in 480 B.C. at least partially involved dysentery. Centuries later dysentery would be one of the elements that contributed to the defeat of the Crusaders. But dysentery as a disease was hard to pinpoint because the name was used to describe a variety of intestinal fluxes. This situation is well illustrated by the equivocal description of dysentery offered by August Hirsch (1817–1892), professor of medicine at the University of Berlin and author of the monumental *Handbook of Geographical and Historical Pathology*.

> Dysentery is the clinical name for an inflammatory affection of the mucous membrane of the great intestine and rectum, which runs its course either with fever or without fever, is either catarrhal or fibrinous (i.e. diphtheritic), and has among its characters, besides pain, borborygmi [rumblings in the bowels], and profuse watery or mucous discharges with tenesmus, more or less of blood in the stools. [14]

Whatever its antecedents, it is beyond question that dysentery was epidemic in France in the sixth century A.D. Gregory of Tours wrote at some length about an outbreak that occurred in the year 580:

> The kings were at strife and once more making ready for civil war, when a dysentery invaded almost the whole of Gaul. The sick suffered from severe fever with vomiting, exceeding pains of the kidneys, and a heaviness of head and neck; what they passed at the draught was of a yellowish or greenish colour. Many declared that the sickness was caused by secret poison. The country people described the cause as internal pustules, which is not so incredible a belief; for when cupping vessels were applied to the shoulders or

legs, vesicles swelled and burst, the matter escaped, and many were cured. Numbers found a safeguard in drinking a decoction of the herbs which are antidotes to poisons. This sickness, which began in the month of August, first attacked young children and brought them to their death. . . .

In these days Chilperic the king fell sick, and no sooner was he better, than his younger son, who was not yet reborn of water and the Holy Spirit, began to ail. Perceiving him nigh his end, they washed him in water of baptism. He became a little better; but his elder brother Chlodobert was now attacked by the disease. When the mother Fredegund saw him also in peril of death, she repented all too late, and said to the king: "The divine mercy hath long borne with us in our misdeeds; oft have we been seized with fevers and other ills, but there hath followed no amendment. And lo! now we lose our sons; lo! now they are slain by the tears of the poor, by the lamentations of widows, by the sighs of orphans, nor is there any object now left to us for which we may amass riches. We lay up treasures without knowing for whom we gather them together. Behold now our treasures are without an owner, having the taint of things plundered and accursed. Were not our store chambers full of wine, our granaries of corn? were not our treasuries filled with gold, with silver and precious stones, with necklaces and other royal ornaments. And lo! now we lose that which was lovliest of all that was ours. Come, therefore, if thou wilt, let us burn all the unjust tax-lists; let that be sufficient for our treasury which sufficed thy sire, King Lothar, before us." With these words the queen, smiting her breast with her clenched hands, bade them bring her the books which had been brought from her own cities [given to her by the bridegroom the morning after the wedding] . . . and cast them into the fire; then, turning once more to the king, she cried: "Wherefore delayest thou? Do now as thou seest me do, that if we must needs lose our dear children, we may at least escape eternal punishment." Thereupon the king, smitten to the heart, cast all the tax-lists into the fire, and when they were consumed, sent messengers to forbid assessment in future. But now the younger boy died, too feeble to resist decline, and his life was quenched. With exceeding grief they bore him from the domain of Berny to Paris, and caused him to be buried in the church of the holy Dionysius. Chlodobert they laid upon a stretcher, and took him to the church of the holy Médard at Soissons; then they set him down before the saint's tomb and made

vows for his recovery. But in the middle of the night, worn to a
shadow, and hardly drawing breath, he gave up the ghost. They
buried him in the church of the holy martyrs Crispin and Crispin-
ian. There was great lamentation of all the people; for men showing
their grief, and women in the sad weeds they wear at their husbands' burial, followed this prince's bier. And afterwards king Chilperic made great largess to cathedrals and churches, as well as to the
poor.

On these days, Austrechild, queen of Guntram, was consumed by
the same disease. But ere she breathed out her vile spirit she had
perceived with many a deep sigh that she could not escape; therefore
would she have companions in her death, and so wrought that at her
obsequies there should be sound of others wailing their own dead.
She is said to have made petition to the king . . ., saying: "I should
yet have had hope of life, were I not undone by the treatment of evil
physicians; the draughts which I have had from them have robbed
me of my life, and caused me thus swiftly to lose the light of day.
Wherefore I entreat thee, suffer not my death to pass unavenged; I
adjure thee under a solemn oath to have them slain with the sword
the moment that I shall have departed this light. If I may no longer
live, let these also have no power to glory after my passing, but let a
common grief fall on their friends and on mine." So saying she gave
up her unhappy soul. But the king, the funeral rites duly performed,
was constrained by the oath sworn to his unjust queen and fulfilled
her wicked behest. For he ordered the two doctors who had served
her well to be slain by the sword. It stood plain in the judgement of
thinking men that such fulfilment might not be without sin.

In 591 Aredius, abbot of Limoges,

was attacked by dysentery. On the sixth day of his sickness, a
woman, often vexed by an unclean spirit, from which the holy man
had not been able to deliver her, bound her hands behind her back,
and began crying aloud, and saying: "Run, O citizens! leap for joy,
O people! go forth to meet the martyrs and confessors who are now
come together for the passing of the blessed Aredius. . . ." When
she thus cried aloud at nightfall her master put her in bonds; but it
was impossible to hold her; she burst the bonds and rushed to the
monastery, uttering these same cries. Soon afterwards the holy man
gave up the ghost, not without true testimony that he had been

taken up of angels. During his funeral, when the grave was closed upon him, he delivered the woman from the evil of the infesting demon, together with another woman vexed by a yet more evil spirit.[15]

THE PESTILENCE OF 664

"In the same year of our Lord's incarnation, 664," wrote the Venerable Bede, "a sudden pestilence also depopulated the southern coasts of Britain, and afterwards extending into the province of the Northumbrians, ravaged the country far and near, and destroyed a great multitude of men. . . . This plague did no less harm in the island of Ireland." [16]

MacArthur has pointed out that "in editorial notes to several printed translations of Bede's writings [as in the case of the one used here] and other works, this pestilence is stated to have been a return of the Yellow Plague, a wrongful identification that has been spread far and wide by these blind guides. The editors, however, are not primarily responsible, because this distraction of the imagination was borrowed in the first place from some late copies of recensions of Irish annals where the mortality of 664 is called the Yellow Plague, . . ." After reviewing available source material, MacArthur arrived at a "reasoned conviction that the great epidemic of 664 was bubonic plague, and that in Ireland it was never supposed to be a second visitation of the Yellow Plague until some meddling scribe, writing at a date long after the event, inserted the name as a retrospective gloss in the mistaken assumption that this pestilence had been of the same nature as the true Buidhe Chonaill of the century before." [17]

The eminent British physician-historian Charles Creighton (1847–1927), who chose the year 664 as the starting point of his history of epidemics in Britain "for the reason that it is the year of the first pestilence in Britain recorded on contemporary or almost contemporary authority, that of Beda's 'Ecclesiastical History,' " was, like MacArthur, satisfied that the pestilence of 664 was bubonic plague—"an extension to England and Ireland of the great European invasion of bubo-plague in 543." But he noted ("on doubtful authority," it is true) "that the disease was a *pestis ictericia*, marked by yellowness of the skin, and colloquially known in the Irish language as *buide connaill*," adding that this was not "incompatible" with bubonic plague and was otherwise "unintelligible." He noted, however, that the Irish annals connected the name *pestis ictericia* or *buide connaill* "back to an alleged mortality in 543, or 548." [18]

MacArthur has already suggested how this confusion arose, but what was the so-called Yellow Plague that had broken out in Ireland a century earlier? It was known as the Pestis Flava in Latin, the buidhe (yellow) chonaill and crón (yellow-brown) chonaill by the Irish annalists, and the Fad Felen by the Britons—"all these names meaning the Yellow Plague." MacArthur based many of his conclusions on the *Liber Landavensis* (the Register Book of the Cathedral of Llandaff compiled about the year 1132), parts of which were drawn from entries in an older register attributed to St. Teilo, a prelate of the sixth century, with much added legendary matter. While the account of the Yellow Plague in the *Liber Landavensis* is somewhat "fanciful," it ends with the statement that "Christ, through his mercy, ordered that the aforesaid pestilence, which was called the yellow, should depart and vanish from the whole island of Britain."

MacArthur rejected the suggestion that the Yellow Plague was an epidemic "of severe confluent smallpox, the running together of the pocks masking the nature of the disease," both because "even in confluent smallpox of the greatest severity, when the face was one superficial abscess, the pocks on the body remained discrete and easily recognizable for what they were," and because "the ancient Irish were familiar with smallpox and called the disease by descriptive names of their own, which referred both to the pustules themselves, and to the heavy scabs they left when drying. Had the Yellow Plague been smallpox, they would have labelled it plainly as they did epidemics of that disease which also occurred in the sixth century. And another point: at no period in Ireland was the word 'yellow' used to describe smallpox."

MacArthur noted that the Irish annalists were not writing medical texts but simply recording outstanding events as they saw them. He then offered his conclusion that the only infection that could have caused a widespread and fatal epidemic in Britain and Ireland, with jaundice as a characteristic and predominating sign, was relapsing fever.

> It was many years ago when listening to an old man's account of epidemic typhus and relapsing fever in the last of the Irish famines, that I first thought of this identification of the sixth century pestilence. The old man knew relapsing fever only as "the yellow fever," and he explained that it was given this name because "those who caught it were coloured yellow with the jaundice." At once I remembered an identical explanation in the Liber Landavensis of the epidemic of fourteen centuries before: "It was called the Yellow Plague because it occasioned all persons who were seized by it to be yellow." Since then I have learned that relapsing fever was long called "the yellow fever," a name that pre-dated the one we use today. Thus, [James] Lind [1716–1794] writing of this disease in Haslar [Royal Naval] Hospital in 1761, says that it is "commonly by us denominated the *yellow fever*," and that "The tincture over the skin is universal of a deep yellow tinge." Out of much other evidence, I might mention that in the text-book by Robert [James] Graves [(1796–1853), published three-quarters of a century later] the section on relapsing fever has as its sole title: "The Yellow Fever of the British Islands." [19]

Speaking of a great epidemic of relapsing fever that occurred at the close of the 1820s, Creighton has said that some cases involved jaundice "which lead [William] Stokes [1804–1878] and Graves to speak loosely of 'yellow fever.' " [20]

It is obvious that Lind, Graves, and Stokes were not referring to the tropical and subtropical "yellow fever" that came out of Africa and Central and South America and devastated American port cities in the eighteenth and nineteenth centuries.

THE CRUSADES

The military expeditions known as the Crusades, undertaken by the Christian powers in the eleventh, twelfth, and thirteenth centuries to wrest the Holy Land from the Moslems, were defeated not "so much by the scimitars of the Saracens as by the hostile bacteria of dysentery and other epidemics." [21] The "other epidemics" were not always identifiable. In retrospect, in addition to dysentery and smallpox, malaria, typhoid, bubonic plague, and scurvy have been suggested, but the symptoms described often differ widely from modern criteria. Friedrich Prinzing, a German physician with more than a passing interest in epidemiological history, has stated that "the mortality of the First Crusade, before and after the conquest of Antioch (1097–8), was terrible." Disease broke out initially among the women and children who accompanied the armies, but spread to the troops and in three months carried off a total of 100,000. When 2500 German reinforcements arrived on the scene, they were immediately attacked by disease and almost completely annihilated. Bodies remaining unburied (during the extraordinarily hot summer of 1099) aggravated the situation.

During the Second Crusade (1147–49), "a severe epidemic broke out in the army of the Emperor Louis VII at Attalia [now Antalya] in Asia Minor; the pestilence spread rapidly among the inhabitants of the city, so that many houses, even entire streets, were depopulated." In 1190, a German army besieging Antioch was decimated by a severe pestilence. In the winter of 1191, during the siege of Acre, "a terrible pestilence . . . played havoc in the pilgrim army; it was caused by an inadequate supply of food, and its symptoms (enlargement of the limbs and falling out of the teeth) betoken scurvy. It also appeared in the army of Saladin [(1138–1193), sultan of Egypt and Syria], but was much worse in the Christian army, in which from 100 to 200 crusaders died each day. Duke Ferdinand of Swabia succumbed to this disease on January 20, 1191."

In August 1218 an army of crusaders in Egypt suffered from dysentery and the following December, while besieging the Egyptian port of Damietta, it was hit by what Prinzing has described as "unquestionably a severe form of scurvy." He based his conclusion on the following passage written by the German historian of the Crusades, Friedrich W. Wilken (1777–1840): "The patients were suddenly seized with violent pains in the feet and ankles; their gums became swollen, their teeth loose and useless, while their hips and shin bones first turned black and putrified. Finally, an easy and peaceful death, like a gentle sleep, put an end to their sufferings. A sixth of the pilgrim army was carried away by this disease, which no medicine could cure." When Damietta fell it was discovered that the besieged too had suffered from the destructive pestilence (complicated by granular conjunctivitis) to a point where houses and streets were filled with unburied corpses and "the infection of the air was intolerable." [22]

The French chronicler Jean de Joinville (1224?–1317) accompanied Louis IX (1214–1270), known as St. Louis, on the Seventh Crusade (1249–1254) and left an eyewitness account which covered some of the epidemics that beset the army.

Following two battles (one on Shrove Tuesday and the other on the first Friday in Lent, 1249)

> the bodies of those who had been slain in these two engagements, and thrown into the Nile rose to the top of the water. It was said that this always happens when the gall is burst and rotten. These bodies floated down the river until they came to the small bridge that communicated with each part of our army; and the arch was so low it almost touched the water, and prevented the bodies passing underneath. The river was covered with them from bank to bank, so that the water could not be seen a good stone's throw from the bridge upward.
>
> The king hired one hundred labourers, who were full eight days in separating the bodies of the Christians from the Saracens, which were easily distinguishable: the Saracen bodies they thrust under the bridge by main force, and floated them down to the sea; but the Christians they buried in deep graves, one over the other. God knows how great was the stench, and what misery it was to see the bodies of such noble and worthy persons lying so exposed. I witnessed the chamberlain of the late count d'Artois seeking the body of his master, and many more hunting after the bodies of their friends; but I never heard that any who were thus seeking their friends amidst such an infectious smell ever recovered their healths. You must know, that we ate no fish the whole lent but eelpouts, which is a gluttonous fish, and feeds on dead bodies. From this cause, and from the bad air of the country, where it scarcely ever rains a drop, the whole army was infected by a shocking disorder, which dried up

the flesh on our legs to the bone, and our skins became tanned as black as the ground, or like an old boot that has long lain behind a coffer. In addition to this miserable disorder, those affected by it had another sore complaint in the mouth, from eating such fish, that rotted the gums, and caused a most stinking breath. Very few escaped death that were thus attacked; and the surest symptom of its being fatal was a bleeding at the nose, for when that took place none ever recovered.

De Joinville made no attempt to name the disease, which may have been scurvy. He himself was a victim (though he recovered), suffering "such a rheum in my head it ran through my mouth and nostrils. In addition, I had a double fever, called a quartan, from which God defend us! and with these illnesses was I confined to my bed the half of Lent." The chronicler went on to relate a rather touching incident that occurred during his incapacity.

My poor priest was likewise as ill as myself; and one day when he was singing mass before me as I lay in my bed, at the moment of the elevation of the host, I saw him so exceedingly weak that he was near fainting; but when I perceived he was at the point of falling to the ground, I flung myself out of my bed, sick as I was, and taking my coat, embraced him, and bade him be at his ease, and take courage from him whom he held in his hands. He recovered some little; but I never quitted him until he had finished the mass, which he completed, and this was the last, for he never after celebrated another, but died. God receive his soul!

Easter came but brought no letup in the epidemic.

The disorder I spoke of very soon increased so much in the army that the barbers were forced to cut away very large pieces of flesh from the gums, to enable their patients to eat. It was pitiful to hear the cries and groans of those on whom this operation was performing; they seemed like to the cries of women in labour, and I cannot express the great concern all felt who heard them.

The good king, St. Louis, witnessing the miserable condition of great part of his army, raised his hands and eyes to heaven, blessing our Lord for all he had given him, and seeing that he could no longer remain where he was, without perishing himself as well as his army, gave orders to march on the Tuesday evening after the octave of Easter, and return to Damietta. He issued his commands to the masters of the galleys to have them ready to receive on board the sick and convey them to Damietta. . . .[23]

The Eighth Crusade, also led by Louis IX, set out in 1267 and three years later dysentery took the lives of the king himself and his son, Jean Tristan.

CHAPTER 6

The Black Death

THE second of the three most devastating epidemics to hit mankind—the Black Death—was cradled in Central Asia. Toward the close of the nineteenth century two ancient cemeteries, with tombstone inscriptions indicating that the graves were of Nestorian Christians, were discovered in the vicinity of Lake Issyk-Kul in the province of Semiryechensk in what is now the Kirgiz Soviet Socialist Republic. Among the inscriptions were three dating from 1338–1339 that stated that death had resulted from plague. Furthermore, it was evident that the number of deaths during this two-year period was exceptionally large.[1]

Lake Issyk-Kul is situated in rugged country, and in the fourteenth century trade caravans may not have passed through frequently, but history has demonstrated that bubonic plague goes where travelers go, and its gradual spread from the province of Semiryechensk eastward to China, south into India, and westward to the borders of Europe was inevitable. Its westward journey was hastened by Janibeg Khan, Tartar prince and ruler of the Western Kipchaks (the Golden Horde that had settled in the Crimea a century earlier). In 1346 Janibeg campaigned in the Kirgiz steppes, vast plains that are still the breeding grounds for wild rodents. His army brought back the seeds of plague.

The latter half of the thirteenth century saw the city-states of Genoa and Venice in open conflict over the immense wealth-potential of trade with the East. Ports on the Black Sea were of vital importance in establishing control of the great caravan trails from

China and Turkestan that ended in the Crimea. To secure and maintain their footholds, Genoa and Venice allied themselves with rival khans. In the 1340s Venice had Janibeg as its ally.

Kaffa (now Feodosiya), a well-fortified cathedral town on the Crimean coast, was Genoa's major port-city. On his return from the steppes, Janibeg inflated a trivial brawl into an excuse for laying siege to Kaffa.

The library of the University of Wroclaw, Poland, possesses the original Latin manuscript of a history of the Black Death, from its inception at Kaffa until it reached Piacenza (near Milan) in 1348, written by a Piacenza notary, Gabriel de Mussis (1280–1356).

It has generally been accepted that De Mussis' account of what occurred at Kaffa was that of an eyewitness and that he had been a passenger on one of the ships that carried the plague to Europe, but a "subsequent editor . . . has reluctantly but decisively established that de Mussis, during the critical period, never stirred from his native town of Piacenza." [2]

Nevertheless De Mussis' description of how the siege ended is as good and probably as accurate an account as anything available.

> Infinite numbers of Tartars and Saracens suddenly fell dead of an inexplicable disease . . . and behold the disease invading all the army of the Tartars . . . every day . . . thousands were killed . . . the humors coagulated in the groins, they developed a subsequent putrid fever and died, all council and aid of the doctors failing. . . . the Tartars, fatigued by such a plague and pestiferous disease, stupefied and amazed, observing themselves dying without hope of health ordered cadavers placed on their hurling machines and thrown into the city of Caffa, so that by means of these intolerable passengers the defenders died widely. Thus there were projected mountains of dead, nor could the Christians hide or flee, or be freed from such disaster . . . they allowed the dead to be consigned to the waves. And soon all the air was infected and the water poisoned, corrupt and putrefied, and such a great odor increased. . . .[3]

As a consequence of this early employment of bacteriological warfare, Kaffa became uninhabitable. Those citizens who had not yet succumbed to the plague took to their galleys and headed for the Mediterranean. Plague, of course, traveled with them.

This was not the only route by which bubonic plague reached Europe. From Central Asia it had struck southward into India whence it traveled on ships to the Persian Gulf and Red Sea and overland to Mediterranean ports in Asia Minor, Palestine, and Egypt.

In all, sixteen galleys brought plague to Italy and it seems unlikely that more than four set out from Kaffa. Of these, one reached Venice in January 1348 and the other three made Genoa the same month. But twelve plague-ridden galleys had put into Messina in Sicily three months earlier—October 1347—and where their voyage originated and where they picked up their cargo of death remain questionable. It may even have been Constantinople where plague raged in 1347, numbering among its victims the youngest son of the then Byzantine emperor. (The emperor, Ioannes [John VI] Cantacuzenus [1292?–1383], abdicated in 1355 to write a history of the empire from 1320 to 1356. In it he stressed the universality of the Black Death "which, starting first from the Hyperborean Scythians, attacked almost all the sea coasts of the world and killed most of their people. For it swept not only through Pontus, Thrace and Macedonia, but even Greece, Italy and all the islands, Egypt, Libya, Judaea and Syria, and spread throughout almost the entire world." [4])

Several days passed before the citizens of Messina realized that the surviving sailors and their ships had brought an epidemic pestilence into their midst. The action they then took came too late to save themselves and only served to involve others. They drove the ships out of port to find "safe harbor" where they might. One ship reached Marseilles in November 1347; the rest put in at Corsica, Sardinia, and other Mediterranean islands. Ships from Marseilles carried the pestilence to Barcelona and Valencia, whence plague spread throughout Spain and Portugal.

Like the Messinans, the Genoese drove off the three ships from Kaffa that made their home port, but again action came too late. From plague-infested Messina, Venice, and Genoa, the epidemic spread its tentacles throughout Italy. Pisa, Florence, Bologna, Parma, and Piacenza had succumbed by April 1348. From Venice, what is now Yugoslavia, Austria, Hungary, and Bavarian Germany were attacked.

The plague took two roads out of Marseilles. One followed the Rhone valley to Avignon, the then seat of the papacy, which was hard hit in April, May, and June. The other route led west. Montpellier was quickly involved, Toulouse by early summer, and Bordeaux on the Atlantic coast in August.

By the end of 1348 plague had blanketed all of Italy and most of France. It had crossed the Alps into Switzerland. England was reached in August (by a ship from Calais that put into the Dorsetshire port of Melcombe), and the epidemic, following the south coast, was in London by October. Mid-1349 found the balance of France, Belgium, and half of England under attack; by the end of the year the rest of England, Scotland, Ireland, Denmark, and most of Germany were involved. Norwegian ships carried the plague as far as Iceland and Greenland. It was in Sweden and Poland in 1350 but did not reach Russia until 1351. This is surprising. One might have expected that the pestilence would have journeyed north from the Crimea or northwest from the steppes to European Russia, but that was not the direction in which trade flowed.

The Black Death engulfed more of the populated world and resulted in more deaths in four years than the Plague of Justinian did in fifty.

SICILY

Discussion has so far been limited to the bare bones of the plague's four-year journey. But what of the social, economic, moral, religious, superstitious, medical impact of its passage and other side effects? For such information reliance must be placed on contemporary writers, where they existed, and later commentaries that are not always reliable.

Plague made its entry into Europe through the Sicilian port of Messina and ten years later a Franciscan friar, Michael Platiensis of Piazza, wrote an account of the event.

At the beginning of October, in the year of the incarnation of the Son of God 1347, twelve Genoese galleys were fleeing from the vengeance which our Lord was taking on account of their nefarious deeds and entered the harbour of Messina. In their bones they bore so virulent a disease that anyone who only spoke to them was seized by a mortal illness and in no manner could evade death. The infection spread to everyone who had intercourse with the diseased. Those infected felt themselves penetrated by a pain throughout their whole bodies and, so to say, undermined. Then there developed in their thighs or on their upper arms a boil . . . This infected the whole body and penetrated it so far that the patient violently vomited blood. [Evidently pneumonic in addition to bubonic plague.] This vomiting of blood continued without intermission for three days, there being no means of healing it, and then the patient expired. But not only all those who had intercourse with them died, but also those who had touched or used any of their things. . . . Soon men hated each other so much that, if a son was attacked by the disease, his father would not tend him. If, in spite of all, he dared to approach him, he was immediately infected and . . . was bound to expire within three days. Nor was this all; all those . . . dwelling in the same house with him . . . followed him in death. As the number of deaths increased in Messina many desired to confess their sins to the priests and to draw up their last will and testament. But ecclesiastics, lawyers and attorneys refused to enter the houses of the diseased. But if one or the other had set foot in such a house . . . he was hopelessly abandoned to sudden death. Minor friars and Dominicans and members of other orders who heard the confessions of the dying were themselves immediately overcome by death, so that some even remained in the rooms of the dying. Soon the corpses were lying forsaken in the houses. No ecclesiastic, no son, no father and no relation dared to enter, but they paid hired servants with high wages to bury the dead. But the houses of the deceased remained open with all their valuables, with gold and jewels; anyone who chose to enter met with no impediment, for the plague raged with such vehemence that soon there was a shortage of servants and finally none at all. When the catastrophe had reached its climax the Messinians resolved to emigrate. One portion of them settled in the vineyards and the fields, but a larger portion sought refuge in the town of Catania, trusting that the holy virgin Agatha of Catania would deliver them from their evil. To this town the Queen of

Sicily came and summoned her son Don Federigo. In November the Messinians persuaded the Patriarch, Archbishop of Catania, to permit the relics of the saints to be brought to their town. But the populace of Catania would not allow the sacred bones to be removed from their old place. Now intercessory processions and pilgrimages were undertaken to Catania to propitiate God. But the plague raged with greater vehemence than before. Flight was no longer of avail. The disease clung to the fugitives and accompanied them everywhere where they turned in search of help. Many of the fleeing fell down by the roadside and dragged themselves into the fields and bushes to expire. Those who reached Catania breathed their last in the hospitals there. The terrified citizens demanded from the Patriarch prohibition on pain of ecclesiastical ban [excommunication], of burying fugitives from Messina within the town, and so they were all thrown into deep trenches outside the walls.

The population of Catania was so godless and timid that no one among them . . . offered [the fugitives] shelter. If some relations in Catania had not secretly harboured a number of people from Messina, they would have been deprived of all assistance. Thus the people of Messina dispersed over the whole island of Sicily . . . and with them the disease, so that . . . innumerable people died. . . . As soon as anyone in Catania was seized with a headache and shivering, he knew that he was bound to pass away within the specified time, and first confessed his sins to the priest and then made his last will. When the plague had attained its height in Catania, the patriarch endowed all ecclesiastics, even the youngest, with all priestly powers for the absolution of sin which he himself possessed as bishop and patriarch. But the pestilence raged from October 1347 to April 1348. The patriarch himself was one of the last to be carried off. He died fulfilling his duty. At the same time Duke Giovanni, who had carefully avoided every infected house and every patient, died.[5]

Being situated in the north of Italy it might be expected that bubonic plague would have reached Pisa, the gateway to Tuscany, from Genoa, but it was two freight ships from Messina that brought the disease. "The crews of both the ships were suffering from the plague, and all those in Pisa who spoke to the sailors on the Piazza dei Pesci were seized and died immediately."[6]

FLORENCE

In the mid-fourteenth century the Tuscan city of Florence was one of the greatest cities in Europe. It was so severely hit by the raging epidemic—more so than Rome, Paris, and Milan and at least as violently as London and Vienna—that the Black Death was sometimes referred to as the Plague of Florence. It is appropriate therefore that the best-known eyewitness account of the plague and its impact should have been written in *The Decameron* of the famous Italian author Giovanni Boccaccio (1313–1375), whose father died of the plague in 1348. His narrative began as follows:

> I say, then, that the years [of the era] of the fruitful Incarnation of the Son of God had attained to the number of one thousand three hundred and forty-eight, when into the noble city of Florence, fair over every other of Italy, there came the death-dealing pestilence, which, through the operation of the heavenly bodies or of our own iniquitous dealings, being sent down upon mankind for our correction by the just wrath of God, had some years before appeared in the parts of the East and having bereft these latter of an innumerable number of inhabitants, extending without cease from one place to another, had now unhappily spread towards the West. And thereagainst no wisdom availing nor human foresight (whereby the city was purged of many impurities by officers deputed to that end and it was forbidden unto any sick person to enter therein and many were the counsels given for the preservation of health) nor yet humble supplications, nor once but many times both in ordered processions and on other wise made unto God by devout persons,—about the coming in of the Spring of the aforesaid year, it began in horrible and miraculous wise to show forth its dolorous effects. . . . [I]n men and women alike there appeared, at the beginning of the malady, certain swellings, either on the groin or under the armpits, whereof some waxed of the bigness of a common apple, others like unto an egg, some more and some less, and these the vulgar named plague-boils. . . .
>
> To the cure of these maladies nor counsel of physician nor virtue of any medicine appeared to avail or profit aught; on the contrary,— whether it was that the nature of the infection suffered it not or that the ignorance of physicians . . . availed not to know whence it arose

and consequently took not due measures thereagainst,—not only did few recover thereof, but well nigh all died within the third day from the appearance of the aforesaid signs, this sooner and that later, and for the most part without fever or other accident. And this pestilence was the more virulent for that, by communication with those who were sick thereof, it got hold upon the sound, . . . not only did converse and consortion with the sick give to the sound infection or cause of common death, but the mere touching of the clothes or of whatsoever other thing had been touched or used of the sick appeared of itself to communicate the malady to the toucher.

The impotency of the medical profession and fear of contagion prompted the individual

to shun and flee from the sick and . . . secure immunity for himself. Some there were who conceived that to live moderately and keep oneself from all excess was the best defence against such a danger; wherefore, making up their company, they lived removed from every other and shut themselves in those houses where none had been sick and where living were best; and there, using very temperately of the most delicate viands and the finest wines and eschewing incontinence, they abode with music and such other diversions as they might have, never suffering themselves to speak with any nor choosing to hear any news from without of death or sick folks. Others, inclining to the contrary opinion, maintained that to carouse and make merry and go about singing and frolicking and satisfy the appetite in everything possible and laugh and scoff at whatsoever befell was a very certain remedy for such an ill. That which they said they put in practice as best they might, going about day and night, now to this tavern, now to that, drinking without stint or measure; and on this wise they did yet more freely in other folk's [abandoned] houses, . . . the reverend authority of the laws, both human and divine, [having] fallen into decay, for [lack of] the ministers and executors thereof, . . . Many other held a middle course between the two aforesaid, not straitening themselves so exactly in the matter of diet as the first neither allowing themselves such license in drinking and other debauchery as the second, but using things in sufficiency, according to their appetites; nor did they seclude themselves, but went about, carrying in their hands, some flowers, some odoriferous herbs and other some divers kind of spic-

eries, which they set often to their noses, accounting it an excellent
thing to fortify the brain with such odours, more by token that the
air seemed all heavy and attainted with the stench of the dead bodies
and that of the sick and of the remedies used.

Still others abandoned their possessions and fled to the country,
but this, like the other approaches described by Boccaccio, offered
no guarantee of immunity. These individual attempts at self-
preservation were understandable. What was indeed shocking was
the callousness with which

> brother forsook brother, uncle nephew and sister brother and of-
> times wife husband; nay (what is yet more extraordinary and well
> nigh incredible) fathers and mothers refused to visit or tend their
> very children, as they had not been theirs. By reason whereof there
> remained unto those . . . who fell sick, none other succour than
> that which they owed either to the charity of friends (and of these
> there were few) or the greed of servants, who tended them, allured
> by high and extravagent wage; . . . many of [whom] perished with
> their gain. . . .

Unavoidably, the amenities of death and burial were abandoned.
Instead

> blood-suckers, sprung from the dregs of the people, who styled
> themselves *pickmen* and did such offices for hire, shouldered the bier
> and bore it with hurried steps, not to that church which the dead
> man had chosen before his death, but most times to the nearest,
> behind five or six priests, with little light and whiles none at all,
> which latter, with the aid of the said pickmen, thrust him into what
> grave soever they first found unoccupied, without troubling them-
> selves with too long or too formal a service.
>   The condition of the common people . . . was yet more pitiable
> to behold, for that these . . . sickened by the thousand daily and
> being altogether unattended and unsuccoured, died well nigh all
> without recourse. Many breathed this last in the open street, whilst
> other many, for all they died in their houses, made it known to the
> neighbours that they were dead rather by the stench of their rotting
> bodies than otherwise; and of these and others who died all about

the whole city was full. . . . The consecrated ground sufficing not
to the burial of the vast number of corpses aforesaid, which daily
and well nigh hourly came carried in crowds to every church, . . .
there was made through the churchyards, after every other part was
full, vast trenches, wherein those who came after were laid by the
hundred and being heaped up therein by layers, as goods are stowed
aboard ship, were covered with a little earth, till such time as they
reached the top of the trench.

Conditions in the surrounding country were as bad as those in
the city. The "poor and miserable husbandmen and their families,
without succour of physician or aid of servitor, died, not like men,
but well nigh like beasts," and in their hopelessness abandoned
"the future produce of their cattle and their fields and the fruits of
their own past toils." Just as some residents of the city had fled to
the country, countrymen sought refuge in the city, but seemingly
in greater numbers for, "between March and the following July,
. . . it is believed for certain that upward of an hundred thousand
human beings perished within the walls of the city of Florence,
which, peradventure, before the advent of the death-dealing calamity, had not been accounted to hold so many," which led Boccaccio
to exclaim in conclusion:

How many valiant men, how many fair ladies, how many sprightly
youths, whom, not only other, but Galen, Hippocrates or Æscula-
pius themselves would have judged most hale, breakfasted in the
morning with their kinsfolk, comrades and friends and that same
night supped with their ancestors in the other world! [7]

PARMA AND PIACENZA

The Italian poet Petrarch (Francesco Petrarca [1304–1374]) wrote
from Parma in May or June 1349:

Alas, my loving brother, what shall I say? How can I begin? Where
shall I turn? Everything is woe, terror everywhere. You may see in
me what you have read in Virgil of the great city, with "everywhere

tearing pain, everywhere fear and the manifold images of death."
Oh, brother, would that I had never been born or that I had already
met my death! . . .

I think that my complaints will be excused, if one reflects that I
am not mourning some slight distress but that dreadful year 1348,
which not merely robbed us of our friends, but robbed the whole
world of its peoples. And if that were not enough, now this following year reaps the remainder, and cuts down with its deadly scythe
whatever survived that storm. Will posterity credit that there was a
time when, with no deluge from heaven, no worldwide conflagra-
tion, no wars or other visible devastation, not merely this or that territory but almost the whole earth was depopulated? When was such
a disaster ever seen, even heard of? In what records can we read that
houses were emptied, cities abandoned, countrysides untilled, fields
heaped with corpses, and a vast, dreadful solitude over all the
world? Consult the historians; they are silent. Interrogate the physicians; they are dumbfounded. Ask the philosophers; they shrug their
shoulders, they wrinkle their brows; finger to lip they command
silence. Posterity, will you believe what we who lived through it can
hardly accept? We should think we were dreaming, had we not the
testimony of our opened eyes, encountering on our city walks only
funerals, and on our return finding our home empty of our dear
ones. Thus we learn that our troubles are real and true. Oh how
happy will be future times, unacquainted with such miseries, perhaps counting our testimony as fabulous! . . .

But to turn from public griefs to our private ones, hardly a year
and a half has gone by since, departing for Italy, I left you in tears
by the tearful fountain of the Sorgue. Look no further back; count
these few days, and think what we were and what we are. Where
now are those sweet friends, where are the loved faces, where are
the caressing words, the gay and gentle conversation? What light-
ning bolt destroyed them, what earthquake overthrew them, what
tempest submerged them, what abyss swallowed them? We· were a
close-knit band; and now we are almost alone. We must make new
friendships. Where shall we find them? And to what end, if the
human race is almost extinguished, if, as I surmise, the end of the
world is at hand? . . .

There remained for me here a survivor of the wrecks of last year,
a man distinguished above all, and, on my word, great of soul and
wise in judgment. This was Paganino da Milano. After several trials

of his worth, I found him most congenial. I judged that as my friend he was worthy to be friend to us all. . . .

Now he too was suddenly snatched away by the pestilence that ravages the world. He dined in the evening with friends, and afterward he spent some time with me in talk and friendly discussion of our affairs. That night he was attacked. He bore his sufferings with a stout spirit; and in the morning death came swiftly. And that no evil should be spared him, within three days his children and his whole family followed him to the grave. . . .[8]

While De Mussis may not have been an eyewitness in the Black Sea, his account of what occurred in his home city can certainly be relied upon:

. . . and thus that disease entered Piacenza . . . I do not know where I can begin. Everywhere wailing and lamentations arose . . . the bodies of the dead without number to be buried . . . there was inadequate land for the graves . . . they were compelled to make ditches by the piazza and the courtyards where never tombs existed. . . . infinite number of young people, especially pregnant women died in a short time. . . . the great and the noble were hurled into the same grave with the vile and the abject, because the dead were all alike. . . . By day and by night they were led to the grave with a brief ecclesiastical office . . . one said O father why dost thou abandon me, another O mother where are thou . . . husband and wife who placidly shared the marriage bed now separated. . . . and when the spirit left, the mother often refused to touch the child, the husband the wife . . . the victim lay sick alone at home . . . the physician did not enter . . . the thunderstruck priest administered the ecclesiastical sacraments timidly. . . . what are we to do, oh good Jesus? [9]

FRANCE

France in the fourteenth century did not possess eloquent chroniclers and poets to equal those in Italy, but her place in the history of the Black Death was assured by the unremitting labors of her churchmen, from papal councillor to penniless, itinerant monk.

"During the plague at Marseilles the Capucins and Jesuits distinguished themselves; they hastened from all quarters of the world to
place themselves at the service of those attacked by the plague. At
that time members of these Orders were to be seen in the streets of
Marseilles who had hardly recovered from the disease, and still
covered with plague boils dragged themselves along on their sticks
to hear the confessions of the dying." [10] (Nohl has clearly confused
some other order with the Jesuits because the Society of Jesus was
not founded until 1534.) The papal city of Avignon appears to have
been hit harder by plague than any other city in France. It came so
fast that sixty-six Carmelite friars had died before citizens knew of
the calamity that had fallen on them. Nonetheless the survivors of
the order and members of other mendicant orders served the people with courage and devotion. But they did not serve alone. Seven
cardinals died of the plague. Pope Clement VI (1291–1352) played
a less active personal role (after all, nothing was to be gained by his
death), but he was constantly in touch with the needs of his flock
and ready to take action to alleviate their distress. In time, disposal
of the dead became a major problem. An unidentified canon, in the
train of a visiting cardinal, wrote his friends in Bruges (Belgium) on
April 27, 1348:

> To put the matter shortly, one-half, or more than a half of the
> people at Avignon are already dead. Within the walls of the city
> there are now more than 7,000 houses shut up; in these no one is liv-
> ing, and all who have inhabited them are departed; the suburbs
> hardly contain any people at all. A field near "Our Lady of Mira-
> cles" has been bought by the Pope and consecrated as a cemetery. In
> this, from the 13th of March, 11,000 corpses have been buried. This
> number does not include those interred in the cemetery of the hospi-
> tal of St. Anthony, in cemeteries belonging to the religious bodies,
> and in the many others which exist in Avignon. [11]

As a final measure, Clement consecrated the Rhone River so that
surplus bodies might be dumped in it.

As for Pope Clement himself, his physician in ordinary Guy de
Chauliac (1300–1368), whose eminence as an authority on surgery
lasted through the fifteenth century, promptly recognized plague as

an infectious disease. He required his patient to sit day and night between two enormous fires, kindled to purify the air. "The fires may in fact have been some help in keeping the Pope free of infection, remembering the plague bacillus's low tolerance for heat, for, as anyone who has been in Avignon in the summer can attest, the heat must have been fearsome." [12] But superstitious elements, typical of the age, were not lacking. The pope wore on his finger "as a protection against the plague an emerald which was said to have produced marvellous effects. Turned towards the south it minimized the virulence of the poison, turned to the east it reduced the possibility of infection." [13]

When a majority of regular priests fled Paris, administration of the sacraments was taken over by members of religious orders; the sisters at the Hôtel-Dieu (hospital) particularly distinguished themselves by their care of the afflicted. According to a contemporary chronicler, Guillaume de Nangis, "So great was the mortality in the Hôtel-Dieu of Paris that for a long time more than fifty corpses were carried away from it each day in carts to be buried. And the devout sisters of the Hôtel-Dieu, not fearing death, worked piously and humbly, not out of regard for any worldly honour. A great number of these said sisters were frequently summoned to their reward by death, and rest in peace with Christ, as is piously believed." [14]

"The physicians of the 14th century, during the Black Death, did what human intellect could do in the actual condition of the healing art; and their knowledge was by no means despicable." [15] But their best was not very good, as was revealed by the countrywide devastation in the wake of the plague. Gilles Li Muisis, abbot of St. Martin's, Tournai (just across the border into Belgium), offered this description:

> It is almost impossible to credit the mortality throughout the whole country. Travellers, merchants, pilgrims, and others who have passed through it declare that they have found cattle wandering without herdsmen in the fields, towns and waste-lands; that they have seen barns and wine-cellars standing wide open, houses empty and few people to be found anywhere. . . . And in many different areas, both lands and fields are lying uncultivated. [16]

These conditions are hardly surprising. Estimates of deaths in Europe have run as high as a quarter of its population.

ENGLAND

The chief source of information about plague in England has been church records. Among the compilers of such records was William of Dene, a monk of Rochester (in Kent) who has been described as "one of the few English chroniclers who handles the events of the day with anything like the impressionistic brio of his continental counterparts." [17]

> In this year [1349] a plague of a kind that had never been met with before ravaged our land of England. The Bishop of Rochester, who maintained only a small household, lost four priests, five esquires, ten attendants, seven young clerics and six pages, so that nobody was left to serve him in any capacity. At Malling he consecrated two abbesses but both died almost immediately, leaving only four established nuns and four novices. One of these the Bishop put in charge of the lay members and the other of the religious for it proved impossible to find anyone suitable to act as abbess.
>
> To our great grief, the plague carried off so vast a multitude of people of both sexes that nobody could be found who would bear the corpses to the grave. Men and women carried their own children on their shoulders to the church and threw them into a common pit. From these pits such an appalling stench was given off that scarcely anyone dared even to walk beside the cemeteries.
>
> There was so marked a deficiency of labourers and workmen of every kind at this period that more than a third of the land in the whole realm was left idle. All the labourers, skilled or unskilled, were so carried away by the spirit of revolt that neither King, nor law, nor justice, could restrain them. . . .[18]

THE FLAGELLANTS

"The mental shock sustained by all nations during the prevalence of the Black Plague, is without parallel and beyond description," wrote J. F. C. Hecker (1795–1850), who was generally recognized in his day to be the most learned medical historian and one of the most able medical writers in Germany. This state of shock left most people without hope for the future. The pious "closed their accounts with the world" while the transgressor repented, devoting "his remaining hours to the exercise of Christian virtues."

As so often happens when the times are out of joint, groups of bigoted fanatics usurped the absolving functions of ecclesiastical orders and brotherhoods that had tended to become hidebound in their performance. Originating in Hungary and moving into Germany and neighboring countries, the Brotherhood of the Flagellants (also known as the Brethren of the Cross, or Cross-bearers)

> took upon themselves the repentance of the people, for the sins they had committed, and offered prayers and supplications for the averting of this plague. This Order consisted chiefly of persons of the lower class, who were either actuated by sincere contrition, or, who joyfully availed themselves of this pretext for idelness, and were hurried along with the tide of distracting frenzy. But as these brotherhoods gained in repute, and were welcomed by the people with veneration and enthusiasm, many nobles and ecclesiastics ranged themselves under their standard; and their bands were not infrequently augmented by children, honourable women and nuns; so powerfully were minds of the most opposite temperaments enslaved by this infatuation. They marched through the cities, in well organized processions, with leaders and singers; their heads covered as far as the eyes; their look fixed on the ground, accompanied by every token of the deepest contrition and mourning. They were robed in sombre garments, with red crosses on the breast, back, and cap, and bore triple scourges, tied in three or four knots, in which points of iron were fixed. Tapers and magnificent banners of velvet and cloth of gold, were carried before them; wherever they made their appearance, they were welcomed by the ringing of bells; and the people flocked from all quarters, to listen to their hymns and to witness their penance, with devotion and tears.
>
> . . . Whoever was desirous of joining the brotherhood, was bound to remain in it thirty-four days, and to have four pence per day at his own disposal, so that he might not be burthensome to any one; if married, he was obliged to have the sanction of his wife, and

give the assurance that he was reconciled to all men. The Brothers of
the Cross, were not permitted to seek for free quarters, or even to
enter a house without having been invited; they were forbidden to
converse with females; and if they transgressed these rules, or acted
without discretion, they were obliged to confess to the Superior,
who sentenced them to several lashes of the scourge by way of
penance. Ecclesiastics had not, as such, any pre-eminence among
them; according to their original law, which, however, was often
transgressed, they could not become Masters, or take part in the
Secret Councils. Penance was performed twice every day: in the morning and evening, they went abroad in pairs, singing psalms, amid
the ringing of the bells; and when they arrived at the place of flagel-
lation, they stripped the upper part of their bodies and put off their
shoes, keeping on only a linen dress, reaching from the waist to the
ancles. They then lay down in a large circle, in different positions,
according to the nature of their crime: the adulterer with his face to
the ground; the perjurer on one side, holding up three of his fingers,
&c., and were then castigated, some more and some less, by the
Master, who ordered them to rise in the words of a prescribed form.
Upon this, they scourged themselves, amid the singing of psalms
and loud supplications for the averting of the plague, with genuflex-
ions, and other ceremonies, of which contemporary writers give
various accounts; and at the same time constantly boasted of their
penance, that the blood of their wounds was mingled with that of
the Savior. One of them, in conclusion, stood up to read a letter,
which it was pretended an angel had brought from heaven, to St.
Peter's church, at Jerusalem, stating that Christ, who was sore dis-
pleased at the sins of man, had granted, at the intercession of the
Holy Virgin and of the angels, that all who should wander about for
thirty-four days and scourge themselves, should be partakers of the
Divine grace. . . .

All this had so powerful an effect, that the church was in considerable danger; for the Flagellants gained more credit than the priests,
from whom they so entirely withdrew themselves, that they even
absolved each other. Besides, they everywhere took possession of the
churches, and their new songs, which went from mouth to mouth,
operated strongly on the minds of the people. Great enthusiasm and
originally pious feelings, are clearly distinguishable in these hymns,
and especially in the chief psalm of the Crossbearers, which is still
extant, and which was sung all over Germany, in different dialects,

and is probably of a more ancient date. Degeneracy, however, soon crept in; crimes were everywhere committed; and there was no energetic man capable of directing the individual excitement to purer objects, even had an effectual resistance to the tottering church been at that early period seasonable, and had it been possible to restrain the fanaticism. . . .

The Processions of the Brotherhood of the Cross undoubtedly promoted the spreading of the plague; and it is evident, that the gloomy fanaticism which gave rise to them, would infuse a new poison into the already desponding minds of the people.[19]

PERSECUTION OF THE JEWS

In every destructive pestilence, the common people at first attribute the mortality to poison. No instruction avails; the supposed testimony of their eyesight, is to them a proof, and they authoritatively demand the victims of their rage. On whom then was it so likely to fall, as on the Jews, the usurers and strangers who lived at enmity with the Christians? . . .

The persecution of the Jews commenced in September and October, 1348, at Chillon, on the Lake of Geneva, where the first criminal proceedings were instituted against them, after they had long before been accused by the people of poisoning the wells; similar scenes followed in Bern and Freyburg, in January, 1349. Under the influence of excruciating suffering, the tortured Jews confessed themselves guilty of the crime imputed to them; and it being affirmed that poison had in fact been found in a well at Zoffingen, this was deemed a sufficient proof to convince the world; and the persecution of the abhorred culprits, thus appeared justifiable. . . .

Already in the autumn of 1348, a dreadful panic, caused by this supposed empoisonment, seized all nations; in Germany especially, the springs and wells were built over, that nobody might drink of them, or employ their content for culinary purposes; and for a long time, the inhabitants of numerous towns and villages, used only rain water. The city gates were also guarded with the greatest caution: only confidential people were admitted; and if medicine, or any other article, which might be supposed to be poisonous, were found in the possession of a stranger,—and it was natural that some should

have these things by them for their private use,—they were forced
to swallow a portion of it. By this trying state of privation, distrust,
and suspicion, the hatred against the supposed poisoners became
greatly increased, and often broke out in popular commotions,
which only served still further to infuriate the wildest passions. . . .
in Basle the populace obliged [the burgomasters and senators] to
bind themselves by an oath, to burn the Jews, and to forbid persons
of that community from entering their city, for the space of two
hundred years. Upon this, all the Jews in Basle, whose number
could not have been inconsiderable, were enclosed in a wooden
building, constructed for the purpose, and burnt together with it,
upon the mere outcry of the people, without sentence or trial, which
indeed would have availed them nothing. . . .

The humanity and prudence of Clement VI., must, on this occasion, also be mentioned to his honour; but even the highest ecclesiastical power was insufficient to restrain the unbridled fury of the
people. He not only protected the Jews at Avignon, as far as lay in
his power, but also issued two bulls, in which he declared them innocent; and admonished all Christians, though without success, to
cease from such groundless persecutions. The Emperor Charles IV.
was also favourable to them, and sought to avert their destruction,
wherever he could; but he dared not draw the sword of justice, and
even found himself obliged to yield to the selfishness of the Bohe-
mian nobles, who were unwilling to forego so favourable an opportunity of releasing themselves from their Jewish creditors, under
favour of an imperial mandate. Duke Albert of Austria burned and
pillaged those of his cities, which had persecuted Jews,—a vain and
inhuman proceeding, which, moreover, is not exempt from the suspicion of covetousness; yet he was unable, in his own fortress of
Kyberg, to protect some hundreds of Jews, who had been received
there, from being barbarously burnt by the inhabitants. Several
other princes and counts, among them Ruprecht von der Pfalz, took
the Jews under their protection, on the payment of large sums; in
consequence of which they were called "Jew-masters," and were in
danger of being attacked by the populace and by their powerful
neighbours. These persecuted and ill-used people, except indeed
where humane individuals took compassion on them at their own
peril, or when they could command riches to purchase protection,
had no place of refuge left but the distant country of Lithuania,
where Boleslav V., Duke of Poland (1227–1279), had granted them

liberty of conscience; and King Casimir the Great (1333–1370), yielding to the entreaties of Esther, a favorite Jewess, received them, and granted them further protection: on which account, that country is still inhabited by a great number of Jews, who by their secluded habits, have, more than any people in Europe, retained the manners of the middle ages.[20]

But even bad things, and the horrors attendant upon them, come at last to an end. "After this, when the plague, the flagellant pilgrimages, the pilgrimages to Rome, and the slaughtering of the Jews were over, the world once more began to live and joy returned to it, and men began to make new clothes."[21]

The Dancing Mania

"THE effects of the *Black Death* had not yet subsided, and the graves of millions of its victims were scarcely closed, when a strange delusion arose in Germany, which took possession of the minds of men, and, in spite of the divinity of our nature, hurried away body and soul into the magic circle of hellish superstition. It was a convulsion which in the most extraordinary manner infuriated the human frame, and excited the astonishment of contemporaries for more than two centuries, since which time it has never reappeared." [1] Known as the dancing mania (or epidemic chorea from the Greek word for dance) and embracing tarantism in Italy as well as St. John's and St. Vitus's dances in the north, this psychic epidemic, while not strictly restricted thereto, must be regarded as a phenomenon of the Middle Ages. Otherwise discussion pertaining to it might introduce so-called mental disorders ranging from "hysteria" in ancient Egypt to group manifestations, often "quirky," in the present age of anxiety.

According to Peter of Herental, a monk and apparently an eyewitness, in 1374

> a strange sect, comprising men and women, from various parts of Germany, came to Aachen, and they went as far as Hennegau and France. This was their condition. Both men and women were abused by the devil to such a degree that they danced in their homes, in the churches and in the streets, holding each other's hands and leaping in the air. While they danced they called out the names

of demons, such as Friskes and others, but they were unaware of this nor did they pay attention to modesty even though people watched them. At the end of the dance, they felt such pains in the chest, that if their friends did not tie linen clothes tightly around their waists, they cried out like madmen that they were dying. In Liège they were freed of their demons by means of exorcisms such as those employed before baptism. Those who were cured said they seemed to be dancing in a river of blood, which is why they jumped into the air. However, the people of Liège said that they had been attacked in this way because they were not truly baptized inasmuch as most of the priests kept concubines. For this reason the populace proposed that they rise against the priests, kill them and take their property, which would have happened had not God provided a remedy through the aforesaid exorcisms. When the people saw this their anger subsided to such an extent that the clergy were held in even greater reverence than before.[2]

An unidentified chronicler offered a decidedly different account of the 1374 outburst in the Rhineland and Flanders:

In the year 1374, in summer, there happened a curious thing on the earth, and particularly in districts of Germany on the Rhine and the Moselle—it being that the people began to dance and rush about; they formed groups of three and danced in one place for half a day, and while dancing they fell to the ground and allowed others to trample on their bodies. By this they believed that they could cure themselves of illness. And they walked from one town to another and collected money from the people, wherever they could procure any. And this was carried on to such an extent that in the town of Cologne alone more than five hundred dancers were to be found. And it was found to be a swindle, undertaken for the purpose of obtaining money, and that a number of them both women and men might be tempted to unchastity and succumb to it. And there were found at Cologne more than a hundred women and servant maids who had no husbands. And in their dancing bouts they were all with child, and when they danced they laced up their bodies closely, so as to appear more slender. Hereupon a good many masters, particularly many good physicians, said that many of those who took to dancing were affected with too full-blooded constitutions and other natural infirmities.[3]

Did the St. John's dance (the association of the 1374 outbreak with John the Baptist derived from the fact that the occurrence at Aachen—Aix-la-Chapelle—around July 15 corresponded with St. John's day; the relating to St. Vitus, the curer, came later) involve religious fervor, as suggested by Peter of Herental, or the license described by the other chronicler? Precedent—especially that of an eyewitness account dating back to 1188—suggests the former.

Gerald de Barri (Giraldus Cambrensis [1146?–?1220]), Welsh churchman and author of *Itinerary through Wales*, offered this 1188 account of a solemn feast held annually at the church of St. Almedha in Brecknockshire

> attended by many people from a considerable distance, when those who labor under various diseases, receive the health they desire through the merits of the Blessed Virgin. The circumstances which occur at every anniversary appear to me remarkable. You may see men or girls, now in the church, now in the churchyard, now in the dance that is led round the churchyard with a song, suddenly falling to the ground as in a trance, then jumping up in a frenzy, and representing with their hands and feet, before the people, whatever work they have unlawfully done on feast days; you may see one man put his hand to the plough, and another, as it were, goad on the oxen, mitigating the animal's sense of labor by the usual rude song; one man imitating the occupation of a shoemaker, another walking and arranging the threads for a web; another, as it were, throwing the shuttle and seeming to weave. Upon being brought into the church and led up to the altar with their oblations, you will be astonished to see them suddenly awakened, and coming to themselves. Thus, by the divine mercy, which rejoices in the conversion, not in the death, of sinners, many persons from the conviction of their senses are corrected and amended on these feast days.[4]

Hecker has cited at least two additional manifestations of dancing mania that occurred prior to the fourteenth century. In 1237 about a hundred children of the German town of Erfurt "proceeded dancing and jumping along the road to Armstadt," a distance of about eight miles. "When they arrived at that place they fell exhausted to the ground, and, according to an account of an old chronicle, many of them, after they were taken home by their parents, died, and the rest remained affected, to the end of their lives, with a permanent tremor." Then on June 17, 1278, at the bridge over the Maas River at Utrecht in the Netherlands "two hundred fanatics began to dance, and would not desist until a priest passed who was carrying the Host to a person that was sick, upon which, as if in punishment for their crime, the bridge gave way, and they were all drowned." [5]

ST. VITUS'S DANCE

During the fifteenth century there were sporadic occurrences of compulsive or continued dancing, but all involved single individuals or at most a few. Then in 1518 a great epidemic of continued dancing broke out in Strasbourg (France).

There are several versions of just what happened and two are worth quoting. The able and scholarly medical historian George Rosen of Yale has offered this account:

> Eight days before the feast of Mary Magdalene a woman began to dance, and after this went on for some four to six days she was sent to the chapel of St. Vitus at Hohlenstein, near Zabern. Soon thereafter more dancers appeared and the number grew until more than a hundred danced at a time. Eventually the municipal council forbade all public gatherings and music, restricted the dancers to two guild halls, and then sent them off to the chapel of St. Vitus. According to one account, more than four hundred people were affected within four weeks. Various chroniclers point out that this was a period of ruined harvests, severe famine, general want, and widespread disease. This was also the time of the early Reformation and thus of religious unrest. [6]

According to chronicler Daniel Specklin,

> In 1518 there began a dancing of young and old people; they danced day and night till they fell down; in Strasbourg over a hundred could be seen dancing at the same time. Several guildhalls were

allotted to them, and in the horse and corn market a platform was erected for them and people were appointed to dance with them and make music with drums and pipes, but it was all of no avail. Many of them danced themselves to death. Then they were sent to the monastery of St. Vitus on the Rock, behind Zabern, in wagons, and they were given crosses and red shoes, and Mass was said over them. On the shoes crosses were made, both underneath and above, and chrisam (consecrated oil mixed with balm) was poured over them, and they were sprinkled with holy water in the name of St. Vitus—this cured nearly all. This evil attacked many people in consequence of being cursed by others with the wish that they should have St. Vitus's dance, and much knavery was committed in this respect.[7]

TARANTISM

Tarantism has been described as "a nervous affection characterized by an uncontrollable impulse to dance; especially prevalent in southern Italy from the 15th to the 17th centuries, and popularly attributed to the bite of the tarantula," a large spider that seemingly derived its name from the port city of Tarentum (now Taranto).[8]

The key words in this description are "popularly attributed" which raise the question whether tarantism was basically psychic or somatic in origin. The earliest account of the disorder is ascribed to Nicholas Perotti (1430–1480) and nobody in his day doubted that it was caused by the bite of the tarantula, a ground spider commonly found in Apulia in the extreme southeast of Italy, but Hecker has pointed out that "the fear of this insect was so general, that its bite was in all probability much oftener imagined, or the sting of some other kind of insect mistaken for it, than actually received." Tarantula bite or no, those affected

> generally fell into a state of melancholy, and appeared to be stupefied, and scarcely in possession of their senses. This condition was, in many cases, united with so great a sensibility to music, that, at the very first tones of their favourite melodies, they sprang up,

shouting for joy, and danced on without intermission, until they
sank to the ground exhausted and almost lifeless. In others, the
disease did not take this cheerful turn. They wept constantly, and as
if pining away with some unsatisfied desire, spent their days in the
greatest misery and anxiety. Others, again, in morbid fits of love,
casting their longing looks on women, and instances of death are
recorded, which are said to have occurred under a paroxysm of either laughing or weeping.[9]

It was widely believed that music and dancing distributed the
poison of the tarantula over the whole body and expelled it through
the skin

> but if there remained the slightest vestige of it in the vessels, this be-
> came a permanent germ of the disorder, so that the dancing fits
> might again and again be excited *ad infinitum* by music. This belief,
> which resembled the delusion of those insane persons who, being by
> artificial management freed from the imagined causes of their suffer-
> ings, are but for a short time released from their false notions, was
> attended with the most injurious effects: for in consequence of it
> those affected necessarily became by degrees convinced of the incur-
> able nature of their disorder. They expected relief, indeed, but not a
> cure, from music; and when the heat of summer awakened a recol-
> lection of the dances of the preceding year, they, like the St. Vitus's
> dancers of the same period before St. Vitus's day, again grew de-
> jected and misanthropic, until, by music and dancing, they dispelled
> the melancholy which had become with them a kind of sensual en-
> joyment.[10]

To effect even a temporary cure the music must not be interrupted. An unidentified chronicler drew this picture:

> If during the dance the clarionets and drums broke down, for these
> maniacs wore out the most energetic musicians, they immediately let
> their joyfully agitated limbs relapse, they sank sick and exhausted to
> the ground, and could find no other relief than in renewed dancing.
> On that account care was taken that the music should continue till
> they were quite exhausted, and it was preferred to pay a few extra
> musicians to relieve one another than to allow the patients to relapse

in the midst of the health-restoring dance into so discomforting a
malady. A no less surprising symptom was the longing of the patients for the sea. As the dancers of St. John's night in their imagination saw the heavens open and all the glory of the saints, those who
were suffering from the bite of the tarantula felt themselves attracted
by the endless blue surface of the sea and lost themselves in its con-
templation. [11]

Hecker also noted the patients' "ardent longing for the sea . . ."
and the part played by color, such as the blue of the ocean, in dis-
turbing or aiding the excitable Italian victims—more so

> than was the case in the St. Vitus's dance with the more phlegmatic
> Germans. Red colours, which the St. Vitus's dancers detested, they
> generally liked, so that a patient was seldom seen who did not carry
> a red handkerchief for his gratification, or greedily feast his eyes on
> any articles of red clothing worn by the by-standers. Some preferred
> yellow, others black colours, of which an explanation was sought,
> according to the prevailing notions of the times, in the difference of
> temperaments. Others again were enraptured with green; and eye-
> witnesses describe this rage for colours as so extraordinary, that they
> can scarcely find words with which to express their astonishment.
> No sooner did the patients obtain a sight of the favourite colour
> than, new as the impression was, they rushed like infuriated animals
> towards the object, devoured it with their eager looks, kissed and
> caressed it in every possible way, and gradually resigning themselves
> to softer sensations, adopted the languishing expression of en-
> amoured lovers, and embraced the handkerchief, or whatever other
> article it might be, which was presented to them, with the most in-
> tense ardour, while the tears streamed from their eyes as if they
> were completely overwhelmed by the inebriating impression on
> their senses. [12]

By the beginning of the seventeenth century the dancing mania,
certainly in epidemic proportions, had died out in Germany. However tarantism was at its height in Italy. The eighteenth century
saw its steady decline to a point where such cases as occurred were
isolated ones.

"Both the St. Vitus's dance and Tarantism belonged to the age in which they appeared," wrote Hecker. "They could not have existed under the same latitude at any other epoch, for at no other period were the circumstances which prepared the way for them combined in a similar relation to each other, and the mental as well as corporeal temperaments of nations, which demand of causes such as have been stated, are as little capable of renewal as the different stages of life in individuals." [13]

Hecker's limitation of the dancing mania to a special time and place in history is only acceptable if one views St. John's dance, St. Vitus's dance, and tarantism in their epidemic aspects, because communal dancing as a form of ecstasy has not been an uncommon phenomenon through the ages. To cite just one example, the eighteenth-century Shakers of New York State performed their rites of worship

> by a perpetual springing from the house floor, about four inches up and down, both in the men's and women's apartment, moving about as thick as they can crowd, with extraordinary transport, singing sometimes one at a time, and sometimes more than one, making a perfect charm . . . This elevation draws upon the nerves so as that they have intervals of shuddering as if they were in a strong fit of the ague. They sometimes clasp hands and leap so as to strike the joyce above their heads. They throw off their outside garments in these exercises and spread their strength very cheerfully this way . . .[14]

CHAPTER 8

The Sweating Sickness

ON August 22, 1485, Henry VII became the first Tudor king of England by defeating the forces of Richard III in a short and decisive battle at Bosworth Field, northwest of Oxford, but "the joy of the nation was clouded by a mortal disease which thinned the ranks of the warriors, and following in the rear of Henry's victorious army, spread in a few weeks from the distant mountains of Wales [where Henry had landed from France] to the metropolis of the empire." [1] This epidemical disease, the sweating sickness (*Sudor Anglicus*), which hit England on five separate occasions (1485, 1508, 1517, 1528, and 1551—spreading to northern Europe in 1529 but on no other occasion) and never again, "remains a mysterious ailment unlike any infectious disease known in the succeeding four centuries." [2]

The first description of the epidemic of 1485 (and of that of 1508) was from the pen of the Italian scholar and man of affairs, Polydore Vergilio (c. 1470–1555), who came to the court of Henry VII in 1501:

> The same year (1485) a new disease pervaded the whole kingdom, during Henry's first descent into the island, a pestilence horrible indeed, and before which no age could endure, a well-known fact; suddenly a fatal sweat attacked the body wracking it with pains in the head and stomach, moreover there was a terrible sensation of heat. Therefore the patients cast off the bed coverings from the beginning, as some of them suffered less heat if they lay in bed; if they were dressed they stripped off their clothes, the thirsty ones

drank cold water, others suffering from this fetid heat, provoked a sweat which had a foul odor, by adding bed clothes, all of them dying immediately or not long after the sweat had begun; so that not one in a hundred evaded it. Nor did any article of medicine or science avail to help it, meanwhile, for this strange disease escaped all their knowledge. In fact, after twenty four hours (the severity of the disease continued for that length of time) the sweat departed bringing this conclusion i.e. that they were not cleansed by the sweat as many of them perished. But that fact pointed out a final measure in the treatment for this great torture; those who had sweat once, since they sickened again, put into use those things which they had discovered to have been beneficial in the first attack. Evenso, when the calamity befell the sickly race again, (1508) from earlier observations they had forgotten how to care for themselves, in order that they might bear more easily the strenuous sweating. Thus from experience, after such a huge slaughter of human beings, it follows that the most prompt relief should have been found, which was this: if anyone was seized during the daytime he should go to bed forwith, with his clothes on; if, while he was in bed at night, he should lie quietly and not move from that place, remaining so for twenty four hours exactly, covered with not enough bed clothes to provoke the sweat but just enough to allow him to sweat spontaneously, taking no food, if possible to bear the hunger, and drinking no more water than usual or of less warmth, which should satisfy in a way and quench the thirst; in the first stages of this treatment care should be taken that there should be no occasion either for warming up or cooling off the hands or feet as to do so means death. Such was the treatment found for this plague which covered so much of England at this time and in times past has so often afflicted it, for the first year that Henry began to reign was remarkable for the plague, which was taken by many as a bad omen.[3]

The 1508 epidemic appears to have centered on Chester (south of Liverpool and the river Mersey and on the border of Wales) and London; in the epidemic of 1517 London, Oxford, and Cambridge were hardest hit.

While the third epidemic "is generally conceded to have been the most severe in its mortality and virulence" and more is known of it than of the previous ones "through state papers, letters of envoys,

and private correspondence," these documents are largely concerned with events and deaths in high places and there is seemingly
no contemporary account comparable to Vergilio's description of
the epidemics of 1485 and 1508.[4] One turns perforce to Hecker
who, after recounting favorable events that "took place in April and
May of the ever memorable year 1517" went on to report that

> London was again indulging in hopes of better days, when the
> Sweating Sickness once more broke out quite unexpectedly in July,
> and in spite of all former experience, and the most sedulous atten-
> tion, inexorably demanded its victims. On this occasion it was so vi-
> olent and so rapid in its course, that it carried off those who were at-
> tacked, in two or three hours, so that the first shivering fit was
> regarded as the announcement of certain death. It was not ushered
> in by any precursory symptoms. Many who were in good health at
> noon, were numbered among the dead by the evening, and thus as
> great a dread was created at this new peril as ever was felt during the
> prevalence of the most suddenly destructive epidemic: for the
> thought of being snatched away from the full enjoyment of existence
> without any preparation, without any hope of recovery, is appalling
> even to the bravest, and excites secret trepidation and anguish.
> Among the lower classes the deaths were innumerable. The city was
> moreover crowded with poor; but even the ranks of the highest
> classes were thinned, and no precaution averted death from their
> palaces. . . . Mourning supplanted the hilarity and brilliancy of the
> festivals, and the king [now Henry VIII], while in miserable soli-
> tude, into which he had retired with a few followers, received mes-
> sage after message from different towns and villages, announcing,
> that in some a third, in others even half the inhabitants were swept
> off by this pestilence. It had never before raged with so much fatal-
> ity. The minds of men had never before been so frightfully appalled.
> The festival of Michaelmas, (29th September,) which in England
> was always kept with much religious pomp, was of necessity post-
> poned; nor was the solemnity of Christmas observed, for there was a
> dread of collecting together large assemblies of people, on account of
> the contagion; . . .
> Thus the Sweating Sickness lasted full six months, reached its
> greatest height about six weeks after its appearance, and probably
> spread from London over the whole of England. In Oxford and
> Cambridge it raged with no less violence than in the capital. Most of

the inhabitants of those places were, in course of a few days, confined to their beds, and the sciences, which then flourished, for they were never more zealously cultivated in England than at that time, suffered severe losses by the death of many able and distinguished scholars.[5]

The first three outbreaks saw no better treatment than the rudimentary precautions outlined by Vergilio, but in the fourth epidemic (of 1528) a more rational method of therapy was successfully undertaken in at least one case. The victim was Margaret, daughter of the high-principled statesman and author, Sir Thomas More (1478–1535). Margaret was married to William Roper, who would be More's biographer. Here is Roper's account of what occurred:

My wife, as many others that year were, was sick of the sweating sickness. Who, lying in so great extremity of that disease, as by no invention or devices that physicians in such cases commonly use (of whom she had divers both expert, wise, and well-learned then continually attendant upon her) she could be kept from sleep; so that both physicians and all other there despaired of her recovery, and gave her over—her father, as he that most entirely tendered her, being in no small heaviness for her, by prayer at God's hand sought to get her remedy.

Whereupon, going up after his usual manner in his foresaid New Building, there in chapel upon his knees, with tears most devoutly besought almighty God that it would like His goodness—unto whom nothing was impossible—if it were His blessed will at his mediation to vouch safe graciously to hear his humble petition. Where incontinent came into his mind that a clyster should be the only way to help her. Which, when he told the physicians, they by and by confessed that if there were any hope of health, that was the very best indeed; much marveling of themselves that they had not before remembered it.

Then was it immediately ministered unto her sleeping, which she could by no means have been brought unto waking. And albeit after that she was thereby thoroughly awakened, God's marks, an evident undoubted token of death plainly appeared upon her; yet she contrary to their expectations was, as it was thought, by her father's fervent prayer, miraculously recovered and at length again to perfect health restored.[6]

The objective was clearly fluid replacement. In modern times a clyster (rectal enema) is employed with a view to emptying the bowel. "However, Celsus, circa 25 A.D., recommended nutrient enemas, and Eudemus of the Methodic sect, which flourished during the first two centuries A.D., recommended clysters of cold water, and in the early decades of the twentieth century the proctoclysis, either of saline or dextrose, remained the standard method of administering fluid to those in whom the oral route was interdicted. Only later was it succeeded by the hypodermoclysis and subsequently by intravenous infusion." [7]

Another notable escapee was Anne Boleyn. When on June 18 Henry VIII heard that Anne's maid de chambre had contracted the sweating sickness he fled to Waltham in Essex. (Three days later, when members of his own household were stricken, he moved on to Hunston in Hartfordshire.) The fact that Anne herself succumbed to the disease and recovered prompted medical writer and editor Francis Cornelius Webb (1826–1873) to comment: "The occasion of this illness produced one of that remarkable series of love letters which have since become so celebrated, and the originals of which are preserved at Rome. . . . Happy indeed would it have been for the ill-fated Anne had the dart penetrated more deeply."[8]

The fourth epidemic seems to have been at its height between May and August 1528 and "there are not even the slightest data by which it can be made out that it was still in England during the summer of 1529." [9] Yet it was in July 1529 that the sweating sickness invaded continental Europe for the first and only time. Here is a summary by Hecker of its passage through the more northerly countries:

> 1529. 25th July, outbreak of the epidemic Sweating Sickness in Hamburgh. Termination on the 5th August. On the 19th July in Lübeck. On the 14th August in Zwickau. About the 1st September the English Sweating Sickness appears to spread universally all over Germany. On the 31st August in Stettin; termination on the 8th September. On the 1st September in Dantzic; termination on the 6th September. On the 24th August in Strasburg. On the 5th, 6th and 7th September in Cologne, Augsburg and Francfort on the Maine. About the 20th September in Vienna and among the besieg-

ing Turks. On the 27th September in Amsterdam. Termination on
the 1st October in Antwerp and the rest of the Netherlands; simultaneously, at the end of September, in Denmark, Sweden and Norway. At the commencement of November a universal cessation of
the epidemic Sweating Sickness.[10]

According to Hecker, "The alarm which prevailed in Germany
surpasses all description, and bordered upon maniacal despair. As
soon as the pestilence appeared on the continent, horrifying accounts of the unheard-of sufferings of those affected, and the certainty of their death, passed like wild-fire from mouth to mouth."
Generally speaking, attempts at treatment showed no advance over
the primitive methods (excepting that of Sir Thomas More) employed in England.

At the same time, the unfortunate delusion existed, that whoever
wished to escape death when seized with the English pestilence,
must perspire for twenty-four hours without intermission. So they put the
patients, whether they had the Sweating Sickness or not, (for who
had calmness enough to distinguish it?) instantly to bed, covered
them with feather-beds and furs, and whilst the stove was heated to
the utmost, closed the doors and windows with the greatest care to
prevent all access of cool air. In order, moreover, to prevent the sufferer, should he be somewhat impatient, from throwing off his hot
load, some persons in health likewise lay upon him, and thus oppressed him to such a degree, that he could neither stir hand nor
foot, and finally in this rehearsal of hell, being bathed in an agoniz-
ing sweat, gave up the ghost, when, perhaps, if his too officious relatives had manifested a little discretion, he might have been saved
without difficulty.

But Hecker could report on one all but forgotten man of medicine who adopted a sensible approach:

There dwelt a physician in Zwickau—we no longer know the
name of this estimable man—who, full of zeal for the good of mankind, opposed this destructive folly. He went from house to house,
and wherever he found a patient buried in a hot bed, dragged him
out with his own hands, everywhere forbad that the sick should thus

be tortured with heat, and saved by his decisive conduct, many, who but for him, must have been smothered like the rest.[11]

The first in-depth study of the sweating sickness by a physician was undertaken by John Caius (1510–1573), cofounder of Gonville and Caius College, Cambridge, and its master from 1559 to 1573. In 1552 Caius published his *A boke or counseill against the disease commonly called the sweate or sweatyng sicknesse.* Since he was only seven years old at the time of the third epidemic and eighteen at the time of the fourth, Caius' eyewitness data necessarily spring largely from the fifth and final epidemic of 1551.

While the custom of his day required that scientific works be in Latin or Greek, Caius wrote about the sweating sickness in English because

> this disease is almoste peculiar vnto vs Englishe men, and not common to all men, folowyng vs, as the shadowe the body, in all countries, albeit not at al times. Therfore compelled I am to vse this our Englishe tongue as best to be vnderstande, and moste nedeful to whome it most foloweth, most behoueth to haue spedy remedie, and often tymes leaste nyghe to places of succourre and comforte at lerned mennes handes: and leaste nedefull to be setfurthe in other tongues to be vnderstand generally of all persons, whome it either haunteth not at all, or els very seldome, as ones in an age.

Having settled the matter of language, Caius indicated that he would

> first declare the beginnynge, name, nature, and signes of the sweatynge sicknes. Next, the causes of the same. And thirdly, how to preserue men frō it, and remedy them whē they haue it.

After briefly noting the first four epidemics of what he preferred to call *ephemera* (the title of his *boke* notwithstanding), Caius turned to the final visitation in 1551, which

> beginning at Shrewesbury in the middest of April, proceadinge with greate mortalitie to Ludlowe, Prestene, and other places in Wales,

then to Westchestre, Couentre, Oxenfoorde, and other tounes in the Southe, and such as were in and aboute the way to London, whether it came notablie the seuenth of July, . . . Then ceassing there, it wente from thence throughe al the east partes of England into the Northe untill the ende of Auguste, at whiche tyme it diminished, and in the ende of Septembre fully ceassed.

Caius then considered the nature of the disease which he declared to be

> not a Sweat onely, (as it is thought & called) but a feuer . . . in the spirites by putrefaction venemous, with a fight, trayaile, and laboure of nature againste the enfection receyued in the spirites, whervpon by chaunce foloweth a Sweate, or issueth an humour compelled by nature, as also chanceth in other sicknesses whiche consiste in humours, when they be in their state, and at the worste in certein dayes iudicial, aswel by vomites, bledinges, & fluxes, as by sweates. . . . In which labors, if nature be strõg & able to thrust out the poisõ by sweat (not otherwise letted) yᵉ persõ escapeth: if not, it dieth.

Ephemera was to be recognized

> First by the peine in the backe, or shoulder, peine in the extreme partes, as arme, or legge, with a flusshing, or wind, as it semeth to certeine of the pacientes, flieng in the same. Secondly by the grief in the liuer and the nigh stomacke. Thirdely, by the peine in the head, & madnes of the same. Fourthly by the passion of the hart. . . . [I]f any do sweate [without the propre signes], I take theym not to Sweat by this Sickenesse, but rather by feare, heate of the yeare, many clothes, greate exercise, affection, excesse in diets, or at the worst, by a smal cause of infection, and lesse disposition of the bodi to this sicknes. So that, insomoche as the body was nat al voide of matter, sweate it did when infection came: but in the mattere was not greate, the same coulde neyther be perilous nor paineful as in others, in whom it was greater cause.

Caius then discussed the causes of this "pestilente Sweate of English ephemera," and found them to be twofold: "Infection by the

aier, and impure spirites by repletion." [12] Was the sweating
sickness unique in that it was limited to five isolated English epidemics (plus one in continental Europe)? Attempts to identify the
Sudor Anglicus with other disease entities have been made repeat-
edly and are continuing in the present day, but the various authorities and would-be authorities are rarely in agreement and no proposed solution has so far fitted the three basic features of the
sweating sickness apparent from the various accounts: that the
onset was usually abrupt, the duration short, and the case mortality often high. As a random example, an attempt to identify sweating sickness with recurrent (relapsing) fever was thwarted by the
latter's three- to ten-day lapse between its outbreak and its crisis in
contrast with the sweating sickness crisis in twenty-four hours.

The Morbus Gallicus

"THE eruption of syphilis in Europe at the end of the fifteenth century is the great puzzle of the history of epidemic disease, and two
schools of medical opinion are still arguing about its origin. The
Columbian school opines that the disease was endemic among the
aboriginal inhabitants of the West Indies, and that it was transmitted by the Carib women—who were quite promiscuous in their
sexual relations—to the sailors of Columbus, who then imported it
into the virgin population of Europe. American medical writers,
however, indignantly repudiate what they seem to regard as a libel
upon their nation, and aver that the disease had been slumbering
unnoticed in Europe for centuries before it made its historical
debut in A.D. 1493, and that it—or a closely similar disease—was
known to the ancient Romans." [1]

Fortunately in the present context the question is academic since
it is clear that the first *epidemic* of syphilis occurred at the close of
the fifteenth century.

If the Columbian theory is accepted, there was indeed a *quid
pro quo* in the introduction of smallpox into the West Indies.
According to Dr. Howard N. Simpson of Springfield, Massachusetts, "the Europeans were able to conquer America, not by
their military genius, . . . but by waging unpremeditated and
unrecognized biological warfare. . . . When Columbus discovered
Hispaniola, that island paradise had an estimated population of
300,000 natives. Within half a century the Tainos had been practically exterminated by slaughter, starvation and 'so many diseases,

especially certain pestilential small-pox which prevails generally in
all the island, that in a short time the Indians will be ended.' So
wrote Oviedo in 1548." [2]

Gonçalo Férnandez de Oviedo y Valdés (1478–1557) must be
regarded as an eyewitness to much that occurred in the Caribbean
islands in the first half of the sixteenth century, for not only was he
among the earliest explorers of the area, but he also visited it several times, was for a time viceroy of Mexico, and was the author of
two books on the plant life of the Indies (Seville, 1525 and 1535).

Francisco López de Villalobos (1473–1556) was the first doctor in
Spain to write about *las buvas*, which, explained George Gaskoin,
translator of and commentator on *The Medical Works of Francisco
López de Villalobos*, "are nothing but that which hath been known all
along as the French pockes." [3] In 1498 he published in Salamanca a
Latin poem of 740 lines of which Ellis Herndon Hudson, emeritus
professor of hygiene, Ohio University at Athens, has said, "Although it bore the grandiose title *A Summary of Medicine*, the subtitle more exactly described the contents, A Treatise concerning
the Pestilential Buvas." [4]

Villalobos gave no indication of how long it may have taken him
to collect his material and convert it into Latin verse, or what delay
occurred between completion and publication, but there is intrinsic
evidence that suggests that the actual writing took place between
1493 and 1495. In the first stanza he spoke of the "kings don Fer-
nando and Donna Isabel" in these words:

> *Through all the whole universe their fame now was spread,*
> *Where men and laws are found, and aught of culture springs,*
> *Now all of blighting arrogance was captive led;*
> *At this time all their land in peace was swayed,*
> *All tyrants were destroyed, whether vassals or kings.* [5]

Hudson has pointed out that 1493 "was the earliest that this
compliment would have been appropriate [the capture of Granada
having occurred in 1492], and within two years thereafter the rum-
bling of approaching war was audible." [6]

Furthermore, it was at this time that *las buvas* struck:

> *Even thus as they dwelt in fair and stately show,* . . .
> *There came forth from God a gen'ral malison,*
> *That fell on all the land, each province and nation,*
> *All countries that we know or where we penetrate.*
> *It was a pestilence ne'er to be found at all*
> *In verse or in prose, in science or in story,*
> *So evil and perverse and cruel past control,*
> *Exceeding contagious, and in filth so prodigal,*
> *So strong to hold its own, there is little got of glory.* [7]

After dealing with the opinions of the theologians and the astrologers as to the cause of the pestilence, Villalobos turned to the physicians:

> *Physicians say the secret of its power*
> *In melancholy humour and salt phlegm doth lie,*
> *Which occasion in all organs what obstructions do occur,*
> *Proceeding from a mighty distemperature*
> *Of the liver, which is turned to hot and dry;*
> *And this from something baneful in the air is bred,*
> *And also from bad habits and from sustenance,*
> *And joined along with this the aforementioned;*
> *Even so the mischief works, and gets so far ahead,*
> *That neither cure nor regimen can check its insolence.* [8]

Villalobos noted that the disease made its first appearance in what he called "the parts of shame," the liver throwing morbid matter "to these valuable friends of ours." Hudson has pointed out that Villalobos "listed sexual excess coordinately with other excesses"—gluttony, drunkenness, and the like—but he "did not attribute *las buvas* to venery *per se*, nor warn against intercourse with prostitutes. Although he recognized that the eruption appeared first on the genitals, he did not ascribe this to sexual contact, but to 'weakness' of the genitals relative to other organs." ("Being very tender flesh, and much prone to alteration" as Villalobos put it.) "He seems," Hudson continued, "to have missed the point that the genital sore was the place where the infection entered the body, and that it was concerned equally with the skin eruption in the process of transmission, although this epidemiologic fact was being recognized elsewhere in Europe, new cases being ascribed here and there to intercourse with leprous, scabby or menstruous women." [9]

From causes and symptoms Villalobos turned to cure to which he devoted the remaining three hundred lines of his poem.

Villalobos studied medicine at the university of Salamanca, about eighty miles southwest of his birthplace. When he composed his poem he was still a student but had received his license to practice.

> Salamanca was a relatively isolated provincial town in an agricultural district of northwest Spain. It was not a commercial or industrial center; it was not a crossroads town with traffic flowing through, but a "town at the end of the road," for beyond it was the deadend of the Portuguese border. The nearest port was hundreds of miles away over mountainous terrain, no sailors were coming and going, and there was no licentious water-front. . . .
>
> Consequently, the people with *buvas* that Villalobos saw must have been natives of Salamanca town and country, and not soldiers, sailors, strangers, travelers or refugees. He did not invent a name for the "new disease, but adopted the one his patients were using, a genuinely Spanish word. He was quite content to assume that the disease had originated right there; he accused no one of having "brought it in." . . . If he had heard of Columbus and the discovery of the New World he could hardly have imagined that this event had any relation to his "new" disease, especially if he had been seeing cases of it among the patients at the medical school. [10]

It would appear therefore that the syphilis that Villalobos observed and treated was endemic rather than part of the epidemic of 1493, but this does not detract from the fact that his poem offered the first professional description of the disease.

Close on the heels of Villalobos was another Spaniard, Gaspar Torella (fl. 1500) who was physician to the notorious pope Alexander VI (Rodrigo Lanzol y Borja—1431?–1503). In 1497 he published at Rome a tract on the French disease (or *pudendagra*, the name he suggested for it). Whether Torella drew his data strictly

from the cases he encountered at the papal court and in the house
of Borgia or there was a widespread epidemic in Rome that centered on the corrupt entourage of Alexander VI is open to question, but Torella noted that he observed seventeen cases in a two-
month period. It was his belief that the epidemic (which historians
generally agree was raging in 1495) originated in France in 1493
(justifying the use of the designation *morbus gallicus*), spreading
from there to Spain, the islands of the Mediterranean, and Italy.
Giovanni di Vigo (1460–1520) of Rapallo (near Genoa), who came
to Rome in 1503 as surgeon in the train of the ascending pope
Julius II (1443–1513), is credited with being the first, in his treatise
of the French disease (1514), to attribute the outbreak of the epidemic to the siege of Naples by the army of Charles VIII of France
(1470–1498), which began in December 1494. His belief was amplified by Rodrigo Ruiz de Isla (1462–1542) in his *Treatise on the Ser-
pentine Malady* written between 1510 and 1520 and published in
Seville in 1539:

> In the following year of 1494 the most Christian King Charles of
> France who was then reigning having gathered a great army passed
> into Italy. And at the time he entered the country with his host
> many Spaniards infected with this disease were in it and at once the
> camp began to be infected with the aforesaid malady and the
> French, as they did not know what it was, thought it came from the
> atmosphere of the region. The French called it the disease of Na-
> ples.[11]

(De Isla incidentally lends some credence to the Columbian hypothesis.)

Mala napoletana as an alternative to *morbus gallicus* was not the
only topical name given to the "new" disease. "After it became epidemic, it was called the Spanish, Polish, German, or Turkish
'pocks,' from the anxiety of different nations to shift the blame
upon one another." [12] The disbanding of Charles's army of mer-
cenaries inevitably spread the disease far and wide in Europe.

Torella offered this description in the case of a young man who
had relations with a woman with *pudendagra:*

An ulcer developed on the penis associated with a red streak and glands in the groin. Six days after, the ulcer became partly scarred and he then developed severe pains in the head, neck, shoulders, arms and legs, ribs. Ten days later he developed a number of pustules on the head, face and neck.[13]

In 1514 Di Vigo confirmed and amplified Torella's description:

The disease usually appeared first on the genitals as a livid pustule with a firm base and then spread to other parts of the body. Sometimes crusty elevated scabs occurred on the forehead, face and head. At the same time and for some weeks after, cruel pains occurred in the head, shoulders, arms and legs. Some months later hard nodes arise apparently from the bones themselves . . . rotting bones . . . gummosities or ganglion like tumors of the muscles, puffy swellings, stiffness of the joints. After a long time, malignant ulcers appeared and are hard to cure.[14]

FRACASTORO

"The name and reputation of JEROME FRACASTOR (1478–1553) of Verona has survived," wrote British physician, writer, and traveler James Johnston Abraham in his introduction to an English translation of Fracastoro's *Syphilis or the French Disease*, "not because he was a poet, a physician, and a philosopher with, in his time, a European reputation, but because he invented the word 'SYPHILIS.' "[15]

Born in Verona, a city that had no university, Girolamo Fracastoro in his teens attended the university in the nearby town of Padua. He first studied mathematics but later turned to medicine (for which Padua was famous), his studies including botany, geology, astronomy, and philosophy, subjects requisite for the medical student of his day. In 1501 he was appointed lecturer in logic at Padua, a post he held for six years. He might have remained to occupy a professorial chair but for the political misfortunes of the Republic of Venice, under whose sway were both Padua and Verona. The university was closed when the papal, Austrian, German, French, and Spanish enemies of Venice formed the League of

Cambrai and marched into her territory, Padua being one of the first cities captured and sacked by the Austrians. Fracastoro and most of his friends joined the Venetian general Alviano at his stronghold at Pordenone, about forty miles northeast of Venice. In April 1509, under the illusion that Venice would defeat her enemies, Fracastoro returned with Alviano to Verona, but a month later the general was defeated at the battle of Agnadello, east of Milan, and the Germans captured and sacked Verona. When plague broke out in the city in 1510, Fracastoro retreated to his villa at Incaffi on the shore of Lake Garda where "he would appear to have remained, botanising, thinking, writing, until the *Peace of Noyon* restored Verona to the Venetians again in 1516." [16] After the departure of the Germans, Fracastoro returned to Verona where he lived and practiced for twenty years. His retirement was mostly spent at his villa at Incaffi where he died. During his lifetime he did considerable writing on a variety of subjects, but his medical fame rests upon his poem in Latin hexameters, *Syphilis sive Morbus Gallicus* (Verona, 1530) and his treatise *De Contagione* (Venice, 1546).

Syphilis or the French Disease was divided into three books. In the first Fracastoro discussed the origins, causes, and symptoms of the malady; in the second, remedies; while the third book is largely concerned with the fable of Syphilus the shepherd.

"What various chances in Life," the first book begins—the translation is in prose—"what seeds conveyed this strange disease, unknown to any through long centuries, which, in our own day, has raged throughout Europe, through portions of Asia, and through the cities of Africa; but which broke into Italy through the grievous wars of the French [the siege of Naples], and took its name from that race: . . ." [17]

Fracastoro went on to reject the theory held by many of his contemporaries that the Spanish brought the disease from the New World:

Was it borne by the Western Sea, and so came to our world at the time when a chosen band [Columbus and his sailors] set sail from the shores of Spain, and dared to attack the foam and the unknown waters of the wandering ocean and search out lands lying in a new world? For there, they say, that sickness held sway with everlasting ruin through all the cities, and wandered hither and thither by endless fault of heaven, sparing but a few. Must we then think that by means of traffic this contagion was carried to reach us—a contagion which, small in the beginning, but soon gaining strength and matter to feed on by degrees, spread itself throughout all lands? . . .

But, indeed, if true observation deserves belief, we must not so consider. For certainly it is not fair to deem that the disease is foreign to us and borne across the ocean: since in the first place, we can show many who of their own accord, without contact with any other, have contracted this same malady and have been the first to suffer it. Besides, a single contagion would not have been able to reach so many lands in so short a time. . . .[18]

Fracastoro seems later to have somewhat modified his attitude toward the Columbian theory. The third book, which was added to the original two between 1525 when these, probably in manuscript, were submitted to Cardinal Pietro Bembo (1470–1547), the dedicatee, and 1530, opens with a reference to the guiac (or guiacum) trees (native to the West Indies and equatorial America), a preparation from which was employed in the treatment of syphilis as late as the eighteenth century:

But now the happy groves of another world and foreign glades call me. Far beyond the Pillars of Hercules the Ocean resounds and far-distant shores make reply. Now must I sing of the great gifts of the Gods brought from an unknown world; of the sacred tree which alone has set bounds to our pain and brought our distresses to an end. Come, Goddess Urania, worship the blessed grove; and be it thy pleasure, with a chaplet of the new leaf in thy hair, to go forth through Latium in robes of healing, revealing the holy boughs to the nations: be it thy pleasure also to tell of new things unseen of any in the days of our fathers, which none has ever recorded.[19]

Later, in the chapter on syphilis in *De Contagione,* Fracastoro devoted better than three pages to the guiac tree and the preparation of its bark and wood for use in the treatment of syphilis.[20]

These pages indicate that Fracastoro had at least become aware that syphilis was prevalent in the West Indies and a remedy, if not the disease itself, returned with Columbus.

In Book I of *Syphilis or the French Disease,* after dealing with origins, Fracastoro turned to causes:

> And when you consider that the seeds of so great a disease cannot lie either in the bosom of the earth or in the sea, you are bound to decide after deliberation that the source and seat of the evil must exist in the air itself; the air which is diffused round all the earth, which insinuates itself everywhere throughout our bodies, and has continually inflicted this plague on the race of living beings. . . .
>
> Now, however, hear in what manner the air carries the infection, and what changes the lapse of centuries can bring. In the first place, then, the golden sun and the multitude of stars shake and perturb the earth, the fluid air, and the waters of the ocean; and as in the heavens themselves the stars have changed their courses and forsaken their former stations, so do the mighty elements transform themselves in various fashion. . . . These things, it is manifest, come to pass in the long course of years and after countless revolutions of the swift heavens; the Gods in this fashion unfold destiny. . . .
>
> Turn, therefore, now with me to contemplate the ever-revolving sky, the mansions of the Gods and the blazing stars; and, moving in thought through the universe, look to the conjunctions of the planets for the signs they have given and the fate heaven has presaged for our years. Because here, perchance, the origin of this novel pestilence, the channels through which disaster came, will be laid open to you. . . .
>
> And yet I know well that it is difficult to say what things the heavens may bring about, and in what order, or to examine the definite causes of all things; for sometimes the heavens drag out the results through long periods, sometimes (which may mislead us) manifold cases are by chance intermingled in one. . . .
>
> Therefore, since pestilences vary so much in their nature and kind, and germs are manifold in wondrous wise, consider this one, beginning in the sky and long unknown, which so strangely broke forth into the air. For, indeed, it did not infect the silent creatures of the sea and the shoals of swimming things, nor the birds and wild

animals that range the lofty forests, nor kine, nor sheep-flocks, nor
herds of horses, but singled out for attack man mighty in mind,
warring on our members. . . .[21]

Fracastoro then turned to symptoms:

To begin with, there was this single fact; though the infection was
there, the moon had often four times circled the earth before clear
symptoms of the disease appeared. For when it had once been received into the body it does not immediately declare itself; rather it
lies dormant for a certain time and gradually gains strength as it
feeds. Meanwhile, however, the sufferers, weighed down by strange
heaviness and irresistible languor, are going through life with increasing weakness, moving sluggishly in every limb. Their eyes,
too, have lost their natural keenness; the colour is driven from their
faces and deserts their unhappy brows. By slow degrees the corruption, arising in the generative organs, consumes the whole body here
and there, or eats away the groin in its triumphant course. Then the
symptoms of the disease reveal themselves more clearly. For as soon
as the kindly beams of departing day usher in the sad shades of
dusk, the natural heat wont to invade the vital parts by night deserts
the outposts of the body, no longer cherishing the parts oppressed
by a gross mass of humours. Then the arms, the shoulder blades,
and the calves of the legs are racked with pain. In fact, where the infection passes through all the veins, and poisons the juices of the
body and its future nourishment, Nature, which always rejects disease, expels the tainted matter from all parts to the surface. But
because the poison is slow to move in a gross body and clings by its
viscosity, much of it on departing cleaves to the bloodless limbs and
muscles, spreading thence to bring grievous pains to the joints. And
even when repelled from the lighter portions of the frame which are
more liable to eruptions, it attacks the surface of the skin and the extremities of the limbs. Forthwith, throughout the body unsightly
scabs break forth, and foully defile the face and breast. The malady
now takes a new form: a pustule resembling the top of an acorn, and
rotting with thick phlegm, opens and soon splits apart flowing co-
piously with corrupted blood and matter. Nay even, eating deeply
in, it hides in the innermost parts and feeds dreadfully upon the
body; and often we see joints stripped of their very flesh, bones rot-

ting, and foully gaping mouths gnawed away, the lips and throat
producing faint sounds. . . .

I myself remember to have seen, where rich Ollius flows past the
lush meadow-lands of Lake Sebinus, an illustrious YOUTH of Verona.
None was more brilliant than he, none of happier promise in all
Italy. Scarce in the bloom of his budding manhood, he was mighty
in wealth and ancestry; and in his body he was beautiful. His eager
pleasure it was to control the swift galloping steed, to don the hel-
met and shine in painted armour, or to harden his tender body in
the strife of the wrestling school; to hunt wild beasts and to outstrip
the stag. Him all the Goddesses of Ollius and the maidens of Eri-
danus desired, the Goddesses of the Groves and the girls of the
countryside. All these wooed him with sighs. Perchance one of them
was spurned and called the High Gods to avenge her; and not in
vain, for the Good Powers heard her prayers. The wretched man,
too confident to fear such dire mischance, was attacked by this disease, the most savage anywhere seen in the past, or that ever will be
seen in time to come. By slow degrees that shining springtide, that
flower of young manhood, fell to ruin as his vital force declined;
then, dreadful to relate, foul corruption fastened on his wretched
limbs, and deep within, the larger bones began to swell with loath-
some abscesses. Foul ulcers (shame on the mercy of heaven!) began
to devour the fair eyes which the light of day loved to look upon; to
feed, too, on nostrils gnawed away by bitter wounds. And then,
doomed too soon by unkind fate, the luckless youth left behind him
the now hateful air of heaven and the light of day. . . .[22]

To destroy the scabs, Fracastoro recommended "the force of fire,"
which included fumigations.

But most people do better by dissolving everything in quicksilver,
since the power inherent in this is wonderful. Whether because it is
destined by nature to relieve both chills and fever, by drawing
swiftly to itself our bodily heat, or because, being of great density, it
dissolves humours and acts more powerfully, just as glowing flame
more keenly consumes iron: or whether the active particles of which
it is wonderfully compacted, when they lose their internal links and
bonds and are carried separately into the body, dissolve away the
concretions and dry up the seeds of the pestilence. Or, indeed, it

may be that the Fates and Nature have endowed it with some other
power. The discovery of the gift of heaven of this remedy I will now
turn aside to relate. . . .[23]

Mercury was employed in the treatment of syphilis as late as the
mid-nineteenth century.

The myth which Fracastoro turned aside to relate involved a
Syrian hunter named Ilceus who contracted syphilis as a punishment for shooting a sacred stag. He is told by the gods that "if any
hope of cure remains, it must be sought in the depths of the earth,
and under the blackest night." His underworld savior is Lipare,
"whose task is to watch over the birth of silver and gold." She
bathed him three times in a fountain of mercury ("spring of healing
silver") and "thrice she poured the shining fluid over his limbs with
virgin hands, and thrice purified the youth throughout his body:
who, his frame cleansed of the foul pestilence, greatly marvelled at
the slough of vileness he had left in the depths of the stream." [24]

Fracastoro's introduction of the word syphilis as the name for the
disease derives from another myth. When the flocks of Syphilus,
shepherd to King Alcithous of Ophyre (Haiti) died of drought, he
renounced Apollo, raised altars to his master, the king, and made
sacrifice to him, and "the rustic crowd and all the band of his
fellow shepherds did likewise." The king "rejoiced in the divine
honours rendered him; and gave his royal decree that no other God
should be worshipped in the land." By way of retribution, Apollo
sent "a pestilence unknown" which "sprung up on the unhallowed
earth. The first among them all, Syphilus . . . manifested the foul
sores in his own body; he first knew sleepless nights, whilst his
limbs were racked with pain. And from him, the first to suffer it,
the disease took its name and was called Syphilis by the native
race. Before long the deadly infection spread itself among the folk
in all the cities, nor in its virulence did it spare the King's person." [25]

Fracastoro offered no reason for calling his shepherd Syphilus
and scholars have endlessly argued its possible Greek derivations to
a point of no satisfactory conclusion. Perhaps the most plausible
explanation is that Fracastoro was echoing a tale told by Ovid in

his *Metamorphoses*. Niobe (daughter of Tantalus and wife of Amphion, both sons of Zeus) had claimed that she should be worshiped on an equal footing with Leto, mother of Apollo, boasting that she had borne seven times as many children as Leto. In retaliation, Apollo with his arrows destroyed all her sons, including one named Sipylus. (Incidentally Niobe herself was turned to stone on Mount Sipylus in Asia Minor while weeping for the loss of her children.) "Thus," concluded Heneage Wynne-Finch, translator of *Syphilis or the French Disease*, "Niobe's *Sipylus* was the victim of a God's wrath like Syphilus the shepherd in the present poem." [26]

AFTER 1500

It is within the bounds of reasonableness to conclude that the epidemic of syphilis that swept Europe at the close of the fifteenth century is the only epidemic of syphilis that ever occurred. To put it another way, sporadic outbreaks in the centuries that followed were more endemic than epidemic.

> With the spread of the Renaissance influences of education, sophistication in dress, and improved personal hygiene, the complex known so widely as *Morbus Gallicus* faded from central Europe. Residua were found in the most backward areas, causing sporadic outbreaks.[27]

Prostitution was one factor that kept the disease alive, with the licentiousness of invading armies spreading it to pristine localities. For example, the appearance of syphilis (under the name of *sibbens* or *sivvens*) in Scotland in the middle of the seventeenth century was attributed to Cromwell's invasion of the southwestern districts. In 1694 troops carried it into the Highlands. The mid-eighteenth century saw its peak in the southwest, but as late as 1825 to 1840 sixty cases from the Highlands were admitted to the Glasgow infirmary. Thereafter reference to the disease disappeared from Scottish medical writings. "It appears that the malady was endemic mostly among the poor, filthy, and neglected inhabitants of certain districts," Hirsch has noted. (He made a similar observation with regard to the fifteenth-century epidemic.) [28]

In Norway and Sweden syphilis was known as radesyge ("bad disorder"). While no army was involved in its 1720 appearance in Norway (where it reached a peak in the final quarter of the century), it was introduced into Sweden in 1762 by troops returning from the Seven Years' War. There was a second importation when Swedish troops returned from war in Finland in 1790. The so-called *Jutland syphiloid* was brought to Denmark in the middle of the eighteenth century either by Russian sailors or troops from Sweden and Norway, but it did not come to the attention of the Danish government until 1817.

> Completely analogous to these endemics is the *Dithmarsian or Holstein disease*. The origin of it is traced to the circumstance of a large number of stranger navvies, especially from East Friesland, flocking into the Süder-Dithmarsian for the work of embanking the Crown-Prince dyke; and if they did not introduce the disease, they certainly were the chief occasion for its spreading. By the year 1789, the malady was so prevalent in the marshes and the Gheest that, in some villages, the whole population was affected; towards the end of the century, it showed itself in other parts of Holstein as well, so that, in 1801, the attention of the government was drawn to it. In 1806 its diffusion was almost universal, reaching at last to Kiel on the east coast; it was not until 1840 that any considerable decrease of this so-called "syphiloid" was remarked, but at the present day it seems to have died out as an endemic.
>
> The *syphiloids of Lithuania and Courland* make another addition to the history of these syphilitic endemics. In the Lithuanian division of East Prussia, syphilis became endemic in 1757, after the invasion of Russian troops during the Seven Years' war; and it retained its hold as an endemic there down to the first twenty years of this [the nineteenth] century, when the strict enforcement of police sanitary regulations put an end to it. In Courland [it] is said to have broken out in 1800 after the landing of Russian troops on the Dondanga coast.[29]

The early nineteenth century saw scattered outbreaks in the Balkans, mostly troop connected.

It is further noteworthy that the development of the sickness in many of these endemic centers was started, or at least materially helped, by the concentration of troops, the contingencies of campaigning and things of a like kind tending to aggravate the hardness of living. Again, the spread of the disease not only through sexual promiscuousness, as usual, but very often by other channels of contagion as well, and, above all, in places where the endemic had lasted many years and had deeply infected the population, by way of inheritance. Lastly, the disease developed unusually often into its most malignant forms, in consequence of the want of rational medical treatment.[30]

When there is an outbreak of influenza in Hong Kong or London it is virtually certain that it will hit America in the not too distant future, but syphilis in either of these cities betokens no ill for New York, New Orleans, or San Francisco. Such epidemic diseases as smallpox, measles, and bubonic plague, to name a few, have been eradicated where methods of control have been put in operation, but syphilis will always be with us (effective treatment and controls notwithstanding) because, in the words of the pioneer English surgeon Richard Wiseman (1622?–1676), it is "most frequently gotten by the most predominant vice of the age." [31] He might have said "of any age."

Reliable statistics as to the prevalence of syphilis have always been difficult to obtain. Beginning in 1860 attempts at estimations were made but they were for the most part based on histories and clinical findings, effective means of diagnosing and treating the disease not becoming available until the first decade of the twentieth century. In 1906 August von Wassermann (1866–1925) introduced his serum diagnosis of syphilis; in 1910 Paul Ehrlich (1854–1915) and his Japanese assistant Sahachiro Hata (1873–1938) produced salvarsan (arsphenamine). But it was not until 1938 that the Syphilis Control Program really got under way in the United States.

Another bar to sound statistics has been what has been called the venereal disease phobia, which was first reported in 1676 by Wiseman where he wrote in his *Severall Chirurgicall Treatises* (London: Royston):

These dreadful Symptoms have frequently possest the imagina-
tions of some people, who having taken the way to get the Pox are
soon perswaded that they have it. These men will strangely imagine
all these pains and other Symptoms they have read of, or have heard
other men talk of. Many of these hypochondriack have come to Sir
Frac [Francis] Pr[ujean], in which case he hath been pleased to send
for me to consider their complaints with him. They commonly went
away from us unsatisfied, nor could they quiet their minds till they
found some undertake that would comply with them; which done
they were never the better, the imagination in which the Disease
was seated remaining still uncured; whereupon presuming they were
not in hands skilful enough, they have gone to others and so for-
wards, till they have ruined both their Bodies and Purses.[32]

How many phobia cases have been included in statistics can never
be known.

Another complication developed in 1943 when the substitution
of penicillin for the arsenic-bismuth treatment (unsuited for use in
the doctor's office) shifted diagnosis and treatment from the public
clinic to the private office. In the early sixties only a little more
than 10 percent of cases of infectious syphilis treated by private
physicians were being reported, which led to the conclusion that,
in the United States in 1962, while only twenty thousand cases
were reported by clinics and physicians, the probable number diagnosed and treated was close to a hundred thousand.

Between 1910 and 1938 the Scandinavian countries, with effective public treatment and control programs, reduced the attack of
syphilis to minimal levels, but the United States delayed positive
action until 1938. However, the upsurge of syphilis expected during World War II was largely contained and, while a peak was
reached in 1947, a sharp decline followed, reaching its low point in
1954. This low level was maintained through 1958, but the number
of cases rose sharply in 1959 and the upward trend has continued.

Syphilis is a classic example of a disease that can be conquered
by modern medical and sociological approaches. However, the
major source of today's problem is that the medical profession can
do nothing without the wholehearted cooperation of patients, no
matter what their age or station.

1. The Aesculapian serpent arrives in Rome to save the city from the plague of 291 B.C. (a Roman coin of c. 150 A.D.)

2. The plague at Ashdod, 1141 B.C., as seen by the French painter Nicholas Poussin in 1630 A.D.

3. Miniature from a manuscript showing the plague at Tournai in 1349.

4. *The Plague*, by the nineteenth-century Swiss painter, Arnold
Böcklin.

5. The St. Vitus dancers, after a painting by Peter Breughel the Elder.

6. A contemporary (1496) representation of the *Morbus Gallicus* as divine punishment.

7. Seventeenth-century illustration of a cure for the pox (syphilis).

8. John Caius, eye-witness describer of the sweating sickness.

9. Thomas Sydenham, "The English Hippocrates." Note that there is also an Aesculapian staff in this 1746 engraving.

10. Protective costume for an Italian physician during the "pestilence" of 1656—from a book published in 1661.

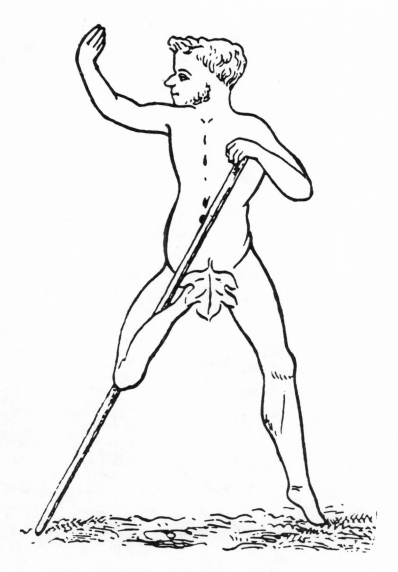

11. Poliomyelitic deformities of the legs, from a fourth-century B.C. Italian jar.

12. Children were removed to isolation over the violent objections of their parents during the nineteenth-century epidemic of smallpox in Montreal.

13. A moving symbolization of puerperal fever.

14. French political caricature drawn during the cholera epidemic of 1832, and showing the swift and violent onslaught of this dreaded disease.

15. Raising a building to eliminate rats' living quarters, during a bubonic plague campaign in New Orleans.

16. A cartoon of Dr. Kinyoun, the courageous public
health officer who was vilified and threatened for
his identification of bubonic plague in San Francisco.

Thomas Sydenham and the
Epidemic Diseases of the Sixteenth
and Seventeenth Centuries

MOST epidemic diseases have plagued man from the earliest times—sometimes identified, sometimes not, often confused. The sixteenth and seventeenth centuries were a period of increasing differentiation, a period culminating in the contributions of Thomas Sydenham (1624–1689).

Thomas Sydenham has come to be known as the English Hippocrates both because he revived the Hippocratic methods of acute observation and empiricism and because he subscribed to Hippocrates' philosophy of assisting nature rather than opposing her. Yet Sydenham "came to medicine more by accident than design," fully sharing "in the military and political vagaries of his family's fortune. His eldest brother, Colonel William Sydenham, was a founder of the Protectorate and one of the handful of men holding a supreme power under Cromwell's military dictatorship. . . . Thomas Sydenham loyally supported his brother throughout the vicissitudes of civil war and the bewildering flux of its political aftermath." [1]

In 1642 Sydenham entered Magdalen Hall, Oxford (where the principal, John Wilkinson, was one of the leading Puritans at the university), but his stay was cut short after a few months by the outbreak of the civil war and his entry into military service. When Oxford and the other royal garrisons surrendered in 1646, Sydenham resigned his commission and prepared to return to Oxford. En route he stopped off at the family home near Dorchester to visit a sick brother (presumably Richard who died soon after the hostilities ended) and there met his attending physician, Thomas Coxe (1615–1685), who had obtained his M.D. degree from Padua in 1641 and would become president of the College of Physicians in 1682.

> With his well-known kindness and condescension, Dr. Coxe asked me what pursuit I was prepared to make my profession [wrote Sydenham many years later], since I was now returning to my studies, which had been interrupted, and was also arrived at years of discretion. Upon this point my mind was unfixed, whilst I had not so much as dreamed of medicine. Stimulated, however, by the recommendation and encouragement of so high an authority, I prepared myself seriously for that pursuit.[2]

The year 1647 found Sydenham at Wadham College but he was unimpressed by a medical curriculum that, "over-burdened with theory, was only vaguely related to the physician's primary task of treating the sick: there was no training in clinical medicine." A fellow student, John Ward, later vicar of Stratford on Avon, would write: "Physick says Sydenham, is not to bee learned by going to Universities, but hee is for taking apprentices; and says one had as good send a man to Oxford to learn shoemaking as practising physick."[3]

Sydenham had only been back at Oxford a year when, on April 14, 1648, he received the degree of bachelor of medicine "by creation." This was a practice instituted by the earl of Pembroke, chancellor of the university, to meet the postwar dearth of candidates for office. Now that Sydenham was eligible he was elected to a fellowship at All Souls College and within the year he had been appointed senior bursar of that college.

April 1651 found him back in the army and it was not until 1655 or 1656 that he began medical practice in London. "I well remember (for it was the first time I was called upon to treat a dropsy)," he wrote in 1683, "having been summoned twenty-seven years ago or thereabouts, to a worthy married woman named Salt-marsh at Westminster." [4] But in these early days his practice was small and uncertain, partly, no doubt, because he was still involved in the politics of his party. Furthermore, it was not until 1663 that he obtained the license of the Royal College of Physicians.

Meanwhile, shortly after the Restoration, Sydenham had begun his clinical study of London epidemics (1661–1675) that was to bring him his niche in the medical hall of fame.

He first classified fevers (comprising two-thirds of his practice) into three main groups: continued, intermittent, and smallpox. Malaria was, of course, the typical intermittent fever. And Sydenham included measles with smallpox from which it was occasionally difficult to differentiate. But his group of continued fevers needs a word of explanation. He believed that there was a natural period for "fermentation" in all febrile illnesses, and continued fevers included all those diseases with prolonged pyrexia. Typhus, or the fourteen day fever, was the commonest one: others were typhoid and relapsing fever. Within the recurring pattern of London epidemics, Sydenham carefully studied the natural history of these diseases (including variations in succeeding epidemics) on the simplest basis of clinical observation. Then he worked out, purely empirically, the most efficacious methods of treating them. . . .

During [the] fourteen years [covered by his investigation] Sydenham recognized the following five periods: (1) 1661–4, (2) 1665–6, (3) 1667–9, (4) 1670–72, (5) 1673–5, each of them being characterized by a particular *epidemic constitution* or disposition of the atmosphere. It was the nature of the epidemic constitution that caused outbreaks of certain fevers. First, intermittent fevers predominated together with a peculiar species of continued fever. Then plague broke out, and was accompanied by other pestilential fevers, analogous to, but different from, the true plague. In the third, or variolous constitution, smallpox predominated, and was accompanied by another fever of the same epidemic constitution which Sydenham called variolous fever. The dysenteric constitution predominated during the fourth period causing cholera, summer diarrhoea, and unspecific fever resembling dysentery, an anomalous type of smallpox, and true dysen-

tery. The fifth constitution was characterized by a comatose fever
and an epidemic cough, probably influenza.[5]

MEASLES

Notwithstanding the fact that almost a century later Richard Mead
would still link measles with smallpox, it is surprising to read that
"Sydenham included measles with smallpox from which it was occasionally difficult to differentiate," for, as Barbara Gastel of Yale
has pointed out, "Among the most famous descriptions of measles
are those by Thomas Sydenham in 'Of Measles in the Year 1670'
and 'On the measles' in [the posthumously published] *Process integri*
(1692)," and I. J. T. Davies of University College Hospital, London, Welsh physician and author, who considers that what Sydenham did for clinical medicine was on a par with what William Har-
vey (1578–1657) had done for physiology and Andreas Vesalius
(1514–1564) for anatomy, has quoted Sydenham's description of
measles during the London epidemics of 1670 and 1674 as one that
would "vie with those in any modern paediatric textbook":

> Measles is apt to run through all that are under one roof. It begins
> with a rigor followed by heats and chills during the first day. On the
> second day there is a fever, malaise, white tongue (not actually dry)
> . . . a humour distils from the eyes and nose; the effusion or suf-
> fusion of tears being the most certain sign of sickening for measles,
> more certain indeed than the exanthem. The child sneezes as if it
> had taken a cold, there may be vomiting, more usually there are
> loose green stools (especially during dentition) and there may be ex-
> cessive fretfulness. On the fourth day red maculae like flea-bites ap-
> pear on the forehead and face, which coalesce as they come out in
> increasing number so as to form racemose clusters. The maculae will
> be found to the touch to be slightly elevated, although they seem
> level to the eye. On the trunk and limbs, to which they gradually
> extend, they are not elevated. About the sixth day the maculae begin
> to roughen and scale from the face downwards and by the eighth
> day they are hardly discernible anywhere. On the ninth day the
> whole body is as if dusted with bran. The common people say that
> the spots had "turned inwards", by which they mean that if it had
> been smallpox they would have remained out longer and have pro-

ceeded to suppuration and maturation. The rash having "gone in", there is an excess of fever attended by laboured breathing and cough, the latter being so incessant as to keep the child from sleep day or night. If they had been treated by the heating regime, they are apt to have chest troubles pass into peripneumonia, by which complication measles becomes more destructive than smallpox itself, although there is no danger if it be rightly treated.

"So accurate was Sydenham's description," Davies comments, "that it became possible to diagnose cases of smallpox and measles coexisting in the same household. On the same day as the Princess of Orange (sister of Charles II) died of smallpox, her sister, Princess Henrietta, was moved to St. James' Palace 'for fear of infection.' After a few days Henrietta left London for France, but the sailing of the ship was delayed owing to the Princess being attacked with 'Mezils'." [6]

SCARLET FEVER

Sydenham has also been credited with being the first to differentiate between measles and scarlet fever, but he was anticipated by the able Wittenberg clinician Daniel Sennert (1572–1637) and even earlier (in 1553) by the Sicilian Giovanni Filippo Ingrassia (1510–1580) of whom E. W. Goodall (1861–1938) wrote,

he described the rash as consisting of very many discrete erysipelatoid spots, large and small, of a fiery red colour and scattered all over the body, which, therefore, appears to be aflame. He disagrees with those who hold that the disease is the same as measles, for he has himself had ample opportunity of contrasting the two affections. [7]

SMALLPOX

Smallpox was pandemic in Europe in 1614 but it was not until 1628 that the first great epidemic occurred in London. Smallpox was again epidemic in England in 1667–68. In 1667, of a London population of 500,000, roughly 1200 died of smallpox; in the next year, almost 1500. In 1669 Sydenham wrote a (never completed) essay on smallpox in which he planned to present "a history and cure of a disease . . . too well knowne both by its terrible aspect and fatal effects to most familys in England," but he was, as was so often the case in his writings, more interested in "cure" than in "history" and in condemning antiquated methods and defending his own.

> I say not this with disrespect to the physitians of former ages, nor reproach to the doctor of this. I know what is to be allowd to pre-possession and education, receivd opinions I confess how false so ever, backed with generall uncontrold practice are not easily to be removed out of the mindes of men. And I quarell not with others for following their own maxims and methods, but yet must take the liberty to vindicate myself from the scandels and calumnys, which the doeing my duty and dealing with my patients as became an honest and conscientious man has drawn upon me.[8]

Sydenham's efforts notwithstanding, smallpox epidemics raged relentlessly. In a forty-year period early in the eighteenth century, one-quarter of London's population was stricken. In 1764 Niles Rosén von Rosenstein (1706–1776), the father of Swedish pediatrics, reported that every year one-tenth of the Swedish children died of the disease. Yet a countermeasure to what was "one of the most feared epidemic diseases of all times, not only because of its high mortality but also because of the horrible and disfiguring changes it produced in its victims" was available to such physicians as would use it—inoculation, to be followed before the century was out by vaccination.[9]

DYSENTERY

Although dysentery apparently did not become epidemic in London until 1670–72, Sydenham produced this description of the disease at the beginning of 1670:

I observe this disease come on for the most part about the beginning of Autumn. It is sometimes accompanied with a feaver and sometimes without but always with great torment in the bowells upon going to stoole with frequent dejections and these for the most part not stercorous but mucous with which are mixt streaks of bloud in the beginning, but in the farther progresse of the disease bloud in larger quantitys and unmixed often is evacuated, (to the great hazard of the patients life if not the certainty of the loss of the same, this large bleeding espetially if unmixed with mucous matter being an argument of the great corrosion of some of the vessells of the intestines.) Upon the continuance of this disease the intestines seeme to be affected successively downwards, and the mucuous stooles only troubleing the lower gut, whilst they are excreting and provokeing frequently to stoole. . . . It is for the most part mortall to old persons, lesse fatall though very dangerous to youth but benigne enough to infants, who if let alone and not tampered with may have it for some months without any prejudice to their lives.[10]

While Sydenham did not refer to it in his 1670 essay (in which he proposed more orthodox treatment), in the early sixties he had devised a novel approach to the cure of dysentery: he treated a woman by causing her son,

a plump, hot lad of thirteen years of age, and her nurse's son of six or seven years, to go to bed to her naked and to lie the one close to her belly, the other close to her back, which they did, and so long as they continued with her she had no stools; but the boys rising at any time the looseness would immediately return. I commanded that she should persist in her course till her cure should be complete (the boys relieving one another by turns in the daytime) and so she fully recovered.[11]

Even more novel was the treatment given during the civil war by a Dr. Bowles, a Royalist physician "called to treat a Parliamentary captain suffering from dysentery. The latter had just torn up some Common Prayer books—whether as a protest against orthodoxy, or on account of the limitations imposed by illness on a man of action, is not related. But the doctor caused the leaves of the prayer book to be boiled up in milk and administered to the patient. When this

preparation wrought a rapid cure, the doctor proceeded to discourse on the misfortunes of tearing up a book with such striking
medical properties. To a sceptic who inquired whether any other
sort of printed paper would have done, the doctor replied: 'No, I
put in the prayer for the visitation of the sick.' " [12]

In 1672 Sydenham described the articular and muscular pains of
dysentery and, in 1676, its seasonable aspects during the 1670–72
epidemic.

MALARIA

Just how ancient a disease malaria may have been is open to question. All intermittent fevers are not malarial and "ague" was used
to describe many fevers. The name *malaria* does not appear to have
been introduced until the eighteenth century. [13]

Malaria, of course, comes from the Italian words *mal' aria* meaning bad air or miasm which was blamed for the disease; from the
earliest times fevers that may or may not have been malarial have
been associated with standing water. (These conclusions were not
unreasonable when one considers that the anopheles mosquito
breeds in standing water and is airborne.)

Hippocrates gave considerable attention to fever, as well he
might, because Greek farmlands, which were rich and productive
thanks to an abundance of water, were becoming depopulated by
fever caused by the bad air put forth by the standing water that
made the farms prosperous. In fact, in 334 B.C. Alexander the
Great (356–323 B.C.) took advantage of the situation in his conquest
of Greece. (By way of retribution, the fever from which Alexander
died may well have been malarial.)

Around 300 B.C. a Greek colony that had settled at Paestum
(near modern Agrippa) in Italy some three hundred years earlier
was hard hit by fever. Faulty irrigation had allowed water to seep
in and form marshlands. The bad air that brought the fever rose
from the marshes.

In A.D. 410 Alaric the Visigoth sacked Rome, but he was in turn
defeated by the bad air arising from the marshes of the Roman

Campagna and his death has been imputed to malaria. The German leaders who succeeded him tried to hold out against Rome's forbidding summer climate, but in the eleventh century they declared the city uninhabitable and abandoned it. On July 5, 1740, Horace Walpole (1717–1797) wrote from Rome: "There is a horrible thing called mal' aria, that comes to Rome every summer and kills one. . . ." [14] Incidentally, the marshes continued to make Rome almost uninhabitable in the summer until Mussolini drained them.

However, it was not until the sixteenth century that an *epidemic* of malaria can be considered to have occurred.

> On the very verge of the period to which the history of malarial epidemics can be traced back, we meet with a pandemic . . . in the years 1557 and 1558, which is said to have overrun Europe. It is impossible to decide from the scanty and incomplete epidemiological data of the sixteenth and seventeenth centuries how often such epidemic outbreaks of malarial fever may have occurred in times subsequent to that pandemic; it is not until the years 1678–1682 that we again meet with definitive facts relating to an epidemic extending over a great part of Europe; and thereafter follow at short intervals reports of the same kind for the years 1718–1722, 1748–1750, 1770–1772, and for a more restricted epidemic in 1779–1783. [15]

In 1602, forty thousand Italians died of malaria; in 1610, the talented but tempestuous Italian artist Michelangelo Merisi da Caravaggio (1565–1609) succumbed to the disease in the fishing village of Porto Ercole as he was trying to sneak back into Rome. The deaths of James I (1625) and Oliver Cromwell (1658) have been attributed to malaria. (Malaria had long been endemic in England, perhaps since the time of the Venerable Bede, and Sydenham declared it to be epidemic between 1661 and 1664.)

TYPHUS AND TYPHOID

Without differentiating between them Sydenham apparently included among febrile diseases in which feverishness is prolonged both typhus and typhoid. Typhus is a rickettsial disease transmitted by human body lice; typhoid involves a Salmonella bacillus that is to be found in the feces and urine of man and transmitted by food contamination in handling or water, especially in poorly sanitized communities.

MacArthur, as has been noted, was satisfied that typhus was the major disease entity in the Plague of Thucydides. There are indications that typhoid, also an ancient disease, was known to Hippocrates, and certainly by the second century B.C., when a fifty-six-mile aqueduct to supply Rome with fresh water was built, the Romans had recognized the importance of clean household water and sanitation to combat waterborne disease.

According to Hirsch, the "earliest references to typhus epidemics, having a degree of definiteness, date from the eleventh century. There is a notice of an epidemic in 1083 at the monastery of La Cava, overlooking the town of Cava near Salerno." The chronicle of Bohemia by Hagecius told of a severe epidemic in 1096 in which no "plague-glands were to be seen, but the complaint was of soreness in the head." Hirsch went on to note: "Similar epidemics of 'pain in the head' (or 'head sickness,' the term that afterwards came into general use for typhus) without 'plague-glands' (thereby expressly distinguished from plague) are often referred to in the German chronicles of the centuries following. Especially towards the end of the fifteenth century, typhus appears to have been widely spread in many countries of Europe; as in 1480 in Carinthia and Carniola (burning fever and pain in the head) in consequence of famine; in 1481–82 under the same circumstances in Friesland and other parts of Germany, and in France; in 1489 in Spain, during the campaign in Granada, having been imported, as was said, by troops from Cyprus, where it was alleged to be endemic; and in 1502–1504 in Germany, . . ." [16]

Epidemics of typhus were rife over a great part of Italy between 1505 and 1530. Fracastoro described the disease and like fevers which, he said, were "vulgarly called 'lenticulae' (small lentils), or 'puncticulae' (small pricks), because they produce spots which look like lentils or flea-bites. Others spell the name differently, and call them 'peticulae.' " Fracastoro recounted instances in which "persons who went from Italy to other countries where no fever of this sort existed, and died of it there, as though they had carried the infection with them. . . .

> This fever, then, is contagious, but it does not infect quickly or by means of fomes, or at a distance, but only from the actual handling of the sick. Though in the early stages all pestilent fevers are gentle and mild, this sort invades so very gently that the sick are hardly willing to call in a doctor. Hence many doctors have been deceived at first; they expected a resolution of the malady in a little while, and so provided no remedy against it; soon, however, the symptoms of malignant fever began to show themselves. For though, according to the nature of fevers of this sort, a moderate temperature was felt, nevertheless a sort of internal disturbance became obvious, then prostration of the whole body, and a lassitude such as follows over-exertion; the patient could only lie flat on his back, the head became heavy, the senses dulled, and in the majority of cases, after the fourth or seventh day, the mind would wander; the eyes became red, and the patient was garrulous; the urine was usually observed to be at first pale, but consistent, but presently red and clouded, or like pomegranate wine; the pulse was small and slow, such as I have described above, the excrement corrupt and offensive in smell. About the fourth or seventh day, red, or often purplish-red spots broke out on the arms, back and chest, looking like flea-bites (punctiform), though they were often larger and in the shape of lentils, whence arose the name of the fever.[17]

Typhus was epidemic in Bologna in 1540, Padua in 1549, Ancona (on the Adriatic) in 1552; in Germany in 1540 and 1543; in France in 1545; in France and Spain in 1557. "Another severe epidemic began in 1566, as war-typhus, in Hungary . . . and spread over Austria, Bohemia, Germany, the Netherlands, and Italy; famine in many parts of Europe gave an impulse to it, and it lasted until 1568. In 1572–74, the disease was prevalent, to a like extent, in the Netherlands, Germany, France, and Switzerland, being again associated with war and failure of the crops. Among the isolated epidemics of typhus during the period, there deserve to be mentioned the notorious outbreaks on the occasion of assizes held at Oxford in 1577 (Black Assize) and at Exeter in 1568. An area of severe famine-fevers, among which typhus was again conspicuous, was formed towards the end of the sixteenth century in *Lombardy* (1578–88), *Italy* in general, with *Sicily* (1590–92), a large part of *Germany* (1591–92) and *Sweden* (1597)." [18]

The beginning of the seventeenth century saw typhus epidemics in Spain, Germany, Italy, and the north of Europe.

> The widest diffusion of the disease was during the Thirty Years' War [1618–1648], in which the political and religious disagreements of Europe were fought out on German soil. *Germany* herself suffered earliest and most severely, but the sickness afterwards reached *France*, the southern provinces of which had already become the seat of widespread epidemics of typhus during the persecutions of the Calvinists and the conflicts connected therewith, as well as the *Northern Kingdoms*, where the war between Sweden and Denmark and Norway furnished new occasion for the extension of the fever. Under the same circumstances typhus appeared in *England* during the Civil Wars, and in the *Netherlands*, while *Italy* was visited by extensive and severe epidemics especially in the famine years 1628–32 and 1646–50. In the latter half of the century we find references to isolated but considerable outbreaks of typhus . . . and in 1688 in the *British Islands*, where the disease is said to have begun in London in May, after which it spread over the whole of Great Britain, and began to spread over Ireland in July. [19]

Turning to typhoid, Hirsch observed that in "the medical writings of antiquity and the middle ages we seek in vain for descriptions or even moderately trustworthy indications of the group of symptoms peculiar to typhoid. It stands to reason that we may not conclude therefrom that the disease occurred rarely in those times, or not at all; on the contrary, there are, in several writings of the sixteenth and seventeenth centuries on the 'febres pestilentes' then observed, accounts of several forms of sickness which can hardly be interpreted otherwise than as referring to typhoid; and still more frequently and more plainly do we encounter the lineaments of this disease in the epidemiographical and clinical literature of the eighteenth century, to which there are not wanting even some anatomical notes relating undoubtedly to typhoid." [20]

Perhaps the first clear description of typhoid was that of Thomas Willis (1621–1675), well-known English physician, investigator, and anatomist, in his *De febribus* published in London in 1659. His account was based on observation of Royalist troops stationed at Oxford in 1643. Sydenham's final publication (1685)—*Schedula Monitoria de Novæ Febris Ingressu*—discussed a new fever which, while not identified as such, resembled typhoid. In 1690, just prior to his retirement, he had attended Lord Ossory, son of the earl of Arlington, who was desperately ill with what was probably typhoid. There were also descriptions by the Italian physicians Giorgio Baglivi (1669–?1707) and Giovanni Maria Lancisi (1654–1720). But the picture remained clouded and Hirsch has offered no evidence of typhoid being epidemic in the sixteenth and seventeenth centuries.

DIPHTHERIA

Aretaeus (A.D. 81–?138) from Cappadocia in eastern Asia Minor offered the first clear description of diphtheria (which he called *ulcera Syriaca*):

> Ulcers occur on the tonsils; some indeed of an ordinary nature, mild and innocuous; but others of an unusual kind, pestilential and fatal. Such as are clean, small, superficial, without inflammation and without pain, are mild; but such as are broad, hollow, foul, and covered with a white, livid or black concretion, are pestilential. Aphtha is the name given to these ulcers. But if a concretion has depth it is an eschar, and is so called; but around the eschar there is formed a great redness, inflammation, and pain of the veins, as in carbuncle; and small pustules form, at first few in number, but others coming out, they coalesce, and a broad ulcer is produced. And if the disease spread outwardly to the mouth, and reach the columella (uvula) and divide it asunder, and if it extends to the tongue, gums, and the alveoli, the teeth also become loosened and black; and the inflammation seizes the neck; and these die in a few days from the inflammation, fever, foetid smell and want of food. But if it spread to the thorax by the windpipe, it occasions death by suffocation within the space of a day.[21]

But Aretaeus was not the first to recognize diphtheria as a disease entity. Diphtheria, known as *ashara* or *serunke* (Greek, *cynache*), was so feared by the Hebrews that the detection of a single case in a community led to the blowing of the shofar, notwithstanding the fact that such a warning blast was ordinarily reserved for the third case of an infectious disease. In Hippocrates' *Epidemics* cynache is described as involving difficulty in swallowing and an escape of fluid through the nostrils when drinking, a nasal voice, and an inability to stand upright. Asclepiades of Bithynia (fl. 110 B.C.) practiced both scarification of the tonsils and laryngotomy.

Since Aretaeus, Caelius Aurelianus (fl. A.D. 400) recognized diphtheria of the larynx and described diphtheritic paralysis of the soft palate; Aëtius of Amida (fl. 550), after giving a description of epidemic diphtheria not unlike that of Aretaeus, also mentioned paralysis of the palate as a sequel. The Sanskrit Samhita of Suśruta (c. 500) spoke of a disease—*valasa*—involving painful swelling of the throat, difficulty in breathing, and ultimately asphyxia.

The Nuremberg city physician Hartmann Schedel (1440–1514) described a diphtheria epidemic that occurred there in 1492. Guillaume de Baillou (1538–1616) followed with an account of a Paris epidemic in 1576. Baillou was considered by Francis Graham Crookshank (1873–1933), himself an eminent English epidemiologist, to be "the first epidemiologist of modern times." [22] His great work on epidemiology—*Epidemiorum et ephemeridium*—published posthumously (Paris, 1640) included the first clear account of whooping cough. Between 1581 and 1638 diphtheria was six times epidemic in Spain.

INFLUENZA

The name influenza is derived from the fact that in the later Middle Ages influenza was regarded as due to a cosmic or celestial "influence" (*influentia coeli*). This name first appeared in Buoninsegni's *History of Florence* (1580) in reference to an epidemic in 1357; Sozomeno applied it to a Tuscan epidemic in 1387. According to Hirsch, before the year 1173 "the epidemiological data, although

they certainly relate to influenza, bear a stamp too little characteristic to make them likely to be useful," but there is every reason to
believe that influenza was spread by the Crusades, if not introduced by them. "Influenza," Hirsch further observed,

> always occurs as an *epidemic* disease, whether within a narrow circle
> or even confined to particular places, or in general diffusion over
> wide tracts of country, over a whole continent, and, indeed, not
> rarely over a great part of the globe as a true *pandemic*. It is in this
> last respect that influenza takes an exceptional place among the acute
> infective diseases; no other of them has ever shown so pronounced a
> pandemic character as influenza.

This "exceptional place" prompted Hirsch to devote ten pages to a
chronological tabulation of epidemics occurring between 1173 and
1875.[23]

Today most of the epidemic diseases have been eradicated or
brought under control where public health measures are enforced
and therapeutic preventive measures taken. Specifics have been developed to treat the few cases that might slip through the cordon.
But a significant exception to this rule is influenza which is as pandemic today as it ever was.

THE GREAT PLAGUE OF LONDON—1665

If one thinks of bubonic plague simply in terms of pandemics and
great epidemics, one is left with the impression of spontaneous
outbreaks occurring centuries apart—the Plague of Justinian in the
sixth century, the Black Death in the fourteenth century, and the
Great Plague of London in 1665. But plague, once introduced,
tends to become endemic, and this is well illustrated by the English
experience. England's first bout with plague—a mild one—occurred when the Plague of Justinian reached her shores (around
558). Her first significant epidemic occurred in 664 and the disease
thereafter was endemic for twenty-five years. The Black Death,
which reached England in August 1348, had not long subsided

"when in 1361 another [epidemic] broke out that would have been considered most calamitous had not the memory of 1349 overshadowed it. This tapered off slowly—York had a plague in 1363 and in 1365 there was quite an upsurge—and it had not entirely disappeared before a renewal of great intensity in 1369. Thereafter the plague was almost constant for twenty years, with conspicuous threats in 1371, 1373, 1375, 1378–1382, and 1390. The century closed with a serious outburst in 1399–1400, sufficient to disrupt the governmental routine and carry off some distinguished victims." [24]

There were at least twenty acute visitations in the fifteenth century. Then a sharp outbreak in 1532 caused the prorogation of parliament; the year 1543 was critical; in 1546 a death on a Venetian ship at London heightened already existing fear.

In 1563, 17,440 of an estimated population of 93,000 succumbed to plague. Shrewsbury has suggested that the Great Plague was only the third most destructive of London's last five great outbreaks, being tagged "the great" only because it was the last and its toll was numerically highest. On the basis of proportionate destruction, however, he awards the laurel to 1563.[25] The other serious epidemics occurred in 1593, 1603, and 1625.

Epidemics of plague were not, of course, confined to London, though attention tended to focus on the capital city. In extreme contrast, for example, was the tiny village of Eyam in Derbyshire (population 350 or less). Between September 1665 and October 1666 all but thirty of the villagers died of plague. How did the disease reach this tightly knit community, shut away from the world? Apparently in a box received from London by the village tailor containing patterns and some articles of discarded clothing. The tailor was the first to die of plague. In June 1666, by which time there had been eighty-five plague deaths, the villagers had panicked and made preparations for flight but the Reverend William Mompesson, rector of Eyam from 1664 to 1669, "pointed out that as each family left the village seeking sanctuary from the plague, they would carry with them, hidden in their baggage, among their garments, upon their hands and lips, the invisible seeds of the disease. Sickness and death would travel with them, as unseen companions, measuring their progress step by step. Wherever they wandered, through whatever town or hamlet they passed, in whatever house they sank to rest, the Black Death would follow, like a terrible shadow. The friends and relatives who proved brave enough to shelter them would be rewarded with a pestilence visited not only upon their own families but upon those of their neighbours and all who lived about them." The villagers accepted his admonition, "isolating themselves from the untainted countryside about them." [26]

It has been general practice to turn to *A Journal of the Plague Year* [27] by Daniel Defoe (1660–1731) for a contemporary account of the Great Plague of London, but in 1665 Defoe was five years old and can hardly be rated as an eyewitness. Nor can Sydenham (who might have been), for he

> prudently sought safety in the country. He has been reproached for joining the vast majority of physicians who left the capital when the sick were so desparately in need of their services. But it would have been foolhardy to have remained with a wife and young family in a plague-ridden area, which was, in any case, depopulated, as the residents on whom his livelihood depended had long since departed to more salubrious areas. [28]

In fact, "London looked like a desert. The King and Queen had gone with the whole court to the West, to uninfected places in the country; the High Councils and the High Court of Justice had been transferred. Parliament, which had just been opened, had moved to Oxford. All rich people with very few exceptions had left the town. The stoppage of industry increased the misery and confusion." [29]

Neither of these accounts takes into consideration the poor who were in no position to flee. It has been observed that plague usually struck at periods of high population when overcrowding led to unsanitary conditions. In 1554 the Venetian ambassador reported home that cases of plague "for the most part occur among the lower classes, as if their dissolute mode of life impaired their constitutions," and in 1566 Dr. John Jones noted in his *A Diall for all Agues*

(London: W. Seres) that "plague in the big cities like London, Bristol and Coventry was always worst in the 'stinking lanes' inhabited by the poor. Little was ever done to improve these poor areas where plague was endemic, and when plague periodically became epidemic and spread to the rest of the city the only solution was for the rich and their physicians to flee, leaving the poor to suffer." [30]

There were, however, two eyewitnesses of the 1665 epidemic who left accounts which are available to us. One is William Boghurst (1631–1685), apothecary in St. Giles in the Fields (London) and the other the diarist Samuel Pepys (1633–1703).

The Boghurst treatise is strictly medical. In fact, the editor of the first printed edition, Joseph Payne, held that it "contains the best medical account of the great epidemic, which has been preserved . . . which constitutes the main reason for printing the document, . . ." [31] Boghurst's contents can best be summarized by quoting his original subtitle: "Demonstrating its Generation, Progresse, forerunning, and subsequent Diseases and Accidents, Common Signes, Good and Evill Signes, Meanes of Preservation, Method of Cure, Generall and Particular, with a Collection of Choice and Tried Medicines for preservation and Cure by the practicall Experience and Observation of WILLIAM BOGHURST." [32]

On the subject of "flight" Boghurst had these interesting observations:

> Beza and some other Divines treating of this point and commending and advising it, doe not like well to have it called flying away, perhaps thinking it a scandalous term, but would have it called only going aside, a more moderate word. All physitians terme it Flight and many of them scruple much the advising of it, soe that some will say nothing at all to it, neither persuade nor dissuade, but leave every man to his choice, but the Divines have beene more bold, and advise it more eagerly and condemn those that betake not themselves to their heels. Nay, they say people are wicked and provoke God in not doing of it. The Turks (they say) neither fear nor fly from it. As to the lawfulness of the thing I see noe reason why people should soe scruple about it, seeing an indifferent understanding may solve the doubt; for sure it is lawful if a man live not in a healthful aire to

remove into another, or if a man doe not sit easy, to remove to another seat; a man hath the world before him and given him to live in. . . .

But there ariseth another question, who may fly, and who may not, for it is not to bee thought that all may run without distinction, care or consideration; but as for children, I think it would bee well if they could bee all put out into the country, for what good doe they in a dangerous place, but make work and trouble, and add fuel to the fire, they being more apt to catch the disease than others? And as for others, I think all may fly that are free and not obliged to stay either by their office, relations or necessities, such as Magistrates, Ministers, and Physitians, Apothecaries, Surgeons, Midwives. But those Apothecaries which have their work and dependence from the Physitians are not, I think, obliged to stay behind, when their Masters lead the way; for who shall direct them? They say it is not our business to direct or undertake to give Phisick of our own heads; therefore they are to bee excused. But those Apothecaries which stand upon their own Legs, and live by their own practize, are bound to their undertakings to stay and help as in other diseases. Every man that undertakes to bee of a profession or takes upon him any office must take all parts of it, the good and the evill, the pleasure and the pain, the profit and the inconvenience altogether, and not pick and chuse; for ministers must preach, Captains must fight, Physitians attend upon the sick, etc.

As for those who stay behind,

> After Humiliation, Confession, and resolution for reformation of life, which is necessary at all tymes, especially at such a tyme, because of the extraordinary fickleness of our lives, wee may the more comfortably and confidently descend to the use of other means of inferior ranke; and in these I will not make many nice divisions, for the avoiding of tediousness, because it overchargeth people's thoughts and memory; but after a few short rules concerning aire, meate, and drinke, fullness and emptiness, exercize and rest, sleeping and waking, and passions of the mind, I shall descend to medicine.[33]

What Pepys had to say was understandably more social than medical. His first reference to the plague, on April 30, 1665, was apprehensive: "Great fears of the sicknesse here in the City, it being said that two or three houses are already shut up. God preserve us all!" On May 24 he spoke of "plague growing upon us in this town; and of remedies against it: some saying one thing and some another." On June 10 he was greatly troubled to "hear that the plague is come into the City, though it hath, these three or four weeks since its beginning, been wholly out of the City." [34]

From this point forward Pepys made almost daily reference to the budding epidemic and it becomes necessary to be selective:

> 15th [June]. . . . The town grows very sickly, and people to be afraid of it: there dying this last week of the plague 112, from 43 the week before; . . . 23rd. . . . Home, by hackney-coach, which is become a very dangerous passage now-a-days, the sickness encreasing mightily. . . . 26th. . . . The plague encreases mightily, I this day see a house, at a bitt-maker's, over against St. Clement's Church, in the open street, shut up; which is a sad sight. . . .12th [July]. After doing what business I could in the morning, it being a solemn fast-day for the plague growing upon us, I took boat, and down to Deptford, where I stood with great pleasure an hour or two by my Lady Sandwich's bedside, talking to her, she lying prettily in bed, [but] the plague . . . renders it unsafe to stay long at Deptford. . . . 17th. . . . But, Lord! to see, among other things, how all these great people here are afraid of London, being doubtful of anything that comes from thence, or that hath lately been there, that I was forced to say that I lived wholly at Woolwich [whither he had sent his wife]. So anon took leave, and for London. . . . 20th. . . . Walked to Redriffe, where I hear the sickness is, and indeed it is scattered almost every where, there dying 1089 of the plague this week. My Lady Carteret did this day give me a bottle of plague-water home with me. . . . Lord! to see how the plague spreads! it now being all over King's Streete, at the Axe, and next door to it, and in other places. 21st. . . . Late in my chamber, setting some papers in order; the plague growing very raging, and my apprehensions of it great. . . .26th. . . . The sickness is got into our parish this week, and is got, indeed, everywhere; so that I begin to think of setting things in order, which I pray God enable me to put, both as to soul and body. . . . 12th [August] . . . The people die so, that now it seems they are fain to carry the dead to be buried by day-

light, the nights not sufficing to do it in. And my Lord Mayor commands people to be within at nine at night all, as they say, that the sick may have liberty to go abroad for ayre. There is one also dead out of one of our ships at Deptford, which troubles us mightily—the Providence, fire-ship, which was just fitted to go to sea; but they tell me, to-day, no more sick on board. And this day W. Bodham tells me that one is dead at Woolwich, not far from the Rope-yard. I am told, too, that a wife of one of the groomes at Court is dead at Salisbury; so that the King and Queene are speedily to be all gone to Milton. So God preserve us! . . . 15th. It was dark before I could get home, and so land at Church-yard stairs, where, to my great trouble, I met a dead corpse of the plague, in the narrow ally, just bringing down a little pair of stairs. But I thank God I was not much disturbed at it. However, I shall beware of being late abroad again. 16th. To the Exchange, where I have not been a great while. But, Lord! how sad a sight it is to see the streets empty of people, and very few upon the 'Change! Jealous of every door that one sees shut up, lest it should be the plague; and about us two shops in three, if not more, generally shut up. . . . 25th. This day I am told that Dr. Burnett, my physician, is this morning dead of the plague; which is strange, his man dying so long ago, and his house this month open again. Now himself dead. Poor unfortunate man! . . . 29th. To Greenwich, and called at Sir Theophilus Biddulph's, a sober, discreet man, to discourse of the preventing of the plague in Greenwich, and Woolwich, and Deptford, where in every place it begins to grow very great. . . . 31st. Up: and, after putting several things in order to my removal to Woolwich; the plague having a great encrease this week, beyond all expectation, or almost 2000, making the general [Mortality] Bill 7000, odd 100; and the plague above 6000. Thus the month ends with great sadness upon the publick, through the greatness of the plague everywhere throughout the kingdom almost. Every day sadder and sadder news of its encrease. In the City died this week 7496, and of them 6102 of the plague. But it is feared that the true number of the dead this week is near 10,000; partly from the poor that cannot be taken notice of, through the greatness of their number, and partly from the Quakers and others that will not have any bell ring for them. . . . As to myself, I am very well, only in fear of the plague, and as much of an ague, by being forced to go early and late to Woolwich and my family to lie there continually. . . . 6th [September]. To London to pack up

more things; and there I saw fires burning in the street [to counteract
plague], as it is through the whole City, by the Lord Mayor's order.
. . . 16th [October]. . . . I walked to the Tower; but, Lord! how
empty the streets are, and melancholy, so many poor, sick people in
the streets full of sores; and so many sad stories overheard as I walk,
everybody talking of this dead, and that man sick, and so many in
this place, and so many in that. And they tell me that, in Westminster, there is never a physician and but one apothecary left, all being
dead; but there are great hopes of a great decrease this week: God
send it! . . . 14th [November]. Captain Cocke and I in his coach
through Kent Streete, a sad place through the plague, people sitting
sick and with plaisters about them in the street begging. . . . 22d. I
was very glad to hear that the plague is come very low; that is, the
whole under 1000, and the plague 600 and odd: and great hopes of
further decrease, because of this day's being a very exceeding hard
frost, and continues freezing. . . . 30th. . . . Great joy we have
this week in the weekly Bill, it being come to 544 in all, and but 333
of the plague; so that we are encouraged to get to London soon as we
can. And my father writes as great news of joy, that they saw York's
waggon go again this week to London, and full of passengers; and
tells me that my aunt Bell hath been dead of the plague these seven
weeks. . . . 13th [December]. . . . Away to the 'Change, and there
hear the ill news, to my great and all our great trouble, that the
plague is encreased again this week, notwithstanding there hath been
a long day or two great frosts; but we hope it is only the effects of
the late close, warm weather, and, if the frost continue the next
week, may fall again: but the town do thicken so much with people,
that it is much if the plague do not grow again upon us. . . . 31st.
. . . But now the plague is abated almost to nothing, and I intend-
ing to get to London as fast as I can. . . . 16th [January 1666].
Mighty troubled at the news of the plague's being encreased, and
was much the saddest news that the plague had brought me from the
beginning of it; because of the lateness of the year, and the fear we
may with reason have of its continuing with us the next summer.
. . . 4th [July]. Thanks be to God! the plague is, as I hear, encreased but two this week; but in the country, in several places, it
rages mightily, and particularly in Colchester, where it hath long
been, and is believed will quite depopulate the place. . . . 7th
[August]. . . . I receive fresh intelligence that Deptford and Greenwich are now afresh exceedingly afflicted with the sickness more

than ever. . . . 9th. . . . I met with Mr. Evelyn in the street, who tells me the sad condition at this very day at Deptford, for the plague, and more at Deale, within this precinct, as one of the Commissioners for sick and wounded seamen, that the town is almost quite depopulated.[35]

Pepys' subsequent alarums notwithstanding, with the coming of the November frosts the great pestilence was over, and plague would never devastate London again. This immunity has been attributed to the Great Fire of London which, in 1666, cleansed the streets, destroying narrow alleys and houses built too close to each other, but the fire was largely confined to the City, possibly the least affected part of London, and spared parishes where the plague had been most violent. Furthermore, the relative immunity extended to other parts of England. Nor can the abatement be attributed to improved hygiene or advances in medicine. The hygiene of English towns was not much better in the eighteenth than in the seventeenth century. Three hundred years after the Great Plague there is still no satisfactory explanation of England's freedom from major epidemics of plague.

CHAPTER 11

The Fruits of Exploration and Colonization

SMALLPOX was confined to the East until avarice persuaded the Persians to overcome their aversion to the sea and their trade ships brought the disease to Arabian ports whence it traveled to Alexandria and Europe. The Plague of Justinian followed trade routes in its spread throughout Europe and the Black Death followed the same paths in its considerably faster circuit. But until the close of the fifteenth century, travel was by land or through the coastal waters of the "known world." Then men like Bartholomeu Dias (1450?–1500), Christopher Columbus (1451–1506), and Vasco da Gama (1469?–1524) had the temerity to venture into uncharted seas and forge passages to new worlds—unsuspected lands and islands for exploration and colonization.

Isolated people lack immunity to unfamiliar diseases. The introduction of such diseases into these receptive fields has been devastating. Sometimes introduction occurred during exploration; other times it waited on colonization. But there was another aspect to the opening up of new territories. Diseases occasionally flourished there of which the existence had been unsuspected in the Old World.

THE WESTERN HEMISPHERE

Because the Indians of the Americas proved highly susceptible to various Old World diseases, a belief has been fostered that they had formerly dwelt in a disease-free paradise. This is open to question. It is reasonably certain that venereal disease was endemic in Santo Domingo when Colombus arrived there; the conquest of Peru in 1533 by a few adventurers under the command of Francisco Pizarro (1470?–1541) was made easier by the fact that the population of the Inca empire had been depleted by 50 percent in the previous decade, thanks to disease which may or may not have been indigenous; and there is the unresolved question whether yellow fever was imported into South America from the Guinea Coast of Africa (as a by-product of the slave trade) or, as some hold, the disease appeared in the Western Hemisphere long before there was contact between the continents.

YELLOW FEVER

Yellow fever is an acute infectious virus disease characterized by sudden onset, fever with relatively slow pulse, jaundice (from which it derives its name), and *vomiting of* (altered) *blood*. Surviving Mayan manuscripts speak of epidemics of *black vomit*, and records exist of epidemics in Santo Domingo from 1495 onward and of many subsequent outbreaks in Central and South America and the Caribbean islands. Unfortunately records of yellow fever in Africa date only from 1764 (Sierra Leone) and 1778 (Senegal), but there is every reason to believe that yellow fever has been present in West Africa for centuries. This conclusion is based on the fact that, unlike the natives of Central and South America, the West Africans enjoy a high degree of tolerance of the disease and, if infected, are rarely seriously ill.

Because accounts of the early activity of what may have been yellow fever were by nonmedical observers, there has been a tendency to disregard them and to date the first reliable reports on the disease in the New World from the mid-seventeenth century. Whatever its past, yellow fever was persistently epidemic in the Caribbean area from 1635 on. In 1647 Barbados, thanks to heavy immigration from England, was overcrowded with whites not previously exposed to the disease, and an epidemic of yellow fever that broke out in the fall may be attributed to the large number of African blacks brought in by Dutch traders in the 1640s. This epidemic spread to Yucatán in 1648. During 1648–49 yellow fever broke out in St. Kitts, Guadeloupe, and Cuba. An epidemic lasting from 1686 to 1694 killed thousands of persons in northeast Brazil, but there were no other Brazilian epidemics during the colonial period, notwithstanding the fact that yellow fever was widespread in the Caribbean, Mexico, and Central America.

In 1668 New York was hit by what the American lexicographer Noah Webster (1758–1843) was later to describe as an "Autumnal bilious fever in its infectious form," so fatal that the governor ordered a fast day (a traditional means of combating epidemics). Medical historians, such as Claude Edwin Heaton, hailed this as the first appearance of the disease in the British North American colonies. Simon Harcourt-Smith has recently stated that yellow fever "despoiled Guadalupe in 1648, and Cuba the next year. By 1686 it was in New York, and soon afterwards in Charleston, South Carolina. Before the century was out, it had reached as far north as Boston, Mass." But the medical historian and teacher John Duffy has taken an opposite view, contending that the "bilious" fever might equally have been "typhoid, dysentery, or several other sicknesses. Had yellow fever been present, the high case mortality and the 'black vomit' would certainly have been noticed." [1]

In Duffy's opinion the first outbreak occurred in 1693 when a British fleet out of Barbados anchored in Boston harbor, bringing, in the words of the famed medical polemicist Cotton Mather (1663–1728), "a most pestilential Feaver, . . . which in less than a Week's time usually carried off my Neighbours, with very direful Symptoms, of turning *Yellow*, vomiting and bleeding every way and so Dying." [2] But the first definitely identifiable outbreaks of yellow fever ravaged Charleston and Philadelphia in 1699. In both cities mortality was high and normal activities were completely disrupted.

The eighteenth century had barely dawned when yellow fever,

which was to dominate the century,[3] hit New York in the summer of 1702. The epidemic, which lasted through October, carried off about 570 out of a population that would not reach eight thousand until 1730. The dead were of all ages and both sexes and included some citizens of note. For the next thirty-five years yellow fever apparently reached no farther north than Charleston which was badly hit in 1706, 1728, and 1732, and possibly in 1711. Epidemics recurred in South Carolina through the thirties and forties, reaching a peak about 1745. "By the arrival of the decade of the 1750's there were few visitations of the familiar disease, and after a mild outbreak in 1758, yellow fever paid its compliments elsewhere. [It] did not return to plague Charleston until the last decade of the eighteenth century, and why there was no serious outbreak this time was an unplainable [*sic*] mystery. But as if recharging itself, the disease descended with full force in the 1790's carrying off many victims in the epidemics of 1790, 1791, 1792, 1795, 1798, and 1799." [4]

The northern incursion was resumed in Philadelphia (1741 and 1747) and New York (1743, 1745, and 1748). John Mitchell (1711–1768), a noted botanist and physician practicing in Urbanna, Virginia, wrote a letter (not intended for publication) in 1744 to Cadwallader Colden (1688–1776), a member of the Governor's Council and a future lieutenant governor of New York, in which he described outbreaks of what he believed to be yellow fever occurring in Virginia in 1737, 1741, and 1742. A copy fell into the hands of Benjamin Franklin (1706–1790) who passed it on to Benjamin Rush (1745–1813). Rush caused it to be published in the *Philadelphia Medical Museum* in 1805. "Thus, unintentionally, Mitchell got into the medical literature as an important man in yellow fever and in early American medicine. To the extent that his common sense attitude was an influence, we will agree. The abstract of his letter was the lead article of the *Philadelphia Medical Museum*. Doctor Rush introduced it briefly and flatteringly. Mitchell's epidemics became accepted as one of the important outbreaks of the eighteenth century and the first in Virginia. He was not doubted by Hirsch or René La Roche, two profound nineteenth-century students. Herbert Thatcher and Brooke Hindle in this century are very respectful. Even the late Wyndham B. Blanton of our own historical fraternity accepted Mitchell's diagnosis. It is evident that none of these authorities read beyond Rush's introduction. . . . The Virginians were febrile and jaundiced but they did not suffer from yellow fever." A review of the "signs and symptoms, gathered from various places in [Mitchell's] paper," including a statement that the "disease raged chiefly in the winter and spring seasons" led Gordon W. Jones, a physician practicing in Fredericksburg, Virginia to his conclusion. "It requires only a paragraph to dismiss this as a yellow fever epidemic," he added. "Yellow fever cannot occur, let alone 'rage,' in the winter in North America in this latitude. The Aëdes aegypti mosquito does not bite at a temperature below 62 degrees Fahrenheit. It hibernates in winter in the Norfolk area." After reviewing several possibilities, Jones favored typhus as Mitchell's epidemic disease.[5] Jones's conclusion that the Virginia outbreaks were not yellow fever has the earlier support of Duffy who drew on a letter written by one of Mitchell's fellow practitioners to John Redman (1722–1808), president of the College of Physicians in Philadelphia, in which he commented that "the yellow fever in Virginia Described by Dr. John Mitchell Differs from that which appeared in Pensilvania in the Same Period of Time." [6]

However, in another letter to Colden the following year, Mitchell explicitly excluded the possibility of typhus (jail fever). Edmund and Dorothy Smith Berkeley, recent biographers of Mitchell, have discussed the various possibilities at some length and come to the conclusion that the epidemics were probably of Weil's disease (leptospiral jaundice). [7]

In 1761 yellow fever was imported into Cuba from Veracruz. The following year it ravaged British forces besieging Havana and was carried by them to Philadelphia. Rush later admitted that it was the experience gained in sixty-two that enabled him to diagnose the virulent Philadelphia outbreak in ninety-three.

For thirty years—from 1763 to 1793—British North America was free of yellow fever. None of the attempts to explain this hiatus has been entirely satisfactory. But when the calm was finally broken, the storm exceeded anything that had been previously experienced. Here are two contemporary pictures of Philadelphia in the late summer of 1793. The first is by Mathew Carey (1760–1839), a publisher; the second, by Benjamin Rush.

> The consternation of the people . . . was carried beyond all bounds. Dismay and affright were visible on the countenance of almost every person. Most people who could . . . fled the city. Of those who remained, many shut themselves in their houses and were afraid to walk the streets. . . . Many were almost incessantly purifying, scowering, and whitewashing their rooms. Those who ventured abroad, had handkerchiefs or sponges impregnated with vinegar or camphor at their noses. . . . The corpses of the most respectable citizens, even if they did not die of the epidemic, were carried to the grave, on the shafts of a chair, the horse driven by a negro, unattended by a friend or relation, and without any sort of ceremony. People shifted their course at the sight of a hearse. . . . Many . . . went into the middle of the streets, to avoid being infected in passing by houses wherein people had died. . . . The old custom of shaking hands fell into such general disuse, that many were affronted at even the offer of a hand.

> The streets every where discovered marks of the distress that pervaded the city. More than one half the houses were shut up, although not more than one third of the inhabitants had fled into the country. In walking for many hundred yards, few people were met, except such as were in quest of a physician, a nurse, a bleeder, or the men who buried the dead. The hearse alone kept up the rememberance of the noise of carriages and carts on the streets. . . . A black man, leading or driving a horse, with a corpse on a pair of chair wheels, . . . met the eye in most of the streets . . . while the noise of the same wheels . . . kept alive anguish and fear in the sick and well, every hour of the night.[8]

The epidemic began in August and by the time it abated with the coming of the October frosts four thousand had died.

There was a great diversity of opinion as to the cause of the epidemic. Hitherto it had been assumed, by citizens and governments alike, that yellow fever was contagious. Massachusetts had established quarantine regulations as early as 1647, Pennsylvania around 1700, and by 1790 rudimentary regulations existed in almost all American ports. (In light of modern knowledge, stricter quarantine measures might have lessened the vulnerability of Northern seaports.) Now anticontagionists, led by James Hutchinson (1752–1793), who was himself a victim of the epidemic, Rush, and Noah Webster, argued that filthy waterfronts were natural places for epidemics to start, the disease appearing only in those climates, seasons, and places in which heat, acting on moist animal and vegetable matter, produced putrid exhalations. (Rush attributed the current epidemic to damaged coffee that had putrefied on one of the wharves.) The anticontagionists therefore discredited maritime quarantine, recommending instead "extensive sanitary measures, including sewer construction, waste removal, broad streets planted with trees, numerous open squares, large house lots, and an end to overcrowding—in short, comprehensive city planning, sanitation, and housing reform." [9]

On the contagionist side, on October 1, 1793, Oliver Wolcott, Jr. (1760–1833), the comptroller of the U.S. Treasury, wrote from Philadelphia to his father in Connecticut:

> I see that the Connecticut Papers propose that measures be taken for the general safety. I sincerely hope that nothing more will be done, than to secure an inspection of Vessells from this Port. You may be certain that the approaches to this City are so watched that a man who can reach Connecticut *by land* cannot have the fever. It is as well ascertained as the case will admit, that the contagion becomes active in the constitution in four days—and it is still more certain that no man can travel after he becomes affected. I should much regret any regulations to interrupt *intercourse by Land*—they will not indicate either good sense or humanity. . . .[10]

Perhaps Wolcott's recommendations made sense, since few people were traveling, but, while Connecticut and New York limited themselves to strict quarantine of incoming ships, Delaware, Maryland, and New Jersey took extreme steps to prevent passengers from Philadelphia from entering their territory.

Faced with conflicting opinions,

municipal and state authorities strengthened existing regulations and instituted new measures based on the possibility that either view might be correct. The Pennsylvania legislature, for example, tightened the quarantine system and provided for a board of health in 1794. During the next few years it passed several more acts directed against yellow fever, and in 1799, largely as a result of the recent epidemics, Philadelphia began work on a public water supply. Baltimore appointed a seven-man health committee in 1794 which adopted quarantine regulations the following year; in 1797 new health ordinances placed sanitary administration under the city commissioner and established a Board of Health to superintend quarantine. New York enacted a series of increasingly stringent quarantine laws, created a three-man Health Office Commission to administer them, and authorized the Common Council to pass sanitary ordinances, abate nuisances, and appoint a sanitary inspector. In 1787 the Massachusetts General Court authorized towns throughout the Commonwealth to appoint health officers or health committees. Two years later the legislature established a 12-man Board of Health in Boston, which proceeded to adopt both sanitary and quarantine regulations for protection against disease.[11]

The 1793 epidemic was limited to Philadelphia, but from 1794 through 1805 there were repeated outbreaks in New York, Boston, Baltimore, Norfolk, and Charleston (in addition to Philadelphia). Less frequently yellow fever hit such smaller seaports as Portsmouth, Newburyport, Providence, New London, New Haven, Wilmington, Delaware, and Wilmington, North Carolina. Thereafter Northern ports were virtually free of the disease until 1819 when there were epidemics in Boston, Philadelphia, and Baltimore. Baltimore was hit severely enough to prompt the mayor, Edward Johnson, to broadcast an appeal for information "in relation to the Causes which gave Origin to this Disease" to the District Medical Society of Baltimore and to individual physicians. Their responses, together with an extract from the mayor's message to the city council and an ordinance reorganizing the Board of Health, were published in a volume running to two hundred pages.[12] After a final visit to New York in 1822, states north of Virginia remained free of yellow fever. "Infected sailors and passengers were landed time after time, but the quarantine and isolation measures appear to have been effective in keeping the disease in check." [13]

In 1795 yellow fever killed 732 out of an estimated New York population of 50,000, but the city's "great epidemic" occurred in 1798 when the death toll exceeded 2000. Prior to that year the municipality was not authorized to issue health regulations. The state legislature now recognized that the city must have power to meet such emergencies through passage of its own health laws. However, a permanent public health administration did not come into existence until 1804 when John Pintard (1759–1844) was appointed city inspector of health.

About the same time, yellow fever played another role in molding the history of America. In 1800 Napoleon, with dreams of a great colonial empire in the New World, had reacquired the Louisiana territory from Spain. By the time Napoleon came to power, Pierre Toussaint L'Ouverture (1743–1803), believing that France, beset with European wars, was in no position to deny independence to Haiti, declared himself governor for life and dubbed himself the Bonaparte of the Antilles.

> In characteristic fashion Napoleon met the situation with force. In the spring of 1802 a strong contingent of French under the command of Leclerc, Napoleon's brother-in-law, landed in Haiti, assumed the offensive and defeated the blacks. And then disaster struck. On the wings of the Aedes mosquito was borne the force that the legions of the French Consul could not combat. Forty thousand men—soldiers, sailors, officers and civilians—died of yellow fever. In November Leclerc, the commanding general, died of the disease, and in January the news of the debacle reached Napoleon. A few weeks later he was telling Talleyrand, "I renounce Louisiana—the whole colony," and was offering two startled Americans, who had come over hoping to buy New Orleans, enough land to make all or part of 15 states. Napoleon had had his fill of the New World, where the swamps swallowed his generals and his legions. [14]

While 1832 saw what was essentially the end of yellow fever in the northeast United States, towns and cities on the Atlantic coast from Virginia south and along the gulf coast from Florida to Texas faced repeated epidemics, so numerous in fact that it would be pointless to write of more than a few unusual ones.

Savannah, Georgia, founded in 1733 ten miles from the sea as the crow flies, was surrounded on three sides by marshes that were later converted to wet rice fields. Here was an ideal breeding ground for disease-bearing mosquitoes but, while malaria became relatively common, mortality records make no mention of a fever involving "marked black vomit" until 1820.

> Foreign shipping had become more abundant in 1816 and im-migrant laborers had begun to come in large numbers. Yellow fever was reported to have occurred in that year, again in 1817 and mildly in 1818. In 1819, according to one report, fifty Irishmen who came in one ship all died before the time of frost in the fall; since yellow fever prevailed it was the presumed though not specified cause of death. This tragedy was no doubt the reason for the passage of "An Act to prevent the introduction of passengers who are aliens into the port of Savannah during the months of July, August, September, and October"—an effort not only to protect the susceptible strangers and townsmen but also to avoid the strain on the city's charitable resources that would be caused by an epidemic.
>
> Savannah's most bitter experience with disease since its founding came in 1820. By that time it was a town with a population es-timated at 7,500, nearly surrounded by rice fields still tended mainly under the customary method of wet culture. . . . A destructive fire in January, 1820, had left part of the town in ruins and extraordi-nary spring and summer rains had filled the many depressions and cellars in the burnt district. The stage was set for the *Aedes aegypti* [the yellow fever vector] to become unusually active. . . .
>
> Summing up the damage from the epidemic, Mayor Thomas U. P. Charlton estimated that one-third of the population, including blacks, had succumbed.[15]

In the summer of 1855 a display of traditional Virginia hospital-ity led to what was probably the most colossal health blunder of the century.

> It all started when the *Ben Franklin*, a steamer fresh from yellow-fever ridden St. Thomas, arrived in Norfolk's harbor in distress.

Her captain begged permission to dock her for repairs. Despite rumors of clandestine burials from his ship and sinister reports of a corpse with orange-hued hands which had washed up on the beach, the over-shrewd captain blandly denied that there was any yellow fever on his ship. . . .

Finally, after a little half-hearted quarantine delay during which two terrified passengers swam ashore . . . the inconceivably good-natured health authorities allowed the ship to dock at Gosport on condition that the hold not be broken open.

Even this pointless agreement was broken by the skipper. In a few days people were fleeing the area of the docks because of a small outbreak of yellow fever. . . .

July and August saw a slow but steady increase in infection. In September the full force of the pestilence struck, continuing into October. "All commerce stopped. The only industry became that of fighting yellow fever. Heroic political leaders, ministers, and physicians of Portsmouth and Norfolk, 'the twin cities of plenty and happiness,' worked and died at their posts." Early in September *The Daily Southern Argus* suspended publication because the epidemic had left only one man in the plant. When publication was resumed on October 15 the editor exclaimed: "How doth the city sit solitary that was full of people!" [16]

In the 1870's, Mrs. Kate Bionda and her husband ran a snack-house in Memphis, Tennessee, catering to riverboatmen. . . . Mrs. Bionda, one insignificant resident of a large city, was not of the sort that history notices or remembers—except for one thing. She got sick in the late summer of 1878, and on August 13, there in her rooms above the snackshop, she died. A physician saw her, noted the symptoms, consulted with other doctors, and then announced to a frightened city that she had died of yellow fever. Mrs. Bionda, age thirty-four, thereby became the first formally designated victim of an epidemic that would claim 5,150 lives, more than a tenth of the city's population, in one of the most severe yellow fever epidemics in American history. [17]

In a sense this single paragraph tells the whole story—except for the process that led yellow fever to Memphis. New Orleans' first yellow fever epidemic occurred in 1796. For the next century epidemics occurred with almost unfailing regularity. Then as railroads were extended—there were three in Memphis—and Mississippi steamboats traveled faster, yellow fever followed in the wake of expanding trade. "The epidemic of 1878 struck first at Baton Rouge and Vicksburg, then pushed on to Memphis, and to Cairo, Ill.; eventually it reached St. Louis. At the same time the disease was carried up the Tennessee River to Chattanooga, and up the Ohio River as far as Louisville." [18] But it was Memphis with its large population that felt the worst impact.

The last epidemic of yellow fever in the United States occurred in 1905 when an infected passenger (or mosquito) slipped by the quarantine station below New Orleans. Four years earlier the U.S. Army Yellow Fever Commission had firmly established the *Aëdes aegypti* as the yellow fever vector, but the Louisiana State Board of Health was divided on the commission's report and the citizens of New Orleans refused to believe that the familiar pest to which they had long adjusted could be the culprit. It took the epidemic of 1905 to spur all parties to action. But at length the installation of municipal drainage, sewerage, and water systems eliminated the favorite breeding grounds of mosquitoes.

With yellow fever endemic in the Caribbean area it was inevitable that it would travel south as well as north, and in 1849 it reappeared in Brazil. It entered through the port city of Salvador, brought there by an American ship that had touched at both New Orleans and Havana. The epidemic spread southward, reaching Rio de Janeiro, where 4160 died, in 1850. It was endemic in the coastal cities for the balance of the century, but the highland areas, just back of the narrow coastal plain, remained relatively untouched.

The presence of yellow fever discouraged European immigrants (which Brazil badly needed) who turned rather to Uruguay or Argentina where the disease was rarely encountered. To make matters worse, in October 1895 the Italian cruiser *Lombardia* put into Rio de Janeiro with a crew of 340 officers and men. Of these only 7 failed to contract yellow fever and 234 died. In 1903 the newspaper *A Gazeta* editorialized: "We all know what yellow fever is: It is the ruin, shame, infamy and curse of our land." [19] But that year the government launched a program that eradicated yellow fever (and smallpox) in most parts of the country within five years.

A ship carrying German immigrants is credited with taking yellow fever from Brazil to Peru where, in 1854, it entered through the port of Callao hard by Lima. Over the next fifteen years it raged along the Peruvian coast (without, however, penetrating the mountainous hinterland), culminating in a severe epidemic in 1868–69. Chile remained free of the disease, but in 1857 it reached Montevideo from Brazil and the following year moved into Buenos Aires.

SMALLPOX

Smallpox spread from Santo Domingo to Puerto Rico early in 1519. The introduction of the disease into Mexico has been credited to Pánfilo de Narváez (1480?–1528), a black soldier in the invading army of Hernando Cortez (1485–1547). The resultant epidemic carried off three to four million natives, including the Aztec king Cuitahuac only four months after he succeeded his uncle and father-in-law, the emperor, Montezuma (1480?–1520). This rapid change in rulers considerably weakened Aztec leadership. (The Aztecs named the pestilence *hueyzahuatl*, meaning "great leprosy" or "great eruption.")

The course and chronology of the New World's first smallpox pandemic from the West Indies and Mexico through the Yucatán peninsula, Guatemala, Panama, and Peru remain uncertain. Accounts were mostly written after the event by Spanish adventurers, members of religious orders, and occasionally natives (though too often, as in Panama and Peru, the Indians had not yet learned to write), and accounts are in conflict. (Did smallpox reach the Inca empire in 1524 [Pedro Sarmiento de Gamboa], 1525 [José Toribio Polo], or 1526 [Pedro Cieza de León]?) [20] It seems that the disease must have reached the west coast of South America by way of the isthmus of Panama, as did Pizarro himself.

If we attempt to describe the first coming of Old World disease to the areas south of Panama, we shall have to deal with ambiguity, equivocation, and simple guesswork, for eruptive fever, now operating from continental bases, apparently outstripped the Spaniards and sped south from the isthmus into the Incan Empire before Pizarro's invasion. Long before the invasion, the Inca Huayna Capac was aware that the Spaniards—"monstrous marine animals, bearded men who moved upon the sea in large houses"—were pushing down the coast from Panama. Such is the communicability of smallpox and the other eruptive fevers that any Indian who received news of the Spaniards could also have easily received infection of the European diseases. The biologically defenseless Indians made vastly more efficient carriers of such pestilence than the Spaniards.[21]

Huayna Capac (1450?–1525), the greatest Inca ruler of Peru, succumbed to what was almost certainly smallpox while campaigning against the peoples of what is today northern Peru and Ecuador. Other victims of the epidemic were the emperor's brother, sister, uncle, and, most fateful, his legitimate son Nina Cuyoche. "Designated by the dying Inca as his successor, Nina Cuyoche died before notification reached him, opening the way for the dynastic struggle still being waged when Spanish adventurers arrived to capitalize upon it." [22]

> The impact of the smallpox pandemic on the Aztec and Incan Empires is easy for us in the twentieth century to underestimate. We have so long been hypnotized by the derring-do of the conquistador that we have overlooked the importance of his biological allies. Because of the achievements of medical science in our day we find it hard to accept statements from the conquest period that the pandemic killed one-third to one-half of the population struck by it. Toribio Montolinía claimed that in most provinces of Mexico "more than one half of the population died; in others the proportion was little less." "They died in heaps," he said, "like bedbugs." [23]

An outbreak of smallpox in Colombia spread to the Quito district of Ecuador where it reached epidemic proportions in 1589 and moved south as far as Trujillo (Peru) but appears to have been kept out of Lima through the foresight of the viceroy, Don Ferdinando de Torres y Portugal, who enlisted the aid of local physicians in setting up preventive measures.

The New World natives had experienced only limited population growth after the smallpox epidemic when measles struck the
area in 1529. After perhaps two-thirds of the population of Cuba
had succumbed, the epidemic hit Mexico and Honduras in 1531
and Nicaragua the following year. Since measles hit Panama in
1531 there are grounds for assuming that the contagion came by sea
rather than overland. Everywhere deaths have been estimated at
one-half to two-thirds of the population. There is some question
whether this epidemic reached Peru. In 1558–59 there was an epidemic of smallpox complicated by what seems to have been influenza. The latter disease had been pandemic in Europe in 1557,
reaching Spain in October. It is reasonable to suppose that Spanish
ships carried influenza to the Spanish colonies where, combined
with smallpox, it would cause considerable mortality. The balance
of the century saw sporadic epidemics of smallpox, measles, and
influenza, sometimes mixed, in the Caribbean and Central America
and the west coast of South America. A further "mix" may have
been provided by the incursions of Sir Francis Drake (1540?–1596).
Drake's expedition, involving twenty-five ships and 2300 men, left
Plymouth, England, on September 14, 1585, and made a first stop
at the Cape Verde Islands. Seven or eight days out from the islands, disaster struck. An epidemic disease carried off two to three
hundred of Drake's men. (By the time he decided that his force was
too weakened to continue his successful campaign and return to
England, the number had swollen to close to six hundred.) Contemporary descriptions suggest that the disease was typhus. "If epidemic smallpox moving west from Cuzco [in the Andes southeast
of Lima] in 1585 spread north to the Caribbean coast, to be followed by southward-moving typhus introduced by Drake's force at
Cartagena [Colombia] and infected Negro slaves at Panama and
ports of the west coast of South America, the high mortality in the
later stages of the epidemic may be more easily comprehended.
. . . The six year-long siege [1585–91] of epidemic mortality in the
Andean area certainly indicates that no sooner had one disease
swept through the susceptible population than another of a quite
different nature and even greater virulence, and to which the earlier one had conferred no immunity, appeared and produced even

greater mortality." [24] It was in 1590 that epidemic disease reached Chile, causing havoc among both the Spaniards and the hostile Araucanian Indians.

It is now generally agreed that smallpox arrived in the British colonies in 1630 with the first governor of Massachusetts Bay Colony, John Winthrop (1588–1649), and a large number of potential colonists. It apparently did not become epidemic until four years later when three or four Dutch traders carried it to Indians on the Connecticut River who died in great numbers. By and large the English settlers had achieved immunity through prior exposure, but such immunity did not extend to their children. A general epidemic of smallpox occurred in the Massachusetts Bay Colony in 1648–49. Boston was hit hard in 1666, and in 1677 English ships brought the infection to Charlestown whence it spread to Boston.

The arrival of a group of infected blacks from the West Indies in October 1689 caused a major epidemic involving New England and New York. Smallpox was so common in the eighteenth century that only the most severe epidemics were noted, including seven in Boston between 1721 and 1792, notwithstanding the introduction there of inoculation in 1721. One dramatic outcome occurred in the winter of 1763–64 when a sharp outbreak in Boston "so frightened the General Court that that august body scrambled over to Cambridge and held its sessions in the college buildings until the festers in the city could heal. The rheumatic and chilblained legislators, however, required such roaring fires in the fireplaces of Harvard Hall that the whole building burned down, destroying the best collection of scientific apparatus and the finest library in the American colonies." [25]

The first epidemic in the Virginia colony occurred in 1667 when a sailor with smallpox arrived at Accomac on the Eastern Shore and, escaping isolation, spread the disease to two Indian tribes. In 1696 smallpox was so prevalent in Jamestown that the Assembly recessed.

There was an epidemic of smallpox in Chile in 1654 and in the jungles of Peru in 1669–70. An Ecuadorian epidemic in 1680, with a mortality in excess of sixty thousand, had spread by the following year to the Amazonian side of the Andes.

With inoculation and then vaccination becoming available in the eighteenth century, smallpox should have ceased to be a serious menace in the following century,

> yet it continued to flare up in every American city. A series of outbreaks in New York City during the 1870s caused 805 deaths in 1871, 929 in 1872, 484 in 1874, and 1,280 in 1875. During three of these same years the annual death toll from smallpox in New Orleans was more than 500, and Dr. Joseph Jones, president of the Louisiana State Board of Health, later declared that 6,432 residents of New Orleans had died of smallpox in the years from 1863 to 1883. As late as the winter of 1899–1900, three of 12 medical students at Tulane University, infected during a widespread outbreak, died of the disease.[26]

Smallpox had been introduced into Canada by the earliest European immigrants and had decimated one Indian tribe after another as it swept the country. Not even the relatively isolated Plains Indians escaped. Nonetheless as late as 1870, when three thousand died, they were still largely relying on their native medicine men. By way of contrast, in the New Westminster district of British Columbia, where memories of an epidemic of 1862 were still alive in 1875, local physicians were able to persuade over two thousand Indians to accept vaccination. This was considered quite an achievement. Measles also plagued the Canadian Indians.

TYPHOID AND TYPHUS

Because typhoid and typhus are so similar they were not differentiated until as late as 1837. Early reports of each were not only confused among themselves but with other diseases as well.

> Of 105 persons who landed at Jamestown, May 13, 1607, more than one-half died the first summer. Year after year additional immigrants came in spite of the high mortality that awaited them. Five hundred and twenty-five died in the first three years. In the first decade-and-a-half, 1607–1624, although 7,549 persons had entered the colony, at the end of that period only 1,095 remained. The death of 6,454 in so short a time abundantly justified the historian's habit of designating this loss as "The Great Mortality."[27]

The symptoms of the sickness that beset the settlers were swellings, bloody fluxes, and burning fevers. Some authorities have thought that what was involved was beriberi, a vitamin-deficiency disease. However, Gordon W. Jones has pointed out that for beriberi to have "actually occurred so soon at Jamestown, there must have been a precipitating or associated factor." While conceding that during "the famous 'starving time' of 1609–1610 there was undoubtedly in Jamestown a veritable museum of avitaminoses . . . meager ration alone for eight weeks in 1607 does not seem enough to cause the development of clinical beri-beri." After all, the 1607 expedition had, prior to its arrival in Virginia, rested in the West Indies, eating fresh fruit and meat and taking on fresh water. Drawing a parallel from the American Civil War, Jones concluded that the "precipitating or associated factor" was typhoid fever, a conclusion in which Wyndham B. Blanton and John Duffy had anticipated him.[28]

If typhoid was the culprit, who was the carrier? When the three ships under the command of Captain Christopher Newport arrived in Virginia, there was only one sick person in the company—the Reverend Robert Hunt—and he had been sick from the outset. When Newport and his crew departed homeward bound, there was no illness aboard. One of those who remained behind was the carrier.

It is hard to resist the temptation to point the finger of suspicion at the Reverend Robert Hunt. It will be recalled that he was desperately ill for five or six weeks at the beginning of the voyage. The illness was very likely typhoid fever. The time of the year is no argument against this opinion. Typhoid, while more prevalent in the hot months, can occur at any time. That Hunt did not spread it on shipboard could be explained by the sanitation of the boat and the fact that the typical sailor's dry diet, which he would have no part in issuing, was not conducive to the growth of bacteria. For that matter, even a well carrier on board would have been as dangerous as he. The significant fact is that there is no note that he was sick during the summer under consideration. Many others are so mentioned by name. At a time when many were sick and there was much work and guard duty to be done who was more logical than the kindly forty-year-old priest to tend the kettle, work the sturgeon [*sic*], and mind the ill? [29]

Historical evidence suggests that typhus fever existed among South American natives in pre-Columbian days and that recognizable epidemics occurred in Mexico before the arrival of Cortez at Veracruz, but the disease did not reach the North American colonies until the eighteenth century. James Lind, famous for his epoch-making treatises on scurvy, naval hygiene (of which he was the founder in England), and tropical medicine, attributed its introduction to felons shipped to America, carrying the seeds of "jail distemper," and to impressed seamen and passengers who wore filthy rags. "Lind was convinced that the infection was carried on the bodies of men, upon clothes and other kinds of materials, such as wool, cotton, linen and might cling to wooden beams, chairs and bedsteads." [30] Thus "ship fever" (as typhus was called) threatened such Eastern cities as Philadelphia, Baltimore, New York, Boston, and Portsmouth. As a prophylactic measure, impressed seamen were often stripped, washed, shorn, and provided with fresh clothing before being allowed to mingle with a ship's company.

French ships of the day were notoriously dirty and fever-ridden. In 1746 a French squadron under the command of the Duc d'Anville, attacked by what was evidently typhus, put in at Chubucto, near Halifax, Nova Scotia. "Blankets and old clothes used in the tents and hospitals were left behind when the squadrons returned to Europe. Mimack Indians used these discarded French garments for clothing and distributed them throughout the tribe. Lacking any natural herd immunity, the whole nation of Indians was virtually wiped out by French blankets. Either infected lice surviving in the blankets or dried rickettsial-laden feces could have initiated the epidemic." [31] Palatine ships carrying German immigrants, bond servants, and convicts brought typhus to Philadelphia on several occasions, culminating in 1754 when the "provincial council ordered the secretary to have doctors visit all ships and places in town where Palatines were housed." [32] In 1759 typhus broke out among the Moravians of North Carolina, and in the 1760s Annapolis, Maryland, suffered from shipborne outbreaks. But it was not until the Revolutionary War that the infection manifested itself on a large scale. One casualty, for example, was Major General Nathanael Greene (1742–1786) of Rhode Island who in August 1776 was appointed commander in chief of ground forces in New York. He succumbed to typhus on the fourteenth and was out of commission until September 5. Meantime 8528 of his command (roughly one-third of its strength) were down with what was almost certainly typhus. There has been speculation that, but for the concurrent defeat of the rebel forces at the critical battle of Long Island by General William Howe (1729–1814) and Admiral Richard Howe (1726–1799), the war might have ended two years earlier, that but for "lice and typhus His Majesty's forces might have experienced another Breed's Hill [the actual site of the battle of Bunker Hill] sufficiently disastrous to have prompted the Howe brothers to return to England and call the whole thing off." [33]

During the eighteenth century, typhoid was relatively common. A series of epidemics in Connecticut and Massachusetts in 1727, 1734, and 1737 and in South Carolina (1734 and 1738) bore the earmarks of typhoid. Then, beginning in 1740, there were a number of New England epidemics obviously involving dysentery, "but the descriptions of many of the long, nervous, continued fevers leave little doubt that typhoid was fighting alongside the other bowel infections." [34] Boston seems to have escaped these epidemics, but in 1759 and the 1760s typhoid was present in Philadelphia, Delaware, North Carolina, and New Jersey.

DIPHTHERIA, THROAT DISTEMPER, AND SCARLET FEVER

In the summer of 1614 the Peruvian city of Cuzco suffered an epidemic of diphtheria so severe that every household in the city was affected. It killed without regard to race, class, or age.

"Throat distemper," according to Cotton Mather, first appeared in the North American colonies in 1659 and there are records of subsequent outbreaks in the seventeenth century. But there is uncertainty as to the nature of the disease or diseases involved (probably scarlet fever in some areas and diphtheria in others), and it has become customary to regard the severe 1735 attack on entire families, that destroyed the women and children, occasionally the men, as the onset of epidemic throat distemper. Even then, the "devout colonists viewed the disease as an act of God, the fruit of strange sins," while contemporary physicians "attributed the disease to bad air and not contagion, since it attacked families who lived miles apart and had no direct contact with one another." [35]

The throat distemper that raged from 1735 to 1740 was clearly an "epidemiological complex." Severe diphtheria spread from Kingston, New Hampshire, to Maine and Massachusetts; there was an outbreak of scarlet fever (described by William Douglass [1691–1752], who had led the opposition to inoculation fifteen years earlier, "in one of the classic writings of early American medicine") in Boston; New Jersey suffered diphtheria combined with mild scarlet fever; an outbreak of diphtheria in Stamford, Connecticut, spread in a northeasterly direction to coalesce, in 1740, with diphtheria in northeastern New England; and there was fragmentary evidence of both scarlet fever and diphtheria in the province of New York. "The two diseases had not yet been clearly separated as independent entities but were fused and confused in the vague designation 'throat distemper.' " [36]

By and large throat distemper, while continuing to appear sporadically in New England and New York where it had apparently become endemic, moved slowly into other states. Philadelphia had its first cases in 1746 but remained relatively free from infection until 1763 when it suffered a large-scale epidemic—the first major outbreak in the colonies since 1755. South Carolina had recorded its first cases in 1750–51.

In 1769 New York was hit hard. Samuel Bard (1742–1821), professor of physic at King's College Medical School, treated sixteen cases of throat distemper and, on the basis of his experience, produced *An Enquiry Into the Nature, Cause and Cure, of the Angina Suffocativa, or, Sore Throat Distemper, As It is Commonly Called by the Inhabitants of This City and Colony* (printed in New York in 1771), a pamphlet described by William Osler (1849–1919—the greatest physician of his time) as an "American classic of the first rank," and by Abraham Jacobi (1830–1919—the father of American pediatrics) as "brilliant . . . wise and accurate . . . classical and simple," offering a description of diphtheria that "in skin, mucous membrane and larynx is correct and beautiful." [37]

Seven of the children treated by Bard died and he performed autopsies on three. "In each he found whitish sloughs in the back of the throat, at the base of the tongue, and particularly the tough membrane covering the entire larynx, the trachea, and much of the bronchi. Bard believed the sloughs to be inspissated mucus. The membrane was so tough that the entire cast of the trachea could be lifted out and resembled a sheet of thin chamois leather in both thickness and appearance." [38] It may have been this description that led the French clinician Pierre Fidèle Bretonneau (1778–1862), in a famous treatise on the subject (Paris, 1826), to name the disease *diphthérite* from the Greek *diphthera* meaning "leather." All the cases Bard treated manifested suffocation symptoms and he had no doubt that those autopsied died from suffocation.

One final note on diphtheria in the eighteenth century.

On December 12, 1799, a cold, rainy, windy day, George Washington, age 67, rode around his Virginia estate from ten until three, went into dinner without changing his damp clothes.

The next day he had a cold and severe sore throat; he was hoarse but joked about it, even read portions of the newspaper aloud. He woke at three the following morning, scarcely able to speak or breathe; he almost choked trying to swallow the mixture of molasses, vinegar, butter. . . . Washington died the next day of what his physicians called cynanche trachealis, now believed to have been diphtheria. [39]

The first definite epidemic of scarlet fever occurred at the time of Boston's smallpox epidemic of 1702. After outbreaks in 1735–36, there was a jump to 1764 when Rush reported the disease to be general in Philadelphia. It flared anew in 1769 and in the same years was present in the Carolinas. In 1783 both diphtheria and scarlet fever were prevalent in all the states from South Carolina to New England, but in some areas New Englanders seem to have developed a degree of immunity.

Diphtheria, for which, in contrast with smallpox, little could be done, became epidemic in the 1870s.

From 1866 to 1872 diphtheria deaths in New York averaged about 325 per year. In 1873 the figure jumped to 1,151, increased to more than 1,600 in 1874, and then reached a new high of 2,329 in 1875. . . . In New Orleans a health official informed a joint meeting of the city's two medical societies in 1887 that diphtheria had long existed there, but never before had it been "so widespread and abundant as now." By this date diphtheria had spread throughout America, ravaging town and country alike.[40]

INFLUENZA

Blanton believed that a severe respiratory outbreak in Virginia in the winter of 1623 may have been influenza; Hirsch traced the first epidemic of influenza in the Western Hemisphere to an outbreak in New England in 1627, claiming that it spread to the West Indies and South America, reaching as far as Chile; but Duffy has stated that the "first recorded influenza epidemic in North America occurred in 1647." There were influenza epidemics in the New England states, among the Iroquois Indians of Canada, and in Virginia during the second half of the seventeenth century, and influenza ranged from South Carolina to New England through most of the eighteenth century.[41]

Emphasis has been placed on an epidemic of influenza that occurred in the Western Hemisphere in 1789–90 by the fact that Robert Johnson described the outbreak in his inaugural dissertation for the degree of doctor of medicine at the University of Pennsylvania in 1793. To set the scene, Richard E. Shope (1901–1966), a researcher of infectious diseases, then with the Rockefeller Institute for Medical Research, wrote:

> To orient you as to the time of this influenza outbreak, it came in the year that Washington was inaugurated president, that the first Congress met in New York, and that the French Revolution began. The first steamboat did not cross the Atlantic until 1819, and the first steam train did not run until 1830. Air travel, of course, was not even dreamed of. This outbreak occurred before modern means of rapid travel were available and when man could go no faster than his horse could gallop. Despite this, according to Johnson, the influenza of 1789 spread like wildfire.[42]

In 1798 there was a general diffusion of influenza in the United States.

DYSENTERY

It is hard to determine when dysentery first hit colonial North America though it must have been early. Unfortunately its symptoms—fever, diarrhea, cramps, and bloody, mucous evacuation—are not restricted to dysentery. While the weight of authority has favored typhoid, the 1607 outbreak in Jamestown involved "bloody fluxes" and may have been dysentery. The year 1669 saw widespread sickness north of New York and at least one observer listed a flux as the chief source of trouble. "A sore dysentery flux" struck down many Bostonians in 1676. South Carolina suffered virulent attacks in 1710, 1715, 1734, 1740, and 1751, and there were equally severe outbreaks in Salem, Massachusetts, in 1732, New London, Connecticut, and Boston in 1734. A medical society newly formed by William Douglass (the first in the colonies) proposed that its first published article be *A History of the Dysentery Epidemical in Boston in 1734*. In succeeding years, according to Duffy, dysentery took first place among the epidemic diseases afflicting New England. The flux hit New York in 1731, New Jersey in 1745, Philadelphia in 1757.

> Few armies in history have escaped dysentery, and colonial armies were no exception to the general rule. In 1690 Robert Livingston reported that the soldiers in Albany and Greenback in Western New York were afflicted with this disease. General Braddock's campaign in the French and Indian War was hindered considerably by the bloody flux, and on one occasion George Washington wrote, "Our hospital is full with sick and numbers increase daily with the bloody flux which has not yet proved mortal to many."[43]

In course of the civil war there were 233,812 cases of acute dysentery with 4084 deaths and 25,670 chronic dysenteries with 3299 deaths.

MALARIA

In July 1526 some five hundred potential colonists left Hispaniola to settle on the Cape Fear River in North Carolina (then part of "Florida"). The Spaniards included in their ranks some black slaves—both groups originating in countries where malaria was endemic. Scarcity of food and prevalence of disease, including malaria, thwarted this attempt at colonization. In 1659 the vice-director of the Dutch settlement in America complained that he had been confined to his bed for two or three months with what seems to have been malaria. In 1684 a malignant fever attacked both whites and Indians at a Jesuit mission in Canada. Other missions were attacked, suggesting that malaria was well established in French Canada by this date. Either the French took malaria into the Mississippi Valley or it was already there when in 1700–1701 Father Jacques Gravier (1651–1708) traveled from Illinois to the mouth of the Mississippi, for its presence is frequently noted in his journal. Malaria in New England in the seventeenth century was virulent and often fatal, but it had practically disappeared before the revolution. On the other hand virulence seemed to increase in the other colonies as the eighteenth century progressed. In 1687 intermittent fever was listed first among the diseases attacking Virginia colonists, and by the eighteenth century it was a constant threat. The same century saw malaria in parts of New York, New Jersey, Pennsylvania, and the Carolinas.

Lord Adam Gordon, an English army officer who journeyed through the colonies in 1764–65, observed that though malaria was prevalent in the Carolinas, Charleston was relatively free of the disorder. The townspeople attributed this "to the air being mended by the Number of Fires in Town, as much as to its cool Situation, on a point, at the junction of two navigable streams, called Ashley and Cowper Rivers." The real explanation lay, of course, in Charleston's porous sandy soil and its proximity to salt water, but Gordon came close to explaining the spread of malaria when he reasoned that "In general what part of South Carolina is planted, is counted unhealthy, owing to the Rice-dams and Swamps, which as they occasion a great quantity of Stagnated water in Summer, never fails to increase the Number of Insects, and to produce fall fevers and Agues, dry gripes and other disorders, which are often fatal to the lower set of people, as well White as Black." . . .

The significance of malaria in colonial history can scarcely be overrated, for it was a major hurdle in the development of the American colonies. To the newly arrived settlers or "fresh Europeans," it frequently proved fatal, and epidemics of pernicious malaria took a heavy toll of old and new colonists alike. In endemic regions the regular succession of spring and fall outbreaks, with the concomitant sickness and disability, deprived the colonies of much sorely needed labor. . . . Directly or indirectly, malaria was one of the most fatal of colonial diseases and shares with dysentery first place among the colonial infections.[44]

Discussion of epidemic disease in the United States has thus far been essentially limited to the Atlantic and Gulf states. After the War of 1812, settlement of what is now Ohio, Illinois, Indiana, Michigan, and Wisconsin began in earnest.

In retrospect one tends to picture a group of robust pioneer men and women raising large and lusty families, exploring the Great Lakes and the rivers, subduing the forest, tilling the soil, hunting, fishing, and, during leisure moments, bagging an Indian, all in a spirit of good clean fun and in an atmosphere of abundant health and vitality. Nothing could be farther from the truth. The most lethal dangers the pioneers had to face were neither savages nor wild animals. They were typhoid, malaria, dysentery, malignant scarlet fever, pneumonia, erysipelas in epidemic form, spotted fever, or what would now be called meningococcal meningitis, and diphtheria.[45]

But, while these diseases were as widespread as the settlers, it is questionable whether they can be ranked as epidemic.

POLYNESIA AND AUSTRALIA

The medical history of the Polynesians, the Amerindians, the Africans, and the Eskimos has provided dramatic examples of the ferocity of certain microbial diseases when first brought to these peoples by the white man. Suffice it to mention for illustration that when measles was first introduced into Hawaii practically the whole population went down with the disease. Further epidemics of measles, influenza and pertussis struck Hawaii again in 1848 and every child born that year died. In 1853, there were over 9000 cases of smallpox with 6000 deaths out of a population of 70,000.[46]

By way of contrast, Richard K. C. Lee, president and chief executive officer of the Hawaii Board of Health, could state in 1954 that "Hawaii's communicable disease rates are the lowest in the world. As examples, there has not been a single case of smallpox contracted locally since 1913; not a single death from diphtheria since 1946, from scarlet fever since 1942, nor from typhoid fever since 1947, and not a single case of typhoid fever since 1949." This commendable record stems from Hawaii's first board of health, established in 1859 by King Kamehameha III (1813–1854) and his privy council "to provide for the preservation and cure of contagious, epidemic or other diseases" and to enforce sanitary measures.[47]

The original Polynesian inhabitants of Hawaii came from Asia by way of the Malay Peninsula and Java and then by island-hopping in their hundred-foot sailing canoes that could carry ninety settlers with food, water, and livestock. They lived in undisturbed isolation and were well adapted to the diseases they had brought with them. When Captain James Cook (1728–1779) discovered the islands in 1778, he estimated a native population of three hundred thousand. Following Cook's discovery

Hawaii became the port of call for the whalers, the traders in sandalwood, furs, silks, and for all kinds of shipping, and the native people were exposed to new people and new diseases. Epidemics of communicable diseases such as smallpox, cholera, influenza, measles, venereal diseases, leprosy, and plague decimated the native population. Even such diseases as mumps and whooping cough killed both young and old. The epidemic of smallpox in 1853 was so severe that of a population of 19,126 persons on the Island of Oahu, 9,082 cases and 5,748 deaths were reported.[48]

The worst havoc was caused by the six hundred or so whaling ships with thirty thousand men that

> annually descended on the island ports for the winter; they set up countless brothels, bars, and vice dens; procurers scoured the coastal villages, sometimes traveled far inland for women whom they took by force when persuasion failed. By 1840, virtually the entire native population was infected with various forms of venereal disease.
>
> Powerful merchants and other island interests welcomed the whalers' money; they fought efforts at control by physicians, missionaries and royalty.
>
> The demoralized Hawaiian government pleaded in vain for help from France, England and the United States.[49]

Thanks to various epidemics, by 1850 the population had dropped to around seventy-five thousand. (Incidentally Captain Cook was killed by natives who blamed him for the syphilis epidemic.)

The Maoris are Polynesians who migrated to New Zealand from other Pacific islands. Prior to the advent of the Europeans they appear to have been a healthy race. Joseph Banks (1743–1820), naturalist to the Cook expedition that reached New Zealand in 1769, commented, "I do not remember a single instance of a Person distempered in any degree that came under my inspection, and among the numbers of them that I have seen naked, I have never seen an eruption on the Skin or any signs of one by sores or otherwise." (However, a French officer who arrived with Jean-François de Surville at approximately the same time wrote that the Maoris exhibited extreme dirtiness that led to skin diseases and a type of scab or itch.)[50]

In 1642 the Dutch navigator Abel Tasman (1603–1659) anchored off the coast of New Zealand but when some of his sailors in a small boat were killed by Maoris in canoes, Tasman sailed away without landing, "leaving New Zealand with its name but nothing more than a vague line on the map." One of the slain sailors was carried off and presumably eaten and this, according to R. E. Wright-St Clair, assistant medical superintendent at Waikato Hospital (Hamilton, New Zealand), offered the first possibility of

Maori encounter with European infections. However, the length of the voyage (Tasman was four months out of Batavia and two months out of Mauritius) precluded most epidemic diseases. When Cook circumnavigated the islands a century and a quarter later, making close contact with the natives in several places, his crew brought them venereal disease which they had picked up in Tahiti. When Captain Samuel Wallis (1728–1795), the English circumnavigator, had discovered Tahiti two years earlier, the island was disease-free, but meantime it had been visited by the French expedition of Louis Antoine de Bougainville (1729–1811) that "had been island-hopping across the Pacific and no doubt keeping its gonococci and spirochetes active." [51]

Sydney, Australia, was settled in 1788. Only thirteen hundred miles from New Zealand, it was inevitable that Australian visitors would carry infectious diseases there, and there seem to have been localized epidemics of influenza as early as 1791. Following a visit by H.M.S. *Coromandel* in 1826, there was a serious outbreak of the disease, fed by the high susceptibility of the Maoris who had no previous experience with it.

> A more serious epidemic broke out at the end of 1838 and continued into the following year. William Williams, later the first Bishop of Waiapu, who himself had some knowledge of medicine, . . . records that "in the month of December of this year (1838) the northern part of the island was visited with influenza in its most virulent form. Every person seemed to be affected by it, both old and young, and many for a time were laid quite prostrate. Great numbers were carried off, particularly the aged and infirm, and persons who had been weakened by previous disease. [52]

Influenza seems to have been epidemic throughout the Southern Hemisphere in 1852–53, being particularly severe in New Zealand, and the June 1860 issue of the *Southern Cross* reported a great prevalence of the disease in the Auckland area (and in Sydney, Australia).

Measles were introduced into New South Wales by infectious passengers aboard the *David Scott* which arrived in Sydney on October 25, 1834. By January the resultant epidemic was carried to

Hobart, Tasmania, where it also became epidemic. It was probably a Maori returning from Sydney on the brig *Children* that introduced measles into the South Island of New Zealand in March 1835. The effect on the Maoris with no previous exposure was devastating, seriously reducing the population. Measles first reached the North Island in 1854, by ship from Tasmania.

Of considerable interest is the fact that two diseases that attacked children of European descent had a markedly lesser effect on the Maoris, notwithstanding the fact that they had had no known previous contact with them. They were scarlet fever and diphtheria.

In pre-European days the Maoris lived in fortified villages set on hilltops for easier defense. But when the white man provided the natives with muskets (in addition to his diseases), the villages ceased to be impregnable. The natives moved to the lowlands where wheat and corn flourished, but sanitation became a major problem. "Typhoid fever went unchecked," wrote Sir Peter Henry Buck (1880–1951), the eminent Maori anthropologist, "for the old hill-top sites, with their organized sanitation, had been abandoned and indiscriminate defecation on the lowlands led to pollution of pools and springs. The gathering of distant tribes to weep for the dead in a typhoid-infected village led to later weepings in other villages." [53]

For a small, lightly populated country New Zealand moved fast in instituting public health measures. Fear of cholera led, in 1856, to quarantine regulations applicable to the entire country; fear of smallpox inspired the first Public Health Act (1872); fear of plague in 1900 brought the establishment of a Department of Public Health.

The story of Australia differs from that of New Zealand in that the natives (aborigines) were few and scattered. This meant that the victims of epidemic diseases were settlers who had not developed immunity.

In Australasia typhoid held a foremost place among acute infectious diseases, in point of frequency and malignancy. There was an epidemic among English troops in Tasmania as early as 1830 and it appeared on the coasts of the mainland soon after settlements were established. It also plagued ships of war on the Australian station.

A severe epidemic in Melbourne in 1878 drew attention to the increasing frequency of the disease and a rising mortality.

Australia enjoyed absolute immunity from smallpox until 1838 when the disease (probably imported from China) made a brief appearance in Sydney, thereafter remaining absent for thirty years. In 1868 it was introduced by ship into Melbourne, but the spreading was slight and it quickly died out. Thereafter rigorous inspection of arriving ships prevented importations.

Scarlet fever first reached Australia and Polynesia in 1848, breaking out almost simultaneously in Tahiti, New Zealand, and Tasmania, and the following year it was to be found in New Zealand and Australia. An epidemic in 1875–76 in New South Wales, Victoria, and South Australia (which spread to Tasmania and New Zealand in 1876–77) was responsible everywhere for exceptionally high mortality. (It is not known, however, whether the epidemic had an unusually high case fatality or was unusually widespread.)

On the credit side, Polynesia and Australia enjoyed an almost absolute immunity from malarial disease.

AFRICA

The Dark Continent is an apt description when it comes to attempting to trace the history of epidemical diseases in Africa. While the early presence of yellow fever on the west coast must be assumed, if there is to be any validity to the question, already posed, whether this disease traveled from west to east or vice versa, Hirsch was forced to conclude that the "records of physicians and travellers in that region in former centuries are too scanty and unreliable to enable us to decide how soon yellow fever showed itself after the first settlements of Europeans on the coast. The earliest trustworthy information is to be found in the account of Schotte of the epidemic of yellow fever at St. Louis (Senegal) in 1778, an epidemic which, like all the later ones in the same place, could be traced to importation of the disease from *Sierra Leone.* The latter strip of coast appears, indeed, to be the headquarters of the disease, and the starting point of its epidemic inroads into the territories lying to the north and south, as well as into the West African Islands." [54]

The Dutch had colonized Cape Town in 1652, establishing it as a trading post for vessels returning from the East Indies into which they had first ventured in 1595. In 1713 a ship, some of whose passengers had had smallpox during the voyage, arrived at Cape Town. All had recovered before the ship docked but their soiled clothes and linen were sent ashore for laundering and it was these that were responsible for southern Africa's first smallpox epidemic.

> The loss of life among the Europeans was considerable, but it was among the Hottentots that the epidemic was most seriously felt. Whole kraals of natives were swept away, and the Hottentot race was practically destroyed. Other epidemics followed in 1755 and 1767, but were not so severe as the first had been. [55]

A very serious epidemic with a high mortality hit the Cape Town area in 1882.

Smallpox seems to have reached Central Africa by two routes. The first ran northward from South Africa, the second was that followed by slave traders from the east coast.

> In the late eighteenth century and throughout the nineteenth century the Arabs who were settled along the East African coast travelled into the interior to buy slaves and ivory for selling at the East African coast ports and the slave markets of Zanzibar and Madagascar. The major slave route was from Ujiji on Lake Tanganyika to Bagamoyo, which lies on the coast of Tanganyika opposite Zanzibar. . . . To the south there were other slave routes linking Lake Nyasa and the Central African plain with the coast and the slave markets of Madagascar. [56]

On the other hand, since smallpox reached Africa relatively late, some native races were spared from epidemics through the practice of variolation, taught, for example, by the Dutch to the Bantus. In 1822 the Reverend J. Campbell told of an unusual practice of the Mashona of what is now Rhodesia. "When the smallpox comes among them they select the person who seems to have the most favourable kind, and from him take the matter to inoculate other people. The disease is thereby rendered more lenient." And the British explorer Richard Francis Burton (1821–1890) wrote in 1860: "The Arabs have partially introduced the practice of inoculation, anciently known in South Africa. The pus is introduced into an incision in the forehead between the eyebrows." [57]

The French island of Réunion, in the Indian Ocean four hundred miles due east of Madagascar, suffered epidemics in 1729, 1827, 1850, and 1858 introduced by slave ships from Madagascar. Between epidemics there were no cases of smallpox. The nearby British island of Mauritius had like experiences. In Madagascar itself smallpox was seriously endemic as well as epidemic.

Hirsch could find no information "as to the occurrence of smallpox along the southern part of the *West Coast of Africa*. On the *Guinea Coast*, according to the unanimous opinion of observers, the disease is not indigenous; it occurs from time to time as an epidemic, sometimes so disastrously that whole villages are ravaged by it." [58]

Probably the most intensely malarial regions in the Eastern Hemisphere lie in the tropical part of the African continent and adjacent islands. To the west, the disease has been enormously frequent and most malignant in the basins of the Senegal and Gambia rivers. Next in severity was the Guinea Coast from Sierra Leone to Cape Lopez (just south of the equator).

> For an approximate estimate of the frequency of the disease in these regions, the fact may suffice that among 15,469 negro troops landed in the three English stations of Gambia, Sierra Leone, and the Gold Coast (including Lagos) during 1859–75, there occurred 4983 cases of malarial fever; or, in other words, 32 per cent. of the troops (native) suffered from that disease. The amount of sickness among the European population was naturally much greater. [59]

Conditions were better from Cape Lopez southward, with the Cape of Good Hope enjoying almost complete immunity. The east coast was seriously infected from Mozambique north to Zanzibar.

Malaria spread inland along the Ruvuma (dividing Mozambique from Tanzania) and Zambezi rivers, one of the tributaries of the latter carrying it beyond Lake Ngami in Botswana to the northern border of the Kalahari Desert. Off coast, the disease was common and pernicious in the Comoro Islands and Madagascar where, however, the northeast corner and the mountainous interior escaped.

Sleeping sickness, a chronic disease resulting from invasion by protozoa of the genus *Trypanosoma*, is produced in man through the bite of the tsetse fly (genus *Glossina*) which only exists in Africa south of the Tropic of Cancer, and in some outlying islands including Zanzibar. (Trypanosomiasis in animals is far more widespread; in South and Central America man is subject to trypanosomiatic Chagas' disease, predominantly in young children, but the vector is not the tsetse fly.)

Sleeping sickness is characterized by irregular fever, expansion of lymph tissue (particularly of the posterior cervical chain), skin eruptions, and painful localized edema, followed by tremors, headache, apathy, convulsion, and eventually coma and death. Its neurological symptoms were first described in 1734 by John Atkins, a British naval surgeon.[60] In 1792 Thomas Masterman Winterbottom (1765?–1859) graduated in medicine at the University of Glasgow and proceeded to Sierra Leone where he practiced medicine for four years. After returning home he wrote an account of his African experiences that was published in 1803. In it he described the swelling and morbid change in lymph nodes that occurred in "kondee" or sleeping sickness.[61]

References to sleeping sickness prior to 1900 center on the valleys of the Niger and Benue rivers and Lake Chad to the northeast. It seems that the infection was introduced into Nigeria in 1890 by traders who regularly traversed the Benue plateau, but that it had appeared considerably earlier in the Lake Chad basin where there were two epidemics in the nineteenth century. One of these, around 1859, so depopulated the town of Digazore that it was deserted for fifty years. At the beginning of the new century there was an epidemic at Meree near Bauchi, which lies between Lake Chad and the Benue plateau. The Lake Chad natives called the disease *dudduru* which could also mean "a river or stream with shady banks," the reference being to where the infection might be encountered.

The occupation of Central Africa by European nations at the close of the nineteenth century coincided with an epidemic of sleeping sickness that, between 1896 and 1906, took the lives of half a million people in the Congo and, between 1898 and 1908 in Uganda, killed two hundred thousand out of a population of three hundred thousand along the northeast shores of Lake Victoria, while the population of the country as a whole dropped 10 percent.

At this time, Lake Victoria, almost the size of Lake Superior, was truly an international waterway . . . Steamboats used it to connect Kisumu on the Kenya shore with Entebbe on the Uganda side. Missionaries, doctors, and government servants used them. Canoe traffic was also heavy, especially to the islands in the lake. . . .

No one worried about *Glossina palpalis*. In 1900 no one yet knew that tsetse carried sleeping sickness. But sleeping sickness would cast a pall over Kampala (the home of the impala) and over other towns in Buganda along the lake—the area Winston Churchill labeled a "curious garden of sunshine and deadly nightshade."

During the first decade of the twentieth century the tsetse fly began to depopulate parts of Uganda—the population of the Buvuma group of islands, on the Equator in Lake Victoria, dropped from 56,000 people in 1900 to 13,000 in 1907. The Busoga area, on the north shore of the lake east of Buganda, was as badly affected. Busoga, known by some as the prosperous banana garden area, become [sic] notorious for epidemics of smallpox, syphilis, and plague, for famine, and for political upheaval. To determine the severity of the sleeping sickness epidemic here, the government instructed the local chiefs to report to headquarters and to carry with them a twig to represent the deaths of each individual they thought died of sleeping sickness within their chiefdoms. A solemn procession of chiefs came to headquarters on the first day and the twigs numbered eleven thousand. The chiefs continued to bring bundles of twigs to headquarters for several days afterward. . . .

The epidemic that crippled the population of Uganda probably had been incubating for a quarter of a century. This span of time, 1875 to 1900, almost coincided with that of Henry M. Stanley's working years. When Stanley [1841–1904] crashed through the jungle from the Congo to Uganda to rescue Emin Pasha, sleeping sickness carried by *G. palpalis* must have followed him. The people of Uganda would not know this until years later because those species of tsetse already there had been biting them for years and never seemed to do them any harm.[62]

Yimbo, in the Central Nyanza section of Kenya, lies directly on the equator. In 1900 the area was densely populated. It became the first area in Kenya to face (and to be hardest hit by) the Lake Victoria epidemic that raged there until 1911.

British bacteriologist David Bruce (1855–1931), who, as a member of the army medical service, had in the 1880s discovered the causal organism of Malta fever and would during World War I work to prevent tetanus among troops, devoted the interim years to sleeping sickness and nagana (the Zulu name for the disease in cattle). In 1894 he first saw the trypanosome of the disease in the blood of Zululand cattle. He went on to determine that the vector was the tsetse fly. The disastrous Lake Victoria epidemic finally awakened the British to the need for a Royal Society commission to determine the cause of sleeping sickness. In 1903 Bruce was appointed to lead the commission, which had already been established in Uganda. In 1901 J. Everett Dutton (1874–1905) had seen in Gambia the trypanosome in the blood of man, a find that was followed up in 1903 by the Italian Aldo Castellani (1877–1971), working in Uganda, who saw the human trypanosome in the cerebrospinal fluid and blood in five cases of sleeping sickness. Bruce and his co-workers again established that the vector was the tsetse fly, but the *G. palpalis* rather than the *G. morsitans* that attacked cattle in Zululand.

Epidemics of sleeping sickness have continued periodically to plague parts of Africa with seemingly no end in sight. Chemotherapy has helped and fly-free areas have been created. But a new political age has dawned over Africa, and the infant nations have not always kept up the research and prevention activities instituted by their former overseers, often because they cannot afford to.

INDIA AND THE EAST INDIES

India (and China) have already been established as the early breeding grounds of smallpox and measles. Malaria has been endemic in
India, particularly but certainly not exclusively in the northwest,
in Ceylon, and in the East Indies. Typhoid was present in the
same general areas, but, says Hirsch, its investigation has been
hampered by the fact that only in the second half of the nineteenth
century had "observers and authorities . . . arrived at a correct
diagnosis of the forms of fever that come under their observation; . . ." Hirsch has dated the "first trustworthy information" on
bubonic plague in India to 1815.[63] All this adds up to considerable
uncertainty about epidemic diseases and epidemics in the subcontinent and the East Indies, and the picture is further clouded by the
fact that the Portuguese navigator Vasco da Gama (1469?–1524)
explored at least the coast of India, Ceylon, and southeast Asia between 1498 and 1510, with the ever-present possibility of introduc-
ing "European" diseases, and that the Dutch East India Company
was established in 1595 (with the British close behind). Another
complicating factor was the prolonged presence of British troops in
India, armies always being highly susceptible to disease. There
can, however, be no doubt that the subcontinent was responsible
for the disastrous waves of cholera (the subject of the next chapter)
that spread throughout the world in the nineteenth century.

Less certainty attaches to the cradle of another epidemic disease
(not so far referred to)—dengue, an acute febrile disease of sudden
onset, with headache, prostration, postorbital pains, joint and mus-
cle pains, and a rash that appears at the time of the second onset of
fever. (The two periods of fever combined last five to seven days.)
It is a mosquito-borne virus disease, the vectors being *Aëdes aegypti*
and other members of the genus. Dengue seems to have sprung to
life fully armed almost simultaneously in four unrelated locations—
Java and Cairo in 1779, the southeast (Coromandel) coast of India
and Philadelphia in 1780—but there is some justification for believing that the disease had been endemic in Java for some time. David
Bylon, medical officer of Batavia, who is credited with being the

first to describe dengue, called it *knokkel koorts* (knuckle or joint fever), a name already in use among the Javanese.

The picture is complicated by the fact that there are a number of brief febrile illnesses that are "dengue-like," among them chikungunya. This variation has been signalized because Donald E. Carey of the Rockefeller Foundation, Ibadan, Nigeria, has published within the present decade a well-documented claim that what was originally styled dengue was really chikungunya and "breakbone fever" was really dengue. Under his reclassification he has declared the Batavia and Cairo epidemics to be chikungunya and that Philadelphia the following year saw the first epidemic of dengue.[64] The Carey study is too significant to be ignored but it seems immaterial in the present context whether the various epidemics were dengue or dengue-like disease, the prototype viruses of dengue not being isolated until 1944–45, the actual viruses in 1961–63, and those of chikungunya in 1952 and 1964 respectively.

Bylon was himself a victim of the Batavia epidemic and described his own experience, stating that he was well at 5:00 P.M. but

> noticed a gnawing pain in my right hand and in the joints of the hand and arm which gradually increased, extending to the shoulder and then over my whole body, so that 9 o'clock that evening I was in bed with a high fever. I had a restless and sleepless night suffering severe pains over the entire body especially in the legs and arms and in the joints. . . . This is a brief notice concerning a very well known disease which, however, in the memory of man here in Batavia has never reached an epidemic, and which has, therefore, seemed wondrous to the inhabitants.[65]

Hirsch quoted a chronicler named Gaberti on the subject of the Cairo epidemic that occurred in the same year. The disease was

> known as the knee trouble . . . ; it threw all the people into a fever. . . . Its first attack lasted for three days, after which the illness increased or diminished, according to the disposition of the individual. It was accompanied by pain in the joints, knees, and extremi-

ties, as well as inability to move, and often with swelling of the fingers. The after-pains lasted more than a month. The onset was sudden, the body being broken by it, and the head and knees taken hold of. . . .[66]

Hirsch also quoted a missionary named Persin on the subject of a similar fever that was epidemic on the Coromandel coast (that extends from the mouths of the Krishna River to south of Madras) in 1790: "Every one was attacked by it. The symptoms by which it was ushered in were almost the same as those premonitory of the plague—headache, lassitude, pains in the joints; but this epidemic had no bad consequences. The patients got rid of it in three days, under moderate diet and copious beverages." [67]

Benjamin Rush offered a clinical picture of the epidemic of *break-bone fever* that was rampant in Philadelphia from August through October 1780:

> This fever generally came on without rigor. . . . A giddiness in the head was the forerunner of the disease in some people. . . . The pains which accompanied this fever were exquisitely severe in the head, back, and limbs. The pains in the head . . . sometimes . . . occupied only the eyeballs. In some people, the pains were so acute in their backs and hips, that they could not lie in bed. In others, the pains affected the neck and arms, so as to produce in one instance a difficulty of moving the fingers of the right hand. They all complained more or less of a soreness in the seats of these pains, particularly when they occupied the head and eyeballs. . . . its . . . general name among all classes of people was the *Break-bone fever*. . . .
>
> A nausea universally, and in some instances, a vomiting, accompanied by a disagreeable taste in the mouth, attended this fever. . . . A rash often appeared on the third or fourth days, which proved favourable. This rash was accompanied in some cases by a burning in the palms of the hands and soles of the feet. . . . Most of those who recovered, complained of nausea and a total want of appetite. A faintiness, especially upon sitting up in bed, or in a chair, followed this fever. A weakness in the knees was universal. . . . But the most remarkable symptom . . . was an uncommon dejection of spirits. I attended two young ladies who shed tears while they vented their complaints of their sickness and weakness. One of them

very aptly proposed to me, to change the name of the disorder, and to call it, in its present stage, instead of the Break-bone, the *Break-heart fever*. [68]

There is mention of what may have been dengue in Spain, Central America, and Peru in the succeeding forty years, but the next epidemic of any importance occurred in Zanzibar in 1823 when there was an outbreak of *dinga* or *dyenga*. (Zanzibar was hit again in 1870 and Tanganyika in 1952. Otherwise Africa seems to have been dengue-free.) Dengue was epidemic in India in 1824–25 and there were frequent epidemics there and in southeast Asia through 1945.

Dengue has been pandemic in the Caribbean area and the southern United States periodically from 1827 to the present day. To date there have been ten pandemics of which six involved the Caribbean-Gulf-Atlantic region, two the Caribbean alone, and one each Gulf-Atlantic, Caribbean-Gulf, and Caribbean-Atlantic.

The great sailing ships of the nineteenth century that traded between the West Indies and southern United States and the markets of the world undoubtedly carried dengue as well as produce. The first recorded pandemic (1827–28) began in the Virgin Islands, swept west to Cuba, Jamaica, and Venezuela, jumped to Charleston, Savannah, Pensacola, and New Orleans, and disappeared in Mexico. The pandemic of 1850–51 involved the populations of New Orleans, Mobile, Havana, Charleston, Savannah, and Augusta. "In New Orleans and Mobile, the dilemma of differentiating mild yellow fever and dengue was apparent to the laity as well as to the medical profession" whom many persons reproached "for charging them two yellow fever bills, while contending that the disease attacks but once." [69] In Charleston, Dr. Samuel Henry Dickson (1798–1872), who had published an account of the 1828 invasion,[70] found that most of those who had had dengue the first time around were immune in 1850. In 1873 an isolated outbreak in New Orleans affected 40,000 people, but the third pandemic did not occur until 1878–80. It involved New Orleans, Savannah, Charleston, Augusta, and a number of smaller cities.

As commercial activity moved westward to Texas ports, so did dengue. Austin (16,000 cases in an estimated population of 22,000) and Galveston bore the brunt of an epidemic in 1885–86 which followed the railroads inland and hit every railroad town in Texas. Pandemics in 1897–99 and 1905–1907 involved Nassau, the Bermudas, Cuba, Panama, Puerto Rico, the Virgin Islands, probably Venezuela, Texas, and Florida.

In 1922 Texas, Louisiana (overland from Texas—the precautions against yellow fever that New Orleans had taken following the epidemic of 1905 seemingly excluded dengue also), Florida, Georgia, and the Caribbean were hit; in the 1934–38 pandemic, dengue entered the United States from the Caribbean through Miami, possibly by plane, since Miami is not a seaport, and spread through Florida to south Georgia. The last United States outbreak of dengue to date began in Texas ports in 1941 and (between then and 1946) Panama, Bermuda, Sonora on the Mexican Pacific coast, Havana, Puerto Rico, and Venezuela were affected.

The two most recent pandemics in the Caribbean occurred in 1963–64 and 1968–69. The first involved Jamaica, Puerto Rico (27,000 cases), and the Lesser Antilles. The second hit Hispaniola, several islands of the Lesser Antilles, and Puerto Rico (16,665 cases in 1969).

> The increasing size of human population in the Caribbean, the continued presence of *A. aegypti*, the absence of effective vaccines [for all possible antigenic types leading to] the lack of lasting heterotypic protection and the absence of knowledge of origin of epidemics all point to continuing difficulties with dengue. If future epidemics of dengue are to be avoided here, basic virologic solutions dealing with long-term heterotypic immunity and prevention of global spread must be found, or cheap, effective means of vector eradication must be developed.[71]

The fact that the viruses of both dengue and yellow fever are transmitted by *A. aegypti*, plus the fact that the diseases appear to be mutually exclusive, prompted Albert Sabin during World War II to investigate the situation. "One of the reasons the problem of interference between these two viruses was pursued further,"

Sabin wrote in 1952, "is the peculiarity in the epidemiology of yellow fever that it has apparently spared many parts of the world (e.g., India, Indonesia, Australia, etc.) where dengue has been endemic. . . . Since the *Aedes aegypti* mosquitoes serve as natural vectors for both the dengue and yellow fever viruses, and since available evidence indicated that mosquitoes remain infected for life, the possible occurrence of interference between these two viruses in mosquitoes was of special interest and possible epidemiologic significance . . . experiments were performed . . . [and the] results suggested the possibility that the introduction of yellow fever virus in a dengue-endemic area may find enough mosquitoes relatively refractory to the yellow fever virus to prevent the establishment of yellow fever in the same area." [72]

But what about situations in which dengue and yellow fever seem to coexist?

In Havana during the winter and spring of 1828 there were cases of yellow fever. Late in April dengue moved in. Yellow fever promptly disappeared. In the early months of the same year there was a dengue epidemic in Martinique. A yellow fever epidemic followed in the last months of 1828 and January 1829. The greater part of the population of Charleston was affected by dengue in June–July 1828. Yellow fever appeared in August–September. New Orleans reported both diseases in 1828 but dengue reached its peak in June and only twelve cases of yellow fever had been admitted to Charity Hospital by July 25. Subsequently, there were 290 yellow fever admissions and 130 deaths. Such examples could be presented interminably. [73]

In the course of this chapter only two epidemical diseases have been discussed that can strictly be classified as "tropical diseases"—sleeping sickness and dengue. This raises the question of what the term "tropical disease" really means. In 1954 R. N. Chaudhuri, director of the Calcutta School of Tropical Medicine, appears to have provided an answer when he wrote:

> There are not many diseases peculiar only to tropical climates, although admittedly conditions in the Tropics are more favourable to

their growth and spread. Such devastating diseases as cholera, small-pox, plague, malaria, and leprosy that now prevail here were . . . once very common in Western countries, If taken in the sense of lati-tudes, labels such as "tropical diseases" and "tropical medicine" are largely misnomers; what is worse, they perpetuate a false idea that tropical countries, try as they may, are doomed always to suffer from these diseases. "Tropical" diseases disappeared from the West mainly for three reasons: first, better and abundant food as a result of better cultivation at home and the importation of food from over-seas; secondly, the removal of poverty as the result of the industrial revolution and the acquisition of colonies; and, thirdly, the institu-tion of public-health measures, which led to better housing and hygiene, improved sewerage, and a safe water supply. If we con-sider "tropical disease" in this light much of it is reduced almost to "poverty disease." In short, many of our so-called tropical diseases are the symptoms of backward countries and not primarily of tropi-cal climates. Remove food deficiencies in the tropical countries and introduce all the sanitary measures now enjoyed in the West and many of the tropical diseases will be banished.[74]

CHAPTER 12

The Terror of Cholera

"OF all the pestilential diseases, cholera is perhaps one of the most awe-inspiring. It may run so rapid a course that a man in good health at day break may be dead and buried at night fall. The fear of cholera saw the beginning of sanitary awakening in Europe and led to the development of public health in the world." [1] Cholera is characterized by profuse diarrhea, vomiting, muscular cramps, dehydration, and collapse. It is contracted by the ingestion of water or food contaminated by the feces of cholera victims, but since the bacteria—the *Vibrio cholerae* (*V. comma*) remains with a majority of patients for two weeks or less, there is rarely a vector or carrier in the usual sense. Contamination may be caused by cockroaches or house flies that have feasted on the feces of patients, or an infected person with unwashed hands may handle food to be consumed by others, but sewage-contaminated rivers and water supplies have been the major cause of serious epidemics, cholera being essentially a waterborne disease.

Cholera in the popular mind is a disease of the nineteenth century that is still rampant in the twentieth century. (The World Health Organization reported 36,380 cases in twenty-four countries in the first six months of 1974, with 80 percent occurring in eleven Asian countries. There were 40,561 cases in eighteen countries [90 percent in nine Asian countries] in the first six months of 1973, and 58,303 cases in twenty-five countries [of which three-quarters were in seventeen African countries and one-quarter in eight Asian countries] in the first six months of 1971.) [2] There is some justification for this belief in a nineteenth-century origin. John Parkin, who had formerly been medical inspector for cholera in the West Indies, wrote in 1887 of cholera as "a new and inscrutable malady [that] had suddenly sprung up in the delta of the Ganges, in 1817," and Hirsch had this to say:

> In the nineteenth-century annals of pestilence, the year 1817 stands as one charged with fatality to the human race. It was in that year there began the epidemic extension over India of a disease which had previously been known only as an endemic in a few districts of the country; in that and the following year it overran the whole peninsula, in a short time it crossed the borders of its native territory in all directions, penetrated in its farther progress to almost every part of the habitable globe, and thus acquired the character of a world-wide pestilence, which has repeatedly since then entered on its devastating campaigns and has claimed its many millions of victims.[3]

Just how old a disease cholera may have been is uncertain. Attempts to link it with the Greeks in the fifth century B.C., contracted as a consequence of military adventures deep in Asia, seem unfounded. Approximately a thousand years later the great Hindu physician Suśruta ambiguously described an entity that may have been cholera. But L. M. Bhattacharji, chief of epidemiology at Calcutta's All-India Institute of Hygiene & Public Health, has relied on a number of sources to place cholera in India as early as 1325, with outbreaks in Gujarat in 1438, Goa in 1503, and Surat in 1612, but the first "reliable information" that Hirsch could find dated from 1768–69 when the disease was prevalent "in the neighborhood of Pondicherry and over the whole Coromandel coast, and which carried off 60,000 victims in one year. Next come the trustworthy accounts of an epidemic of cholera in 1781 in the French army of occupation under General Anderne, of epidemics the same year in Calcutta, and in Madras, where the disease, according to the report of Curtis, was epidemic the following year as well (1782); further, in 1783, on the Madras coast; and among the pilgrims collected at Hurdwar, twenty thousand of whom are said to have died in less than eight days; then at Arcot in 1787, Bellary in 1788, Travancore in 1792, and at various points in the Presidency of Bengal during the years 1811–13." Outside India, Hirsch reported outbreaks in Java (1629 and 1689) and Ceylon (1782, 1790, and 1804). To these Bhattacharji added Burma, China, and Sumatra "towards the end of the 19th century." An epidemic of what was apparently cholera in Ethiopia in 1634–35 has been viewed as an extension of the outbreak in Java in 1629.[4]

THE FIRST PANDEMIC 1817–23

An outbreak of cholera originating to the north of Calcutta in 1817 became so widespread in India that by 1821 little, if any, of the country remained untouched. In December 1818 the disease entered Ceylon, moving on early in 1819 to Burma, Siam, Sumatra, and Singapore, and the following year penetrating as far as Java, Borneo, and adjacent islands. "From Ceylon, the disease was imported in 1819 into *Mauritius* and *Réunion* (then called Bourbon), and thence, in the beginning of 1820, to the *East Coast of Africa*, where it was limited, at this its first outbreak, to the Zanzibar coast. The *Moluccas* and *Philippines* were reached in 1820, and in the same year the cholera appeared for the first time in the *Chinese Empire*, through which it spread devastation from one end to the other during the two years following, and crossed to Nagasaki (Japan) in 1822."[5] Cholera began a westward movement in 1821 which extended to Muscat, on the east coast of Arabia, Syria, Palestine, and finally entered south Russia through Astrakan, inland from the Caspian Sea on the Volga River. This pandemic left the rest of Europe and America untouched, but Europe had been entered, and cholera in the nineteenth century was to prove "the most persistent, the most widespread, and the most destructive epidemic disease to attack the Russian lands. Between 1823 and 1926 the cholera was a fixture in the Russian landscape, an ever-present threat to human life, and a constant burden on the Russian population. During the period, cholera cases were reported in fifty-eight of the one hundred three years with a total of 5,537,358 cases and 2,140,558 deaths. Moreover these figures probably should be revised upward, not only because reporting and recording techniques were haphazard, especially during the early epidemics, but also because the government officials compiling statistics were not above minimizing losses." [6]

THE SECOND PANDEMIC 1826-37

Cholera broke out again in northeast India in 1826, spread along the Ganges, and had soon covered all of India. From Lahore in the far north the disease traveled the caravan routes, reaching Kabul and Balkh in Afghanistan and Buchara over the border in eastern Russia in 1827. The following year it spread by water to Chiva, about four hundred miles east of the Caspian Sea, and from there it was carried by the Kirghese hordes to Orenburg in the foothills of the southern end of the Ural Mountains on a tributary of the Volga (1829–30). In the fall of 1829 Teheran, the capital of Persia (now Iran), was invaded and by 1831 all of Russia's major cities had been stricken. Efforts here, and elsewhere in Europe, to control the invasion of cholera by quarantine and sanitation measures were ineffective because the rivers became infected and other water supplies contaminated.

Russian troops carried the disease into Poland in February 1831 and from there it crossed into Germany. It reached Hungary in June. Here "the ignorant peasants revolted because they thought that cholera, which largely spared the wealthy classes, was directed by some evil force against them, and the remedies used in its treatment were poisons designed to get rid of them." According to Professor George Polgar of the University of Pennsylvania School of Medicine, this belief was deliberately fostered by political profit-seekers. [7] The approach of cholera caused great consternation in Vienna but the government

> made elaborate preparations for combatting the disease, and was well prepared with hospitals, doctors, food deposits, barriers against travel from one district to another, housing and clothing. Food, clean clothes and lodging were found for poor families, and houses

in the poorer districts were cleaned and fumigated. These precautions aroused considerable apprehension among the Viennese. Business was disrupted, work practically ceased, prices of food and other necessities rose, travel stopped and unrest increased. The government of Austria, however, was equal to this situation. It sent vagabonds and foreign workmen away from the city, and organized public works programs where anyone who wanted to work was employed regardless of physical condition. . . . The epidemic was delayed in arriving and by the time it finally appeared, fears had been calmed, and the outbreak of the disease served to bring people together. . . . It is interesting to note that in Vienna, in contrast to most other cities, cholera tended to confine its ravages to the districts inhabited by the well-to-do, which evidently were less well drained than the poorer neighborhoods. This factor may have played a part in preventing uprisings similar to those in Paris and Hungary.[8]

Cholera reached Paris in 1832. Garrison has summarized "a graphic and memorable account of the outbreak" offered by the famous German poet Heinrich Heine (1797–1856) in a letter dated April 9, 1832.

On March 29th, the night of *mi-carême*, a masked ball was in progress, the *chahut* in full swing. Suddenly, the gayest of the harlequins collapsed, cold in the limbs, and, underneath his mask, "violet-blue" in the face. Laughter died out, dancing ceased, and in a short while carriage-loads of people were hurried from the *redoute* to the Hôtel Dieu to die, and, to prevent a panic among the patients, were thrust into rude graves in their dominoes. Soon the public halls were filled with dead bodies, sewed in sacks for want of coffins. Long lines of hearses stood *en queue* outside Père Lachaise. Everybody wore flannel bandages. The rich gathered up their belongings and fled the town. Over 120,000 passports were issued at the Hôtel de Ville.

Attempts by the government to apply public health measures were thwarted by the ragpickers who saw in the removal of piles of offal from the streets a threat to their livelihood. They rioted, setting up barricades. "The suspicion of secret poisoning was raised, as a counter theory to that of infection, . . . and six persons were murdered and naked corpses dragged through the streets under this belief. Finally the public press quieted the panic, and the *Commission sanitaire* was able to accomplish something." [9]

While cholera was penetrating the heart of Europe, it was also spreading to Mesopotamia and Arabia

> and from those countries was carried in the spring of 1831 by bands of pilgrims, on the one hand to Syria and Palestine, and, on the other hand, by way of Suez to Egypt. It appeared in Cairo in July, and spread along the Nile upwards as far as Thebes, and as far down as Alexandria, so that it overran the whole Delta. The same year it was carried to Tunis by pilgrims. It was not until several years later that cholera attained its wider distribution on the North Coast of Africa. [10]

There appear to have been two epidemics of cholera in Ethiopia between 1831 and 1836, and the infection must have spread to Somaliland which was the alleged source of an outbreak in Zanzibar in 1836–37.

Returning to Europe, its southern section was spared until the beginning of 1833 when cholera, introduced by an English ship, hit hard in Portugal. It appeared in Spain at about the same time. December 1834 found the disease in Marseilles, brought from a Catalonian port. From there, over the next two years, it blanketed the south of France and much of Italy. Malta was hit for the first time in 1837.

CHOLERA IN THE BRITISH ISLES

Carried by a vessel from Hamburg, cholera appeared on the quayside at Sunderland in the north of England in October 1831. Within a matter of months it had spread to neighboring Newcastle and Gateshead and then northward to Edinburgh, reached in February 1832, and Glasgow (where there were over three thousand fatalities). From Glasgow it was an easy step to Belfast and Dublin, and Cork was reached in April.

Back in the eighteenth century many doctors had been aware of the dangers of bad drainage, but public health had not yet become the subject of political agitation and action. In 1823 a select committee of the House of Commons had been appointed to consider the matter of metropolitan sewers but, after collecting evidence, it made no recommendations. In mid-1831, faced by cholera in Hamburg, the government resolved to establish a board of health at the Royal College of Physicians. This Central Board of Health came into being by royal proclamation on June 21, 1831. It consisted of Sir Henry Halford, president, and six Fellows of the Royal College of Physicians (one of whom served as secretary), the comptroller of the navy, the deputy chairman of the Board of Customs, the director-general of the army hospitals, the commissioner of the victualing office, and the superintendent-general of quarantine. Acting with remarkable promptness, on June 29 the board forwarded to the Privy Council (to which it had been made responsible) a draft of proposed rules and regulations that read, in part:

> As there are strong reasons for believing that the disease called Cholera Morbus now prevailing in Russia and the North of Europe is infectious, it is of the utmost importance that the very first cases that appear should be known as early as possible and that concealment of the sick should be guarded against. With this view it is submitted, that in every Town or Village commencing with those on the Coast there should be established a local Board of Health to consist of the Chief Magistrate and Clergymen, one or more of the Professional Gentlemen and Principal Inhabitants. One of the medical members to be appointed to correspond with the Board of Health in London. . . .
>
> In each Town or its Neighborhood one or more Places to be immediately pointed out as places to which every case of the Disease as soon as detected might be removed in conveyances appropriated exclusively for the purpose. . . .
>
> The Houses from which the Sick Persons have been removed should be purified in the following manner. The wearing apparel and household furniture should be thoroughly washed and scoured, the walls and ceilings lime washed, the doors and windows of each apartment left open for many days. . . .[11]

The Privy Council received the recommendation but was reluctant to act because of the coercive nature of the proposed regulations and because the idea of local boards of health on a wide scale was novel, but on August 8 it reluctantly gave its assent. As an outcome, some 1200 local boards were set up in Great Britain, 822 in England and Wales, and about 400 in Scotland.

Meantime the citizens of London awaited the approaching epidemic in something akin to terror, the quarantine imposed on ships arriving from the north notwithstanding. A day of national fasting and penance was announced for February 6, 1832. Four days later the first case in the London area was reported from Rotherhithe.

Publication of the official *Cholera Gazette* had been begun in January with the objective of making public communications to and from the Central Board of Health. It was issued every two weeks, the first three issues bearing the dates January 14, January 28, and February 11, but on February 14 there appeared a supplement (it is styled "Second Edition") giving "details of cases of cholera in Rotherhithe, Limehouse, Southwark, &c. &c."

Rotherhithe, 10th Feb. 1832

SIR,

A case having yesterday occurred in this parish, in which a man died under peculiar symptoms; and the medical practitioners differing materially in opinion, as to the cause of his death; the churchwardens and overseers of the poor are very desirous of immediately ascertaining the disease he died of, and whether such death has been occasioned by the *Spasmodic Cholera*, for which purpose they will feel much obliged by your polite early attention to afford them the opinion of the medical gentlemen attached to your Board. They will cause the body not to be interred, in order that such examination and inspection as may be requisite, may take place, and they will feel obliged by an immediate answer.

I am, Sir, your obedient servant,

M. NOTTINGHAM, *Vestry Clerk.*

W. Maclean, Esq., Secretary, Central Board of Health.

The death, of course, turned out to be from cholera as did three deaths at Limehouse and one at Southwark, reported on February 13.[12]

From Rotherhithe, Limehouse, and Southwark, the disease spread locally and then with its usual unpredictability [leaped] to outlying districts such as St Marylebone and Hoxton. By the autumn, when few new cases were occurring, some 5,300 Londoners had died, and during the second short attack in 1833 there were another 1,500 victims.

Cholera in Rotherhithe was a great deal more alarming than cholera on distant Tyneside, and within little more than a week of its first appearance in London an Act was passed "to prevent, as far as may be possible, by the Divine blessing, the spread of the disease." The Act empowered the Privy Council to issue instructions for the prevention of contagion, and within a few weeks doctors were being required to notify all cases of cholera, while the local Boards of Health were peremptorily ordered to set up temporary hospitals, provide the poor with medical attendance and when necessary pay for their funerals. In July the Nuisances Removal Order conferred hitherto unheard-of powers, authorizing the local Boards to scour sewers, close cesspools, clean slaughter-houses and even to enter infected private houses to wash and fumigate them. The first rudimentary machinery of public health administration was in fact being established.[13]

In 1827 the governors of London's St. Bartholomew's Hospital had recognized that the hospital's sanitary arrangements were totally inadequate. The extensive corrective measures undertaken were near completion when cholera hit in 1832, but the governors refused to admit cholera patients "because they did not want to endanger other patients," there being a difference of opinion whether the disease was or was not communicable. Instead, "they proposed to nurse them in a house specially arranged for sufferers of cholera. Their first choice was a house in Christopher Street off Finsbury Square, but neighbours made such a protest that a house in Smithfield was prepared instead . . ." Of fifty-seven patients admitted to this house between March 12 and November 9, twenty-one died.[14]

ACROSS THE ATLANTIC

Asiatic cholera, the most feared of all diseases in the 19th century, arrived in the Western World as a by-product of the Industrial Revolution. Because of its short incubation period and rapid course, the

disease was restricted to the Far East almost until the advent of
steam power and rapid transportation. At the same time, indus-
trialism brought massive urbanization with all its concomitant problems: crowded slums, limited and contaminated water supplies,
hopelessly ineffective methods for eliminating sewage and garbage,
and city governments ill-equipped to deal with the explosive growth
of population. Thus the Industrial Revolution provided both the
rapid transportation necessary for spreading the disease and seed
beds where it could flourish in the crowded cities.

Improvements in communication contributed further to enhancing
the role played by cholera, for no disease in American history was so
widely heralded at its first appearance (1832). The introduction of
cheap newspapers and journals had made it possible for the American public to follow the disastrous course of this pestilence as it advanced through Russia, Eastern Europe, and pushed northwestward
to the Atlantic. The accounts of its destructive progress built up
growing apprehensions which were intensified by urgent warnings
from health authorities and medical societies that the filthy state of
American communities had already set the stage for explosive out-
bursts of disease.[15]

It was Irish immigrants who carried cholera into Canada at the
beginning of June 1832. The European epidemic had spread
throughout Ireland at a time when the potato famine was causing
widespread hardship. Rather than starve, those who could scrape
together £3 for passage money left for America. An estimated
45,000 arrived in Quebec and Montreal. To make out financially
the ship owners crowded 500 passengers in space intended for 150.
The resultant unsanitary conditions and squalor were an open invi-
tation to the spread of cholera. According to *The Cholera Gazette*
(*Philadelphia*), between June 10 and July 14 there were 3724 cases
with 1220 deaths in Montreal. Between June 9 and September 2
there were 2127 deaths in Quebec.[16]

From Montreal the disease moved rapidly up the St. Lawrence
and its tributaries and along the shores of Lake Ontario. Entry into
the United States was three-pronged. For a waterborne bacterium
Detroit was an obvious target, the more so because, ignoring an in-
exhaustible supply of fresh water flowing by in the Detroit River,
most of the inhabitants used water from wells. Because the land

was low and marshy and outhouses were placed with no regard to location, contamination of well water was the rule rather than the exception. The second route involved the almost continuous waterway extending through Lake Champlain to the upper reaches of the Hudson River. (Whitehall, New York, was attacked by June 14 and Mechanicsville, just north of Albany, by the eighteenth.) The third was direct entry of immigrants into the port of New York.

> Late Monday night, June 26, an Irish immigrant named Fitzgerald came home violently ill. The pain in his stomach grew worse during the night, and in the morning he called a doctor. When the doctor arrived, Fitzgerald was already feeling better, but his two children were sick, complaining of agonizing cramps in their stomachs. The children died on Wednesday, but not before they were seen by many physicians, all of whom agreed upon a diagnosis of Asiatic cholera. Mrs. Fitzgerald died on Friday, and the next few days brought a scattering of similar cases: patients suffering with intestinal spasms, diarrhea, and vomiting. Most of them died.

The date—June 26—would allow of either direct importation or indirect importation (through Canada). However, years later, Dr. Westervelt, who was New York's port physician in 1832, stated that "cholera arrived in infected ships prior to its outbreak upon the St. Lawrence, but that for prudent motives, the facts were suppressed by the Board of Health. The sick were cared for in the quarantine hospital, and the well immigrants were shipped rapidly from the city." An attempt in 1874 to verify this story was thwarted by the suspicious fact that, while quarantine records of preceding and succeeding months were intact, those for April, May, and June 1832 were missing. In addition the June 16 issue of the Baltimore *Freeman's Banner* reported that the *Brenda*, out of Liverpool, had docked in Baltimore ten days earlier, having suffered fourteen cholera deaths en route.[17] *The Cholera Gazette* (*Philadelphia*) for July 18 reported that, since the beginning of the epidemic, there had been 1050 cases with 460 deaths in New York City,[18] but this does not represent the full havoc. Of a population of 200,000, 70,000 fled the city, carrying cholera into the interior.

The roads, in all directions, were lined with well-filled stage coaches, livery coaches, private vehicles and equestrians, all panic struck, fleeing from the city, as we may suppose the inhabitants of Pompeii or Reggio fled from those devoted places, when the red lava showered down upon their houses, or when the walls were shaken asunder by an earthquake.[19]

Newark, New Jersey, nine miles west of New York City, was immediately vulnerable and it was on July 6 that the wife of a steamboat captain, just returned from New York where she had been staying in an area where there were several cholera deaths, was the first victim of the disease. Since she died within twelve hours she did not spark an epidemic, but on July 11 the first case of local origin occurred "in 'a small filthy house' situated on the edge of a marsh near the Centre Street wharf. . . . The Board of Health described the house as a 'place of rendezvous for carousal.' In residence were 'about 20 degraded inmates of the most unclean habits [and it was not] surprising that disease should be engendered' [here]. Nine cases developed, all fatal. The other inhabitants were forceably removed to a barracks where they were 'crowded together to live or die, as chance should direct.' The barracks, which served as a cholera hospital for the duration of the epidemic, was located 'a considerable distance from town.' Soon cholera was raging in the areas of the Centre Street wharf, the hospital, and the poor house (which was located about one-quarter of a mile from the hospital)." In all, 127 contracted cholera and 65 died.[20]

In its first issue (July 11, 1832) *The Cholera Gazette* (*Philadelphia*) observed: "It cannot have failed to strike every medical man, who has watched the progress of our diseases, that the condition of things, which have elsewhere been the prelude to the occurrence of cholera as an epidemic, has been gradually coming upon us . . . and that within the last few days a more than usual number of cases of cholera morbus have occurred." Then, after admitting to one death on July 9, the writer added that there could be little doubt that cholera would be epidemic in Philadelphia that summer, but would not result in "extraordinary ravages" because the city was "so well prepared for a visitation, that we shall not have here that *panic* which has elsewhere so greatly augmented the victims of the disease and occasioned evils infinitely more deplorable than those of the pestilence itself." July 18: "During the past week, the epidemic constitution alluded to in our last number, has been gradually developing itself." July 25: "no marked changes." August 8: "The epidemic whose approach we confidentally announced a month since, is now prevailing among us, and appears as yet scarcely to have attained its maximum." There were 84 deaths from malignant cholera and 31 from cholera morbus in the week ending August 4. August 15: "The cholera has passed its height in Philadelphia, and is manifestly on the decline. . . . Whatever may be the causes, and we are not prepared to point them out at present, it is a fact that the pestilence has visited our city, comparatively, but lightly." The claim for a "decline" seems hardly justified. There were 370 deaths from malignant cholera and 35 from cholera morbus in the week ending August 11. (Through August 10, there had been a total of 984 cases of malignant cholera and 392 deaths.) But the drop in deaths did begin the following week and for the week ending August 25 they were down to 116 and 28 respectively. By the week ending September 15 deaths had dropped to 8 from malignant cholera and 28 from cholera morbus; a week later, to 6 and 13.[21]

August found cholera in Maryland, Virginia, and Kentucky, and it then followed the Ohio River into Ohio, Indiana, and Illinois. But Illinois had already been "breached" in July when troops under the command of General Winfield Scott (1786–1866) came by water from Buffalo to Fort Dearborn to help put down an "Indian uprising."

There are several conflicting versions of what this uprising was about, ranging from a belief that Black Hawk (1767–1838), chief of the Sac and Fox tribes, in collaboration with the Winnebago and Potawatomi, hoped, with British aid, to drive the Americans out of Illinois and Michigan, to a peaceable crossing of the Mississippi to resettle and cultivate land in the Rock River valley which they had formerly occupied. Since the "war party" was only a thousand strong, including six hundred women and children, it seems unlikely that their approach was belligerent, but both Governor

Reynolds of Illinois and Governor Mason of Michigan overreacted, calling for, in addition to local militiamen and volunteers, enough Federal troops to fill four lake vessels. (This overreaction may have been inspired to some degree by the fact that, at a first encounter, a handful of warriors routed the Illinois militia, causing many of the settlers to take refuge in Fort Dearborn.)

On July 2 the *Henry Clay* and *Sheldon Thompson*, the first two of four lake vessels hired to carry troops, left Buffalo. (The others followed two days later.) The *Sheldon Thompson* carried General Scott and his immediate staff. At the time of departure, no cases of cholera had been reported in Buffalo, but on July 4 one of the soldiers on the *Henry Clay* became seriously ill. The next day he was dead from cholera. By the time the vessel was off Fort Gratiot (now Port Huron), her decks were covered with dead and dying. As soon as she docked, a great many soldiers deserted and fled into the wilderness, but they did not escape death. After some regrouping of the remaining troops, the *Henry Clay* was ordered back to Buffalo. En route she brought cholera to Cleveland. The *Sheldon Thompson* continued north to Mackinac Island where cholera promptly took hold, causing civilian inhabitants to take refuge on the mainland. She brought cholera to Chicago on July 14. In all, Scott lost about five hundred men to cholera. Ironically, by the time he and a handful of his officers arrived in the combat area to take command, the Illinois militia and some regulars from Fort Dearborn had wiped out Black Hawk's braves at the battle of Bad Axe on August 2.

Meantime the disease had reached New Orleans and spread rapidly through the Mississippi Valley. With cholera in north and south Ohio towns and the state well-nigh surrounded by the disease, and with people from infected towns constantly coming into Columbus by stagecoach and canal boat, it is surprising that this city remained inviolate until the second week in July 1833. When cholera arrived it was confined to a small area but nonetheless produced about a hundred deaths in its two and a half months' activity. In 1833 cholera also devastated Indian territory and crossed the Rockies to the Pacific, but the Eastern states were almost cholera-free. However, it returned to them in 1834, extending on this occasion as far north as Halifax, Nova Scotia.

On January 4, 1833, Bernardo González Angulo, the minister of foreign affairs, officially advised governors of all Mexican states that cholera had appeared in the province of Chiapas, bordering on Guatemala. The announcement was inaccurate—probably based on passage the previous August by the Guatemalan government of an anticholera quarantine decree—but it at least brought to Mexico an awareness of impending disaster. Cholera broke out in Cuba in February and by March was raging there. On May 24 cholera entered Mexico, possibly from Cuba, possibly from New Orleans, through the port of Tampico, just two days before the revolution in the Pacific coast province of Michoacán that led to the civil war. By the latter part of June the epidemic had spread from Tampico to the populous upland areas of central Mexico. At roughly the same time a ship from Tampico brought cholera to Campeche, a port city on the Yucatán peninsula with a population of around twenty thousand. From Campeche the disease spread northwest to Mérida, the capital of Yucatán.

The first city of importance in central Mexico to be attacked was San Luis Potosí where an initial case was certified on June 28. By the end of October there had, allegedly, been 4366 deaths. Whether this number, unusually precise for the place and times, included the French tailor Enrique Androis cannot be determined, but his experience was novel to say the least. Androis came down with cholera, became unconscious, appeared dead, and was taken to the cemetery by the dead cart's last trip for the day.

> It was the custom of the grave diggers not to bury the bodies collected on their last round, but simply to leave them in the open ditch until the following morning. During the night Androis regained consciousness, climbed out of the trench and managed to get back to his house. Unable to rouse his servants, he noticed that the window of his bedroom, which was on the first floor, was open (the maid had done this to air the room in which he had "died") and climbed in. Then he knocked as loudly as his failing strength permitted on the door leading from his bedroom to the patio, which was also locked. The servants, terrified at hearing knockings from the dead man's room in the middle of the night, got up and went in search of a priest who, with the police, returned to investigate. Androis lay

stretched out on his bed, but he gave clear answers to the priest who questioned him from the window. The investigators then opened the door to the room from the patio, and sent to the apothecary and the doctor on duty, who came and took care of his patient. In a very few days Androis was back in his shop. The lucky chance which saved him was that he had been taken to the cemetery on the last round of the dead cart, and so had not been buried.[22]

From San Luis Potosí the epidemic moved northwest to the wealthy and progressive mining state of Zacatecas. To the south Guadalajara, the second largest city in Mexico, saw its first death on July 24. The death toll over two months was estimated at 3275, with 238 dying on a single day (August 21). During the latter part of July and early August cholera spread in all directions in the interior. On the coast, rather remarkably, the country's largest port, Veracruz, escaped until August 20, thanks largely to a strict quarantine that was imposed when cholera appeared in Tampico and Campeche.

At the beginning of August cholera entered Querétaro, something over a hundred miles northwest of Mexico City. On August 6 a woman and her daughter in the capital died of the disease in three hours. Carlos María Bustamente (1774–1848), the indefatigable chronicler of contemporary events in Mexico, wrote in his diary: "What is going to happen in a city that is so populous, so damp, and so impregnated with filth?" [23] What happened (approximately) was that 48,863 persons contracted cholera, of whom 10,332 died. The figures are *approximate* because they "only represented those who were charity cases. The many who had been able to pay for their own treatment had not come to the dispensaries and had not been counted. Also, some of the cemeteries did not send in figures for burials, and there was no way of checking the numbers of those buried in secret (the compilers estimated that not less than 500 were probably buried secretly). Furthermore, figures were lacking from some of the hospitals." [24]

THE THIRD PANDEMIC 1846–63

The epidemic that by 1846 had smothered India and already had spread to the Philippines and China, in one direction, and to Persia in the other had its beginnings as early as 1840–41. By 1848–49 it had covered continental Europe (with the exception of the Iberian Peninsula which escaped until 1853) and was again in England. This second great epidemic on British soil had caused fifty-four thousand deaths, mainly in the large ports and industrial centers, by the end of 1849. This epidemic, and another widespread visitation in 1853–54, taken together, are noteworthy for the conclusions to which they led John Snow (1813–1858) who, incidentally, was a pioneer in inhalation anesthesia. Snow first stated the theory that cholera was waterborne and taken into the system by mouth in an essay which was awarded a thirty-thousand-franc prize by the Institute of France in 1849. He proceeded carefully to map the incidence of the disease in London and

> determined that most of the people who died had drunk water from the Broad Street pump. The water, drawn from the Thames River, had taste and odor of sewage. Snow advised the guardians of the parish to remove the pump handle, and the epidemic quickly waned. . . .
>
> Snow's well-reasoned conjecture that the epidemic had arisen from the contaminated water, not from "miasmic vapors" or supernatural causes, was soon dramatically confirmed. In 1854 the city was struck by another severe cholera outbreak. In the intervening years one of the two private water companies serving the city had changed its water source, drawing from a clean area of the Thames instead of the sewage laden area. Among the users supplied by this company . . . relatively few persons were affected by the 1854 cholera epidemic, the number of deaths in a 14-week period being 461, or 2.6 per 1,000. In the population served by the other company, which was still drawing from the sewage-laden waters, the deaths from cholera totaled more than 4,000, or 15.3 per 1,000.[25]

In April 1848 cholera was again in Canada, reintroduced by immigrant ships from European ports. On December 1, the *New*

York, twenty-one days out of Le Havre, dropped anchor at quarantine at the port of New York. A distressed captain reported seven immigrant deaths from cholera and other passengers with unmistakable symptoms of the disease. On the sixth and eighth, vessels from Hamburg and Bremen brought cholera to New Orleans. The immigrants from the vessels fanned out, taking cholera to steamboat landings along the Mississippi, the Arkansas, and the Tennessee rivers. As early as March 1778 St. Louisans had discussed the advisability of a sewerage system, but to no purpose. In 1843 the state legislature gave St. Louis the right to "establish, erect, and keep in repair bridges, culverts, and sewers," but next to nothing had been done when the city was hit by the cholera epidemic at the beginning of 1849. In March 1850 construction on a public sewer was begun, causing a contemporary to observe: "The weakness of humanity is generally to procrastinate; and what could have been done in 1848 in the way of sanitary precautions, was postponed, which, while it might not have precluded the appearance of the direful disease, would have disarmed it of half its deadly power." [26]

By the early months of 1849 all of the United States east of the Rockies was infected. In addition, the disease traveled from Panama to San Francisco whence it spread through the valleys of the great California rivers—the San Jose, San Joaquin, and Sacramento.

In 1849 the sickness again appeared in Mexico; first from Texas through the border town of Matamoras and also from the seaports on the east coast. From Panama Cholera came to Acapulca and Mazatlon. In the same year all major Mexican cities were infected. In Central America only Panama suffered with the pestilence as the other small states in this area escaped. In the West Indies Cholera was severe. In 1850 Cuba and Jamaica reported Cholera and here the disease raged continuously for four years. The mortality rate was astonishing with tens of thousands of deaths. In 1851 it was Santo Domingo, followed by the Bahamas, Puerto Rico and many of the adjacent islands. In 1855 Venezuela became infected and Brazil soon followed. The disease lingered in many places only to disappear after fifteen years having brought death to millions. [27]

The fifties saw cholera in Java, Sumatra, and the East Indies generally, in Japan, China, and Korea, in Afghanistan, Turkistan, Mesopotamia, and Syria, in Egypt, Tripoli, Tunis, Algiers, and Morocco, in Ethiopia, Somaliland, Mozambique, Madagascar, and the Comoro Islands. In 1856–57 cholera hit Central America— Nicaragua, Costa Rica, Guatemala, San Salvador, Honduras. "The third pandemic of cholera embraces, therefore, a period of some fifteen years, during which the disease had spread over the whole Northern Hemisphere, and to 25° S. in the Old World and to 30° S. in the New." [28]

THE FOURTH PANDEMIC

Starting in the lower basin of the Ganges in 1863 cholera spread throughout India, the East Indies, China, and Japan. Indian pilgrims carried the disease to Mecca, the outbreak causing panic and general flight. Cholera was speedily carried in all directions by the homebound pilgrims. The epidemic spread along the Mediterranean coasts, involving north Africa, Asia Minor, and Central Asia, the south of Europe, and finally the rest of Europe. On this occasion the impact on the British Isles was limited and less severe. In the Western Hemisphere the Caribbean islands of Guadeloupe, Martinique, Santo Domingo, Cuba, and St. Thomas were hit before the disease entered New York, New Orleans, and Halifax. As usual the infection fanned out from the points of entry. Apart from New York and New Orleans, the towns hardest hit were Memphis, Nashville, and St. Louis. But, Duffy has said, in 1866 and 1873 (the final appearance of epidemic cholera in the United States) prompt sanitary measures limited cholera's effect. "Without knowing precisely why, health authorities recognized that the infection was spread through the feces of infected persons, and they resorted successfully to disinfecting procedures." [29] The fourth pandemic is notable because it brought cholera to the west coast of South America for the first time.

AFTER 1875

An epidemic that had broken out in India four years earlier reached Europe in 1883. In 1892 cholera from India again appeared in Europe. Russia lost a million people, including Pëtr Ilich Tchaikovsky who died of cholera on November 6, 1893, at the age of fifty-three. In 1902 cholera spread over India, China, and the Philippines and returned to Russia causing many deaths. World War I saw the disease among the troops of several nations. Since 1923 Western Europe has been relatively cholera-free, but there have been repeated outbreaks in Russia, especially in the Ukraine.

In 1905 the German public health investigator Felix Gotschlich isolated a variety of *V. cholerae*—*V. el-tor*, which was to be responsible for outbreaks of cholera on the Indonesian island of Celebes in 1937–38, 1939–40, 1944, and 1957–58. A further outbreak in January 1961 swelled into a pandemic that is still raging in some parts of the world.

The first phase (1961–62) involved southeast Asia—Java, Sarawak, Borneo, Macao and Hong Kong, the Philippines, Sumatra, Timor, Taiwan, and Irian Barat (formerly West New Guinea). The second phase (1963–69) saw the extension of the pandemic to the Asian mainland—Malaya, Singapore, Thailand, Cambodia, Burma, Vietnam, Korea, East Pakistan (now Bangladesh), India, West Pakistan (now Pakistan), Afghanistan, Iran, Asian USSR, and Iraq. Up to this point (August 1966)

> the countries involved showed their good co-operative spirit by notifying the World Health Organization of the disease in compliance with the stipulations of the International Health Regulations.
>
> It is regrettable, however, to state that disturbance of this attitude of international co-operation ensued when the seventh pandemic approached the door through which its predecessors had passed, threatening more spread westwards. Unwarranted scare took hold of some health administrators and made them take excessively restrictive measures causing economic loss in international trade. The range of these measures was incredible and "included among others, the disinfection of mail and printed matter, prohibition of importation of tinned fruit, iron beams, carpets, teak, mineral oil, etc.,

prevention of entry of the westbound Orient Express with 70 passengers for more than a week, prevention from disembarkation of
the passengers from a plane including a minister of health, for many
hours in the heat of a summer's day, and finally the detention of
cholera vaccine at an airport for three days because the plane sent to
collect it could not get permission to land" (Carter, 1970).

The net result of these unwarranted restrictions was inopportune
announcement of freedom of infection without its adequate surveillance proof, and/or intentional refusal to notify the presence of
the disease. Hence the lull which characterized the *status quo* of the
pandemic during the three years 1967–1969. During those years the
pandemic, as far as official documents go, took a halt, as no extension to new territories was reported. The only new state that joined
the pandemic was Laos in 1969.[30]

The third phase (1970 to date) has seen cholera involving most of
the Middle East countries, much of west and central Africa north
of the equator, and Ethiopia, Afars and Issas, and Somaliland. Of
great significance, however, was the return of cholera to Europe. In
1970 the USSR was entered through Astrakhan and cholera appeared in Istanbul and Czechoslovakia. Single cases were reported
by France and Britain. In 1971 Spain and Portugal experienced
outbreaks, seeded by returning tourists and seasonal workers from
North Africa. There was one case in West Berlin and three each in
Britain, France, and Sweden.

As recently as August 1973 cholera occurred in several cities in
Italy. During the same month there was a single unaccountable
case in Calhoun County, Texas, unaccountable because the "patient had not traveled in cholera-infected parts of the world or
knowingly been exposed to any persons from such areas." Thus the
terror of cholera remains with us. However, Eugene J. Gangarosa
and William H. Barker of the Bureau of Epidemiology of the U.S.
Public Health Service Center for Disease Control, offered some
consolation when they wrote in 1974:

> Sporadic cases of cholera may occur in the United States. Cholera
> is a life-threatening, but fully controllable, acute disease that is com-
> pletely responsive to therapy when physicians are familiar with diag-

nosis and treatment. Cholera is best controlled through proper treatment and surveillance. Cholera vaccine is not needed in the
management of imported cases or in outbreaks that may occur in this
country. Quarantine and mass chemoprophylaxis are not effective
control measures. Laboratory technologists should be taught how to
isolate and identify cholera vibrios.[31]

Hospital-Related Epidemics

As LONG as there have been hospitals they have been called into service whenever an epidemic disease invaded their territories. These demands have, of the very nature of epidemics in the generally accepted sense, fallen upon them sporadically. But there is a different type of epidemic that springs to life in a hospital, or a part thereof, but does not spread, as an epidemic, beyond the walls of the particular hospital, or of a limited area within it.

PUERPERAL FEVER

Puerperal (or childbed) fever is not the only hospital-related epidemic disease but it deserves primary consideration because it is one of the most common causes of death in childbearing. It is, in reality, a postpartum wound infection of the birth canal. Such septic inflammatory complications have occurred from the earliest times and were observed by clinicians dating back to Hippocrates, but they only assumed *malignant* epidemic status when the hospitalization of maternity cases became common.

What may have been the first epidemic of puerperal fever was reported in an article published in Paris in 1694 by Philippe Peu (d. 1707), who stated that a very large number of postpartum patients had died at the Hôtel Dieu in 1664. But the fact that the corpses of the women showed multiple abscesses and that they had been housed above a ward filled with wound cases suggests that the

outbreak was (in modern terms) staphylococcal rather than streptococcal, which would more likely have been the case with puerperal fever. Less doubt can attach to a 1746 account by Paul-
Jacques Malouin (1701–1778) of a number of women confined in
hospitals (particularly the Hôtel Dieu) who perished with a high
fever. In 1750 there was a further outbreak in Paris and an epidemic in Lyons. Puerperal fever hit hospitals in London (1760),
Copenhagen (1765), Dublin (1767), and Edinburgh (1778). That
eighteenth-century hospitals should be natural hotbeds of infection
was well illustrated in 1788 when Jacques-René Tenon (1724–1816)
published a series of memoirs on Paris hospitals. In the winter of
1789 he visited the maternity ward of the Hôtel Dieu.

> He writes that upon opening the door of the maternity ward, the air
> was so heavy as to give one the impression of something tangible
> rushing upon one, and so fetid as to be pungent.
>   Owing to the defective heating, generated by a single stove in the
> middle of the large ward, the windows had to be kept closed. . . .
> The beds were high, curtained and each bed—of large dimensions—
> contained three patients. The dying laid side by side with the par-
> turient and the desperately sick. The deliveries took place—as did
> the cutting of stone in the men's section—in the middle of the ward
> surrounded by feelings of sympathy mingled with fear from those in
> their first labor, or of contempt and derision from the hardened mul-
> tipara or of indifference from the dulled desperately sick.[1]

In 1773 Charles White (1728–1813) of Manchester, England,
published *A Treatise on the Management of Pregnant and Lying-in
Women* in which he advocated, as preventive measures, personal
cleanliness, ventilation, isolation, and disinfection. "He emphasized
the frequency with which puerperal sepsis followed the practice of
certain men, emphasized its contagiousness, and presented an un-
broken record of not a single death in a long and large obstetrical
practice. This was corroborated and followed with equally happy
results by his pupil, Kirkland, who further emphasized the importance of cleanliness and avoidance of contagion."[2] Thomas Kirkland (1721–1798) was the author of *A Treatise on Child-bed Fevers,
and the Methods of Preventing Them* (London, 1774).

A Treatise on the Epidemic Puerperal Fever of Aberdeen (London, 1795) by Alexander Gordon (1752–1799), physician to the Dispensary, begins:

THE disease, which I propose to describe, made its appearance in Aberdeen in the month of December 1789, and prevailed as an epidemic among lying-in women till the month of March 1792, when it finally ceased.

This epidemic seemed, in every respect, to answer the description of the Puerperal or Child-bed Fever, on which many authors have written, particularly Doctors Hulme, Denman, and Leake, who have described it with great ability.

The Puerperal Fever, according to the account given of it by authors, is more frequent and fatal in large towns, and in hospitals, than in the country, and private practice. . . .

It prevailed principally among the lower classes of women, and, on account of my public office, and extensive practice in Midwifery, most of the cases came under my care. But women in the higher walks of life were not exempted, when they happened to be delivered by a midwife, or physician, who had previously attended any patients labouring under the disease.

Gordon's book included a table covering seventy-seven cases attended by him during the period mentioned of which twenty-eight (36 percent) died. (Of those who died, four were delivered by Gordon himself.) Gordon's analysis of a number of the cases led him to two significant conclusions:

That the Puerperal Fever is of the nature of erysipelas, was supposed by Peauteau forty years ago, and has been the opinion of Doctors Young and Home, of Edinburgh, since that time. I will not venture positively to assert, that the Puerperal Fever and Erysipelas are precisely of the same specific nature; but that they are connected, that there is an analogy between them, and that there are concomitant epidemics, I have unquestionable proofs. For these two epidemics began in Aberdeen at the same time, and afterwards kept pace together; they both arrived at their *acme* together, and they both ceased at the same time.

> That the cause of this disease was a specific contagion, or infec-
> tion, I have unquestionable proof [for it] seized such women only, as
> were visited or delivered, by a practitioner, or taken care of by a
> nurse, who had previously attended patients affected with the dis-
> ease.

The second of these conclusions led Gordon to recognize the es-
sentiality of preventive approaches that would still be matters of
dispute a half-century later. Fresh air and cleanliness alone could
not avert contagion.

> The patient's apparel and bed-clothes ought, either to be burnt, or
> thoroughly purified; and the nurses and physicians, who have at-
> tended the patients affected with the Puerperal Fever, ought care-
> fully to wash themselves, and to get their apparel properly fumi-
> gated, before it be put on again. [3]

There is little reason to believe that Gordon's treatise attracted
much attention (or acceptance) among the obstetricians of his day,
but his "very forthright document [in which he named names] did
not make him popular in Aberdeen, and he found it expedient to
leave that city and take service in the Navy, where there was no
obstetric practice. He died of tuberculosis at the early age of 48." [4]

Oliver Wendell Holmes (1809–1894) was born ten years after
Gordon died. He was an anatomist, not a practicing obstetrician,
but he was driven to make inquiries by the death of a colleague,
who had performed an autopsy on a woman who had died of puerperal fever. He found, among other things, that after the autopsy
but before taking to his deathbed, the doctor had continued in
practice and that several women then delivered contracted puerperal fever. On February 13, 1843, Holmes presented his conclusions to the Boston Society for Medical Improvement in a paper
entitled "On the contagiousness of puerperal fever." In it, he offered the following conclusions:

> 1. A physician holding himself in readiness to attend cases of
> midwifery, should never take any active part in the postmortem ex-
> amination of cases of puerperal fever.

2. If a physician is present at such autopsies, he should use thorough ablution, change every article of dress, and allow twenty-four hours or more to elapse before attending to any case of midwifery. It may be well to extend the same caution to cases of simple peritonitis.

3. Similar precautions should be taken after the autopsy or surgical treatment of erysipelas, if the physician is obliged to unite such offices with his obstetrical duties, which is in the highest degree inexpedient.

4. On the occurrence of a single case of puerperal fever in his practice, the physician is bound to consider the next female he attends in labor, unless some weeks, at least, have elapsed, as in danger of being infected by him, and it is his duty to take every precaution to diminish her risk of disease and death.

5. If within a short period two cases of puerperal fever happen close to each other, in the practice of the same physician, the disease not existing or prevailing in the neighborhood, he would do wisely to relinquish his obstetrical for at least one month, and endeavor to free himself by every available means from any noxious influence he may carry about with him.

6. The occurrence of three or more closely connected cases, in the practice of one individual, no others existing in the neighborhood, and no other sufficient cause being alleged for the coincidence, is prima facie evidence that he is the vehicle of contagion.

7. It is the duty of the physician to take every precaution that the disease shall not be introduced by nurses or other assistants, by making proper inquiries concerning them, and giving timely warning of every suspected source of danger.

8. Whatever indulgence may be granted to those who have heretofore been the ignorant causes of so much misery, the time has come when the existence of a *private pestilence* in the sphere of a single physician should be looked upon not as a misfortune but a crime; and in the knowledge of such occurrences, the duties of the practitioner to his profession, should give way to his paramount obligations to society.[5]

Publication of his paper brought violent reactions, especially from two obstetricians in Philadelphia, Hugh Lenox Hodge (1796–1873) and Charles D. Meigs (1792–1869), the latter of whom committed the gross blunder of attacking the author's youth. Later

Holmes characterized these critics as "two professors, learned men both of them, skillful experts, but babies, as it seemed to me in their capacity of reasoning and arguing." [6]

At Vienna's Lying-in Hospital there were two maternity wards known as the First Division and the Second Division. When Ignaz Philipp Semmelweis (1818–1865), of Budapest and Vienna, became assistant to the First Division in 1846, he found that deaths from puerperal fever not only ran at roughly 10 percent of admissions but that, over a six-year period, the mortality rate of the First Division had been three times that of the Second Division. (This situation was so well known that women tearfully begged not to be put in the First Division.)

Before Semmelweis assumed his duties in 1846 he had devoted two years to the study of the pathological anatomy of obstetrics and gynecology under the tutorship of Karl von Rokitansky (1804–1878), the ablest descriptive pathologist of his time, who is alleged to have undertaken more than thirty thousand postmortems in the course of his career. Now that Semmelweis was at the point of practical application of what he had learned, he came face to face with the question of the remarkable difference in puerperal mortality between the two divisions. This in a sense put him in an advantageous position over White, Gordon, Holmes, and others who had attacked the problem, empirically or theoretically, without a "control" such as was provided by the Second Division. Semmelweis could rule out potential causative factors common to both divisions, but this did not relieve him of weary months of speculation and rejection.

Prior to October 1840 male and female students had been assigned indiscriminately to both divisions. It was only after that date, when male students were sent exclusively to the First Division and student-midwives to the Second, that the marked mortality differences appeared. But what further differences were involved? Semmelweis painstakingly eliminated factors. His final conclusion came tragically. Early in 1847 Professor Jacobus Kolletschka, assistant to Rokitansky, died of a dissection wound incurred during a postmortem. Semmelweis, who held him in the highest regard, was "shocked by the sad news." "In the excited condition in which I then was, it rushed into my mind with irresistible clearness that the disease from which Kolletschka had died was identical with that from which I had seen so many hundreds of lying-in women die. . . . The cause of the fatal illness of Kolletschka was well known: it was the wound produced by a dissecting scalpel which was foul with cadaveric particles. It was not the wound, but the wound rendered unclean by cadaveric material, which had produced the fatal result; . . . In the case of Kolletschka the cause of the disease was the cadaveric material carried into the vascular system: I must therefore put this question to myself: Did then the individuals whom I had seen die from an identical disease also have cadaveric matter carried into the vascular system? To this question I must answer, Yes!" [7]

The follow-up conclusion was obvious. The First Division students (and doctors) came directly from the dissecting room to make vaginal examinations with unclean hands, at best with hands washed with soap and water that never really removed cadaveric particles; the student-midwives were required to pay greater attention to personal cleanliness.

> If this theory that the cadaveric material adhering to the hand can produce the same disease as the cadaveric particles adhering to the scalpel be correct, then if the cadaveric material on the hands can be completely destroyed by chemical agencies, and the genitals of the women in labour or in the lying-in state be brought into contact with the clean fingers only, and not simultaneously with cadaveric particles, then the disease can be prevented to the extent to which it originated by the presence of cadaveric material on the examining fingers. [8]

Beginning in May 1847 Semmelweis required every student to wash his hands with *chlorina liquida* before making an examination. (Later chlorinated lime was substituted because it was cheaper.) For May 1847 the First Division mortality rate was over 12 percent. For the whole of 1848, during which chlorine disinfection was diligently practiced, the rate was 1.27 percent (compared with 1.33 percent in the Second Division).

Now, in the autumn of 1847, was the Discovery of Semmelweis complete, and the Doctrine firmly established in his own mind. It amounted to this: that puerperal fever was caused by a decomposed animal organic matter conveyed by contact to the pregnant, parturient or puerperal woman without regard to its origin, whether from the cadaver or from a living person affected with a disease which produced a decomposed animal organic matter.

We shall find that with years of experience Semmelweis found many varieties of illustration, but he never modified his Doctrine in any manner or degree, whatever opponents in later years may have alleged as an excuse for carelessness in the reading of his works, or for their own hostility and the eager levity with which they misrepresented or misunderstood him.[9]

Like Holmes, Semmelweis had his detractors—Friedrich Wilhelm Scanzoni (1821–1891), Carl von Braun (1822–1891), and the orthodox obstetricians of the day—but Rokitansky, Josef Skoda (1805–1881), and Ferdinand von Hebra (1816–1880), all of the New Vienna School, and Gustav Adolf Michaëlis (1798–1848) stood back of him.

As early as 1836 James Young Simpson (1811–1870), who became professor of obstetrics at Edinburgh at the age of twenty-nine, was the first to use chloroform in deliveries (1847), and served as obstetrician to Queen Victoria, began observations that led to a firm belief in the communicability of puerperal fever. After he had assisted in the dissection of two fatal cases, puerperal fever had appeared in his practice for the first time. It then spread to patients attended by a friend. Consequently, as early as 1840 (three years before the publication of Holmes's famous paper) Simpson was lecturing on the contagiousness of the disease. However, his views were not published until 1851.[10]

Simpson welcomed the largely neglected work and conclusions of Semmelweis as a vindication of his own teachings but disputed the Hungarian's claim that puerperal fever was transmitted by animal matter in a state of putrefaction. "It was evident to Simpson that any putrefaction was incidental and that the disease was spread rather by 'an inflammatory secretion, just as the inoculable matter of smallpox, cowpox, syphilis. . . .' Surely for its time a remarkable statement of the specific nature of infection." Acknowledging indebtedness to Alexander Gordon, he further developed his fellow-Scotsman's views on the relationship between puerperal fever and erysipelas by describing what he had himself observed in 1836, namely that "the same focus of contagion producing puerperal fever in puerperal patients [caused] erysipelas, inflammatory sore throat, &c., in patients who were not in the puerperal state." [11]

But what was Simpson's "inflammatory secretion"? From 1850 forward

the problem became largely one of detective bacteriology. The name of the infecting agent was not known; nor where it came from; nor how it was transmitted. Many laboratory workers shared in that investigation during the next 70 years. First, two Alsatian doctors, Coze and Feltz, reported in 1869 that they had seen what they called *microbes en chaînettes*—our "chains" of streptococci—in the lochial exudate of women with puerperal fever. Pasteur (1879) confirmed this and added that he had seen similar *microbes en chaînettes* in the blood of women dying of the disease. He had no doubt that they were responsible for the fever. The story has often been told of the medical meeting in Paris at which a speaker was presenting the conventional vague views about puerperal infections when Pasteur arose in the audience and declared he was talking nonsense. "It is the doctor and his staff," he said, "who carry the microbe from a sick woman to a healthy woman." When the orator expressed doubt about whether anybody would ever see that microbe, Pasteur strode up to the blackboard and drew a picture of a streptococcal chain. "There," he said, "that is its picture." [12]

Leonard Colebrook, in a Jenner Memorial lecture delivered at St. George's Hospital, London, on October 25, 1955, had this to say:

The final picture, then, which emerges to-day—at least in the more fortunate countries—is that childbirth has been largely robbed of the terror of infection. . . . We have gained much greater control over our microbic enemies; and there has been great progress in all that makes for safe midwifery.

To this happy ending I ought to add a postscript. The puerperal fever hazard is *not* a thing of the past. It is still with us. There is still, indeed, more infection than there should be, although it is not reflected in the national death rate. . . .

Finally, we must be on our guard in our practice and teaching against the dangerous doctrine that because puerperal fever is now largely curable its development does not matter. There is evidence . . . that a mother who has recovered from streptococcal infection is very often sterile; and such sterility may be a cause of lifelong unhappiness. We have not yet done our job as obstetricians if we allow mothers to be infected. . . .[13]

HOSPITAL CROSS INFECTION

"Cross infection has been a problem throughout the ages wherever the sick have been housed. It was particularly rife in some of the larger hospitals of Europe in the centuries before Lister, making all but the most imperative operations unthinkable. Paré in the sixteenth century complained that infection at the Hôtel Dieu in Paris was so frightful that no operation could rightly be contemplated in that institution." [14]

During the Middle Ages the Christian church had accepted responsibility for care of the sick poor for whom it organized hospitals in the twelfth century. But even then "the patient's soul obtained better care than his body. Indeed, medical treatment and medical staff did not become regular features of the hospital scene for another few hundred years. Meanwhile, hospitals such as St. Bartholomew's in London and the Hôtel Dieu in Paris became increasingly crowded and insanitary places. 'Hospital fever' (louse-borne typhus) was rife and killed large numbers of patients, as did typhoid, dysentery, and other more obscure 'pestilences.' " [15]

John Pringle (1707–1782), surgeon general of the English army from 1742 to 1758, was the founder of modern military medicine and originator of the idea of the Red Cross. In his *Observations on the Diseases of the Army* (London, 1752) he laid down principles of military sanitation, with special emphasis on the ventilation of hospital wards, but admitted the difficulty of implementing his proposals because neither nurses nor patients recognized the need for reform. James Lind attempted to apply Pringle's approach to naval hospitals. But no attempt was made to improve conditions in civilian hospitals which, in fact, generally deteriorated. As a result, while the scope of surgical operations broadened in the eighteenth and early nineteenth centuries, the outcome of technically satisfactory operations was frequently catastrophic, due to a hospital-related epidemic—surgical fever or hospital gangrene.

At the siege of Rouen (1540) the great army surgeon Ambroise Paré (1510–1590) recommended incision around a wound to form a trench that would keep out hospital gangrene. Hospital gangrene was described in 1722 by Guillaume Mauquest de la Motte (1665–1737) of the Paris Hôtel Dieu as *la pourriture* (rottenness, putrefaction, or corruption). It was established as a distinct disease by the French surgeon Claude Pouteau (1725–1775), who himself contracted it while dressing wounded men. In the early 1800s it ravaged the British navy and Napoleon's armies. During the Crimean War it hit the French much harder than the English because of the latter's practice of immediately removing infected cases from the general wards. Hospital gangrene was practically unknown in the United States until the Civil War, when it hit Confederate soldiers harder than the Union army, a situation that has been "ascribed to the malnourished state of the average Confederate soldier, combined with the pitiful lack of medical supplies and problems which the Confederates faced in regard to adequate physical facilities for the treatment of their wounded men."

Dr. Joseph S. Jones (1833–1896), a surgeon in the Provisional Army of the Confederate States, "spent some time at Andersonville Prison in April of 1864. This notorious prison camp, the child of Ulysses S. Grant who refused to allow prisoner exchange, had thousands of cases of hospital gangrene. The infection could develop in the most trivial scratch, and amputees invariably developed it in the fresh surgical wound with almost 100 per cent mortality." [16]

John Bell (1763–1820) of Edinburgh, the author of major works on surgery and surgical anatomy which he personally illustrated, had written in his monumental *Principles of Surgery* (Edinburgh, 1801–1807):

There is no hospital, however small, airy or well regulated, where this epidemic ulcer is not to be found at times; and then no operation dare be performed! every cure stands still! every wound becomes a sore, and every sore is apt to run into gangrene: but in great hospitals especially, it prevails at all times and is a real gangrene; it has been named the Hospital Gangrene; and such were its ravages at the Hôtel Dieu of Paris (that great storehouse of corruption and disease) that the surgeons did not dare to call it by its true name.

What then, is the surgeon to do? Is he to seek for washes or dressings to cure such a disease as this? Is he to expend butts of wine, contending, as it were, against the elements? No! Let him bear this always in mind, that no dressings ever have been found to stop this ulcer; that no quantities of wine or bark which a man can bear have ever retarded this gangrene; let him bear in mind that this is a hospital disease; that without the circle of the infected walls the men are safe; let him, therefore, hurry them out of this house of death . . . let him lay them in a schoolroom, a church, on a dunghill or in a stable . . . let him carry them anywhere but to their graves. [17]

In 1850 Simpson published a paper showing a close relationship between puerperal and surgical fever [18] but his most comprehensive account of surgical fever was in a series of "clinical lectures" (not published until 1859) in which he said that "every patient placed upon an operating table . . . is in . . . greater danger than a soldier entering one of the bloodiest and most fatal battlefields." Deaths were due less to gangrene than to "some morbific material circulating in the blood producing a special toxaemic state." He saw as the probable vectors of infection the surgeon, his attendants, and nurses. "I believe that surgical fever is often enough propagated in this way, just as puerperal fever is, . . . perhaps . . . to a degree that is at present not yet dreamt of." [19]

The year 1867 produced a scientific answer to wound sepsis when Joseph Lister (1827–1912) introduced antiseptic (the exclusion of infection) surgery. The work of Louis Pasteur (1822–1895) and others had shown that microorganisms in the environment produced fermentation and putrefaction. Lister saw its application to wound infection. Bacteria must be prevented from reaching operation wounds.

In the years that followed, asepsis [the creation of a germ-free zone] largely superceded antisepsis and enormous improvements in hospital, particularly theatre, hygiene were introduced. By about the 1930s the conquest over hospital infection seemed almost complete and operations which would not have been contemplated in the days of Lister became everyday occurrences. Admittedly "clean" operations still sometimes became infected, but this occurred so much less frequently than formerly that little attention was paid, and few, if any, surgeons kept a record of the incidence.

In the last 20 years antiseptics of a new type have appeared on the scene, namely antibiotics. . . . Unfortunately, early hopes with antibiotics have not been fulfilled. The streptococcus has, indeed, lost much of its menace but not so the more adaptable staphylococcus. . . .

Cross-infection in hospital has remained a problem yesterday and today. If enough people take it seriously there is no reason why it should continue tomorrow.

Or as John Bell put it 175 years ago:

No expense should be spared . . . you would willingly expend your own future in such a cause—then do not grudge to employ the revenue of the state for it is employing it and not abusing it! . . . if in the course of a few weeks sixty men die of the disease in your hospital, the government has lost a sum which would trebly buy your hospital itself.[20]

Poliomyelitis and
Other Epidemic Diseases of
the Central Nervous System

IN 1925 the eminent British medical statesman and historian Arthur Salusbury MacNalty (1880–1969) delivered the Milroy lectures before the Royal College of Physicians. His subject was epidemic diseases of the nervous system. "The epidemiological study of these diseases is of absorbing interest, but its presentation is attended with difficulty. I can say in the words of Francis Bacon:— 'In addressing myself to which task I am not ignorant how great a work I attempt, and how difficult a province I take upon me; nor again how far unequal my strength is to my will.' " [1]

These remarks are almost as true today as they were fifty years ago.

POLIOMYELITIS

Mention of an individual who has had poliomyelitis brings to the mind of most people a child (or older person) who must drag his or her way through life, possibly confined to a wheelchair or even an iron lung, but poliomyelitis, while an acute viral disease that can lead to neuron paralysis, can not only be nonparalytic but also inapparent. In fact, inapparent infection has been found to far outrun clinical cases. However, it was not until the twentieth century that focus shifted from earlier emphasis on the crippling effects of the disease to recognition of its broader aspects, and even then the changed concept could not be allowed to obscure the tragedy of severe paralysis, when it resulted, or the need to provide methods of preventing epidemics.

It is generally the opinion of medical scientists, historians, and other authorities that sporadic cases of poliomyelitis "are at least as old as written history," but, while lameness and withered limbs are frequently referred to, descriptions are so brief that it is impossible positively to attribute the deformity to poliomyelitis. The first depiction for which "diagnosis is practically assured" is that of an Egyptian stele (pillar) dating from the Eighteenth Dynasty (1580–1350 B.C.). "We owe . . . original medical interpretation [of the stele] to the Danish physician Ove Hamburger. Here the crippled young man, apparently a priest, is pictured with a withered and shortened left leg, with his foot held in the typical *equinus* position characteristic of flaccid paralysis; his staff is apparently being used as a support. Hamburger rightly concluded that the most probable cause of the priest's deformity was infantile paralysis, and few physicians with appropriate experience who have examined this picture carefully during the more than half century since its publication have doubted the significance of his historic diagnosis." [2] There has been speculation whether some of Hippocrates' reported cases of *clubfoot* were acquired in early infancy (as an outcome of poliomyelitis?) rather than being congenital. Be that as it may, an Italian jar (in the Paris Louvre) dating from the fourth century B.C. pictures a bearded man with "poliomyelitic deformities of the lower limbs . . . supporting himself on a stick." [3]

MacArthur has reported "a strange entry" in the Annals of Ulster "under the year A.D. 708 (*recte*, 709)" involving "the pestilence that is called *baccach* [lameness]." Originally lameness had a wider meaning than it has today, and as late as the eighteenth century Dr. Samuel Johnson, the outstanding English literary figure of his time, spoke of an acquaintance who had "lame fingers." After pointing out that the Annals were believed "to have been compiled in the monastic college of Bangor in County Down, which flourished at the period when Ireland was the chief centre of learn-ing in Western Europe," MacArthur concluded:

> It seems to me that the epidemic of the Lameness could only have been poliomyelitis. It is true that this would pre-date by more than a thousand years the first described epidemic of this disease; but on no other occasion may the factors necessary for such a record have con-joined—the outbreak severe enough to constitute a "pestilence," the eye to see it, the hand to note it down, and the survival of the writer's manuscript through the centuries. The initial febrile phase would hardly have attracted notice in those old days, but no one blessed with eyesight could fail to observe the trail of crippled vic-tims it left behind.
>
> From a window in the college of Bangor where the old scholars wrote their chronicle, they may have seen survivors of the malady limping by, perhaps some of their own monastic brethren among them, and the sad spectacle might suffice, I suggest, to explain this faint and far-away memory of the Pestilence that is called Lame-ness.[4]

At the age of eighteen months Walter Scott (1771–1832), the Scottish poet and novelist in embryo, "was discovered to be af-fected with the fever which often accompanies the cutting of large teeth. . . . On the fourth [day] . . . I had lost the power of my right leg. . . . The impatience of a child soon inclined me to struggle with my infirmity, and I began by degrees to stand, to walk, and to run. Although the limb affected was much shrunk and contracted, my general health, which was of more importance, was much strengthened by being frequently in the open air, and, in a word, I, who in a city had probably been condemned to hopeless and helpless decrepitude, was now a healthy, high-spirited, and, my lameness apart, a sturdy child—*non sine diis animosus infans.*" [5] Scott remained permanently lame, however.

That sporadic cases of poliomyelitis were occurring seems un-questionable, but during the seventeenth and most of the eight-eenth century, physicians (with such rare exceptions as Sydenham who was in advance of his time) did not attach importance to exact diagnosis unless there was an epidemic potential—smallpox, yellow fever, plague—and poliomyelitis did not become epidemic until the nineteenth century. The doctor's concentration on treatment rather than identification and anticipation was abetted in poliomyelitis cases by parents who disregarded the acute forewarning fever of short duration and only called for professional help when lameness was noted days or weeks later.

Attention was first drawn to the relationship between the fever and the onset of lameness by a London obstetrician and pediatrician, Michael Underwood (1737–1820). In 1784 he published *A Treatise on Diseases of Children* but included no reference to anything resembling poliomyelitis. However, in the second edition (1789), under the title of *Debility of the Lower Extremities*, he wrote of a disorder

> not noticed by any medical writer within the compass of my reading, or . . . so described as to ascertain the disease. It is not a common disorder, I believe, and seems to occur seldomer in *London* than in some parts. Nor am I enough acquainted with it to be fully satisfied, either, in regard to the true cause or seat of the disease, either from my own observation, or that of others; and I have myself never had opportunity of examining the body of any child who has died of this complaint. I shall, therefore, only describe its symptoms, and mention the several means attempted for its cure, in order to induce other practitioners to pay attention to it.
>
> It seems to arise from debility, and usually attacks children previously reduced by fever; seldom those under one, or more than four or five years old.[6]

When was poliomyelitis first viewed as a contagious disease, potentially an epidemic disease? Almost certainly not prior to the nineteenth century, although Christopher Carlander (1759–1848), officer of health at Göteborg, Sweden, seemed to have an inkling when he wrote on September 22, 1808, to Professor Pehr Afzelius of Uppsala:

> Now that I am writing so unrestrainedly, I must mention a curious disease: two children attended by me, one attended by Dr. Dubb and one by Regimental Barber-Surgeon Evert, all less than

three years old, fell ill in the beginning of August with symptoms of
mild fever, which disappeared within eight days; but, lo and behold!
the children could then no longer walk but had flaccid paralysis of
their trestle [hips and lower limbs], which they still have. The better
of the two I am now attending is now again able to stand and walk
for a little while—though with the knees pressed strongly back-
wards—but he tires rapidly; the other one can now sit up (which
neither could do in the beginning) and then his toes point straight
inwards. Otherwise the children feel well and are lively and eat and
sleep as usual. What do you think about such a disease? As far as I
can see, the strangest thing is that the disease began at the same time
in several children—at least in the four we know—living in different
houses and belonging to different social classes.[7]

But on the whole half a dozen cases of paralysis in infants, related
in time and place, was not viewed by the rank-and-file physician as
an ominous occurrence, certainly not as an epidemic.

In 1835 John Badham (1807–1840) of Worksop, Nottinghamshire
(near Sheffield), published in the November 14 issue of the *London
Medical Gazette* a paper entitled "Paralysis in Childhood: Four Remarkable Cases of Suddenly Induced Paralysis in the Extremities,
occuring in Children without any apparent Cerebral or Cerebrospinal Lesion." While a small epidemic was evidently involved,
Badham did not suggest contagion or any relation between the
cases, but MacNalty has pointed out, "Badham for the first time
draws attention to the cerebral symptoms presented by the cases.
In two the onset of the disease was preceded or ushered in by
drowsiness, and in the other two by an abnormal state of the
pupil."[8]

The first authoritative study of poliomyelitis was a monograph
by the German orthopedist and exponent of physical medicine
Jacob von Heine (1800–1879), published in Stuttgart in 1840, the
year Badham died. Heine was inspired to relate his own experiences by reading Badham's 1835 account. Of Badham, Yale University investigator and historian of poliomyelitis John R. Paul had
written: "One cannot help feeling a twinge of sadness over the
premature demise of this capable and conscientious young physician. It was a pity that he did not live to see Heine's significant

work on the subject of poliomyelitis, prompted by his own report." [9] Heine was the first to regard acute poliomyelitis as "an affection of the central nervous system, specifically the spinal cord." [10]

An outbreak in St. Helena in the early thirties, reported by the distinguished British neurologist Charles Bell (1774–1842), pointed to the fact that the infection could appear in a remote, isolated island. The first account of poliomyelitis in the United States came in 1843 from London-born George Colmer who had settled in Springfield, Louisiana.

Whether or not the Carlander cases of 1808 represented an epidemic, it is evident that the dishonor of being the cradle of epidemic poliomyelitis must be awarded to Scandinavia. Even so, what was to be considered the first authentic epidemic remained open to question. Was it the fourteen cases which A. C. Bull treated (under the misapprehension that he was dealing with spinal meningitis) near Oslo, Norway, in 1868? Or was it the thirteen cases that were observed by Bergenholtz in Umeå in northern Sweden in 1881, favored by the pioneer Swedish pediatrician Karl Oscar Medin (1847–1927)? In 1886 there were nine cases in and about Mandel, Norway, and the following year Medin investigated an epidemic in Stockholm involving forty-four cases. "The opportunity of dealing with so many acutely ill or even mildly ill school-age children, gave Medin a decided advantage. He brought to it all the talents of a keenly perceptive clinician." [11]

Outside of Scandinavia epidemic poliomyelitis was now becoming more widespread with cases in Italy (1883), France (1885), and Germany (1886). In 1893 twenty-six cases in the environs of Boston led two local pediatricians, James Jackson Putnam (1846–1918) and Edward Wyllys Taylor (1866–1932), to ask "Is Acute Poliomyelitis Unusually Prevalent this Season?" [12] Their paper was remarkable for their conclusion that city dwellers might be more *immune* than their suburban neighbors. This has prompted Paul to observe, "This bit of intuition, to say the least, was far in advance of the times." [13]

The following year the world's first sizable (reported) epidemic occurred in Rutland County, Vermont. There were 132 cases

which were diligently investigated by Charles C. Caverly
(1856–1918), president of the Vermont State Board of Health and
an ardent advocate of public health.

> In retrospect, it seems likely that the Vermont epidemic could
> have been anticipated by the increase in cases in the Boston area the
> previous summer, for Rutland . . . is only 125 miles from Boston.
> This interrupted progression of an epidemic is by no means rare.
> Certainly it had been a common experience for an epidemic to termi-
> nate in a given area with the coming of cold winter and then start up
> again the following spring or summer in an adjacent city, county, or
> rural district. The appearance and character of *epidemic* poliomyelitis
> in the northern lands of Scandinavia and in the sparsely settled parts
> of America's New England were part of the same general epidemio-
> logical phenomenon. This was to become manifest by the shift in
> age incidence which occurred in the two areas. Between 1890 and
> 1905, increasingly older children were attacked during epidemics, in
> contrast to the situation in other middle European countries and in
> most of the United States, where the disease retained its endemic
> character and sporadic cases were still confined to infants and very
> young children.[14]

Ivar Wickman (1872–1914), Medin's pupil, published mono-
graphs on poliomyelitis (Heine-Medin disease as he preferred to
call it) in 1905 and 1907. He had not only witnessed epidemics in
Stockholm in 1899 and Göteborg in 1903, but described the Scandinavian epidemic of 1905 involving (a then staggering) 1031 cases.
Wickman was the first to recognize and describe "the so-called
abortive or non-paralytic cases. These cases are of great epidemiological importance and when they are not reported and isolated are
mainly responsible for the spread of the disease; they are seemingly
as capable of diffusing the infection as the well-marked cases which
develop paralysis. Though having the initial symptoms of poliomyelitis the abortive cases stop short of the paralysis and seem to
recover quickly. In some cases, however, paralytic signs appear
subsequently."[15]

> Within a year after the appearance of Wickman's second monograph,
> came a discovery which was to change the direction of poliomyelitis

research for all time—the discovery of the virus of poliomyelitis. For nearly a generation a fruitless search had been going on to find such a microbial agent. Numerous false hopes had been raised by claimants who championed this or that particular species of bacteria. A search for so-called filterable viruses probably had been made less often, for this presented many more difficulties than did tests for bacteria. . . .

By 1908 only a few filterable viruses as agents of human and animal diseases had been detected. These included the viruses of smallpox and vaccinia, rabies, and foot-and-mouth disease. . . .

Nevertheless, at a medical meeting in Vienna on December 18, 1908, the immunologist [Karl] Landsteiner [1868–1943] and his assistant Popper were able to demonstrate microscopic slides of one human and two monkey spinal cords, all showing the familiar histological picture of acute poliomyelitis.[16]

There are three types of polio viruses, "originally known as Brunhilde, Lansing and Leon, but now more prosaically called types I, II and III."[17] Type I is the strain usually found in paralytic illness, while the appearance of Type III is less frequent and of Type II quite uncommon. Infection is spread by direct contact, the virus probably entering the body via the mouth. While the disease has been endemic throughout the world, epidemics have largely been limited to certain countries, most notably Sweden, Norway, Denmark, the United States, Canada, Switzerland, England and Wales, and Australasia.

An epidemic in New York City in 1907 produced 750 cases (1200 according to one report) and the city faced another large epidemic in 1911. There were epidemics in Mason City, Iowa, in 1910, Cincinnati, Ohio, in 1911, Buffalo and Batavia, New York, in 1912. In 1911 Sweden suffered the largest epidemic of poliomyelitis that that small country, in fact the world, had ever seen—3840 cases by official count as reported by Wernstedt who, according to Paul, "was among the first, if not *the* first, to expound the theory that immunity acquired from inapparent infection during epidemic times was the basis of the age incidence of poliomyelitis. He certainly was the first to be able to back up his argument with proof."[18]

The year 1916 was a big one for poliomyelitis. The entire northeastern United States was involved, and there were 9000 cases in
New York City alone, an incidence rate of 185.2 per 100,000 population. For the years 1909 through 1915 the incidence rate for the
entire country had never exceeded 7.9 per 100,000; now, in the infected area, it jumped to 18.5. The same year there were 1018
cases in New Zealand; a further visitation in 1924–25 produced
1257 cases. A 1931 epidemic in the northeast United States, almost
but not quite as severe as the one in 1916, led to the formation of
the Yale Poliomyelitis Commission (later the Yale Poliomyelitis
Study Unit) under the directorship of James Dowling Trask
(1890–1942). Research and investigation had been continuing since
Landsteiner's 1908 discovery led by such able men, working alone
or in tandem, as the pathologist and bacteriologist Simon Flexner
(1863–1946) of the Rockefeller Institute; Wade Hampton Frost
(1880–1938), the promoter of statistical epidemiology; George
Draper (1880–1959), author of *Acute Poliomyelitis* (Philadelphia,
1917) and *Infantile Paralysis* (New York, 1935); and William Lloyd
Aycock (1889–1951), who developed the theory that the child subject to paralysis was one living in hygienic surroundings who had
not become immune through exposure to the multiple infections to
which the child in dirty surroundings was continuously subjected.
But the Yale unit served an additional purpose by answering calls
for assistance. "The experience of the Yale Poliomyelitis Study
Unit was an example of the frequency of calls for assistance [to university and U.S. Public Health Service research teams] from health
officers between 1932 and 1941. The unit was invited, often urged,
to visit, study, and advise at epidemics in Philadelphia, Pennsylvania, 1932; Los Angeles, California, 1934; Toronto, Canada, 1937;
Charleston, South Carolina, 1939; Buffalo, New York, 1939; Detroit, Michigan, 1940; Miami, Florida, 1941; Cordova, Alabama,
1941; Winnipeg, Manitoba, Canada, 1941; and Huntington, West
Virginia, 1941. All of these were large outbreaks which required
from a fortnight to several months of work on the part of different
members of the unit." [19]

The Los Angeles outbreak in 1934 did not represent the first
visit of the disease to California. There had been epidemics in 1925

(821 cases), 1927 (1298 cases), and 1930 (1903 cases). But there were several interesting facets to the 1934 Los Angeles experience. There have been suggestions that this outbreak did not involve poliomyelitis, and it is possible that a second disease was involved, but of 2499 cases suspected of being poliomyelitis treated in the Los Angeles County General Hospital, 1301 were actually diagnosed as poliomyelitis. (Through July, 2266 cases of poliomyelitis had been reported to the California State Department of Health of which 1564 had occurred in the Los Angeles area.) Secondly, poliomyelitis had long been regarded as a disease of infants and young children—hence the misnomer *infantile paralysis*—but in Los Angeles infection spread to the hospital staff, producing an attack rate of 4.4 percent among hospital employees as a whole, 5.4 percent among physicians, and 10.7 percent among nurses. One of the victims, Dr. Mary Florence Bigler, subsequently published an article in which she stated that the epidemic *was* poliomyelitis "affecting children but also adults of nearly all ages." [20] Thirdly, while most of the cases were relatively mild, there was an excessive display of hysteria, particularly on the part of hospital personnel. This can only be attributed to public and professional ignorance of the fact that the disease is spread more frequently by inapparent infections than by frank cases.

On the question of the "shift" of poliomyelitis from young children to adults, on July 27, 1949, the *New York Herald Tribune* published data supplied by the New York City Department of Health showing changes in age incidence between the epidemic year 1916 and the epidemic year 1947. In 1916, 95 percent of total cases was in the nine-and-under age group; from then, there was a steady decline to 52 percent in 1947. Conversely, the ten-through-nineteen age group accounted for only 3 percent in 1916, rising steadily to 38 percent in 1947. (Percentages in the twenty-and-over group were erratic with only 2 percent in 1916 and 3 percent in 1931—another epidemic year—and a high of 12 percent in 1938.)

Almost from the time that acute poliomyelitis was recognized as a distinct disease, it became clear that an attack almost invariably produced immunity. By 1910 Simon Flexner and others were in pursuit of a method of artificial immunization, but it was not until more than forty years later that an acceptable vaccine was developed.[21]

The Salk vaccine became available for general use in 1955; the Sabin vaccine was licensed by the U.S. Public Health Service in 1961. It is therefore of value to contrast the average annual number of cases in selected countries in 1951–55 and 1961–65. (It should be borne in mind that we are dealing with number of cases without reference to the significantly different populations of the countries involved.)

Country	1951–55	1961–65
United States	37,864	570
United Kingdom	4,381	322
Australia	2,187	154
Denmark	1,614	77
Sweden	1,526	28
Czechoslovakia	1,081	0
Austria	607	70
Belgium	475	79
New Zealand	405	44

The story of poliomyelitis is not yet over but the end of the road may be in sight.

CEREBRAL MENINGITIS

The first known outbreak of this "form of epidemic disease which the medical practitioners . . . failed to recognize" [22] occurred in Geneva, Switzerland, in the early months of 1805. "Its phenomena were of the type of an inflammation of the cerebral and spinal membranes, but it had at the same time the character of a constitutional malady, and it was spoken of, according to the view taken by those who observed it, either as 'meningitis cerebro-spinalis epidemica,' or as 'typhus cerebralis.' " [23] There were thirty-three deaths but, as MacNalty has noted, "Curiously enough, the Commission appointed by the Swiss Government was of the opinion that there had not been enough cases to merit the name of epidemic; they

noted that there had not been a single instance of contagion in the
hospital in which the cases were treated." [24] Geneva doctors were
understandably puzzled by this new disease but the best known
among them, Gaspard Vieusseux (1746–1814), promptly published
a clear account of the symptomatology of epidemic meningitis.
(The meningococcus—*Neisseria meningitidis*—was discovered by
Anton Weichselbaum [1845–1920] in 1887.) A year after the Geneva outbreak "malignant spotted fever" appeared in Medfield, Massachusetts, where, between March 8 and 31, there were nine cases
all leading to death. In the *Medical and Agricultural Register* of 1806,
Drs. L. Danielson and E. Mann described these symptoms and
findings, ". . . the patient is suddenly taken with violent pain in
the head and stomach, succeeded by cold chills, and followed by
nausea and puking; . . . tongue a little white toward the root, and
moist; . . . and in a child of 15 months old, a very violent pulsa-
tion was discovered, at the fontanel . . . the eyes have a wild
vacant stare, . . . the heat of the skin soon becomes much increased, . . ." Postmortems revealed that "The dura and pia mater
in several places adhered together, and both to the substance of the
brain. . . . Between the dura and pia mater was effused a fluid
resembling pus, . . . the veins of the brain turgid with
blood, . . ." [25]

A year later there were cases in Hartford and Windsor, Connecticut, and before 1810 minor epidemics had been reported in other
communities. This prompted a dozen or so physicians to meet in
Farmington in February 1809 to pool their knowledge of this new
disease. They decided to prepare a treatise for public release but
the work was never done because, according to Nathan Strong, Jr.
(1781–1837), they were "prevented by their professional avoca-
tions." [26] Public displeasure at their failure prompted the Hartford
American Mercury to ask editorially, "How is it possible that the
physicians of this state have so long been silent on a subject so
deeply interesting to the community?" [27]

Strong, while generally agreeing with the description offered by
Danielson and Mann, noted certain differences. "Despite the observed differences," Frank J. Grady of the Yale University School
of Medicine has said, "the disease in 1808–1809 was as devastating

to the people of Hartford as it had been to the people of Medfield two years earlier. There were 20 deaths in February and March of 1809, 15 of which occurred within three days of the onset of symptoms. Strong astutely observed the role of vomiting and dehydration, stating that life often depended on their being controlled, and noting that urine volume was often diminished. He realized (as had Danielson and Mann) that the disease was contagious, and noted its seasonal incidence. Fatigue, cold, fear, immoderate stimulation, and general debility were, Strong believed, predisposing factors, but he acknowledged himself to be 'profoundly ignorant of its proximate cause.' " [28] More complete, however, than Strong's dissertation was *A Treatise on a Malignant Epidemic commonly called Spotted Fever* by Elisha North (1771–1843) of Goshen, Connecticut, published in 1811. North, who, incidentally, was without an M.D. degree until one was conferred on him *honoris causa* by the Connecticut State Medical Society in 1813, would establish the first eye infirmary in the United States in 1817. In his treatise he recommended the use of the clinical thermometer in spotted fever cases because he had observed that neither increased temperature nor increased pulse was ordinarily involved. In light of modern knowledge that entry of the meningococcus is usually nasopharyngeal, North showed extraordinary foresight in observing, "If there is any one symptom which may be regarded as a premonitory symptom of this disease . . . it is a sore throat . . . and yet this affection is so slight that few patients mention it unless they are questioned respecting it." [29]

While epidemic meningitis was not exclusively American between 1854 and 1875, the United States was again the chief seat of the disease. The first epidemics (both in 1856–57) occurred in Salisbury (north of Charlotte), North Carolina, and in western and central New York State. During the Civil War the disease was widely spread.

In the winter of 1861–62 it appeared in the army of the Potomac encamped near Washington; at the same time in Livingston county, Mo., both among soldiers and civilians; in that and the following winter among negroes sent by the Confederates to Memphis; and in the winter of 1862–63 among the troops encamped in and around Newbern, Craven county, N. Carolina. In the winter of 1863 a severe epidemic arose at Philadelphia and other places in Pennsylvania; in that and the following year it spread over a large part of the State, and was still going on in Philadelphia as late as the winter of 1865–66. In the winter of 1862–63, simultaneously with the outbreak in Pennsylvania, it appeared in La Grange county and other places in the north and south of Indiana, in Norfolk, Va., among the Confederate troops, in Iowa, at Newport, Rh. I. in the military school, making its first visit, and at Mobile. In the winter of 1863–64 it was epidemic in the southern and central parts of Illinois, in a few localities of New Jersey, in Vermont along the Connecticut river, in Springfield county and some parishes of Licking county, Ohio, at Washington in the two hospitals and an orphanage (having been imported, it was said, from the seat of war) at Mobile and in Green county Alabama, and in the spring of 1864 in Frederick county, Maryland.[30]

Hirsch died in 1892, but it is worth noting what he considered the four peculiarities of meningitis as an epidemic. First, in many instances, "the outbreak of the disease was a perfectly isolated incident in a locality that had been altogether free from it before; it has appeared at one or more places, not unfrequently far apart, while the country around the affected villages or towns, as well as the whole territory lying between them, has remained quite untouched not merely while the sickness lasted, but in many cases often after it had died out in its original seats." Secondly, even when an epidemic "overran considerable tracts of country," it usually progressed "quite irregularly, neither following the highways of traffic nor revealing any other obvious predilection. . . . Thirdly, the comportment of the epidemic in many cases was not less remarkable by reason of the differences it exhibited at the various places affected, and in its several seasons. Often it broke out, over a larger or smaller area, at many points and without concentration at any, the cases being numerous or few at each, or merely sporadic. In other instances, again, it would confine itself almost entirely, or even absolutely, to a particular locality or to one group of the inhabitants; the classical examples of that kind of incidence being the military epidemics, . . . and the outbreaks in workhouses, orphanages and other self-contained institutions. Fourthly, it is very remarkable how different the various epidemics of meningitis have been in their duration and in the number of persons attacked." [31]

While there were outbreaks in the British Isles from time to time the incidence of epidemic meningitis was relatively light until World War I when 6450 cases were reported in England. Military cases numbered 4236 with a death rate of 45.5 percent. (The civilian death rate ran above 65 percent.) "Within a few months after mobilization of US forces, the disease appeared in epidemic proportions. During the first world war, 2,466 military personnel were admitted to hospitals in the United States with this illness, with a fatality rate of 33 per cent. The lower mortality rate compared with previous statistics largely resulted from the use of serum therapy, introduced more than a decade before." [32]

Between 1919 and 1927 meningitis in the United States was relatively rare but in "1928 and 1929, massive civilian epidemics in Detroit and Indianapolis altered the stable trend and instilled lasting dread among the lay population, regarding the contagiousness and seriousness of so-called 'spinal' meningitis. The widely-held misconception of the degree of contagion became evident from the Detroit epidemic. Direct contacts with afflicted patients infrequently became ill and usually only one member in a family was involved. More than one case occurred in 23 out of 692 houses containing an ill patient, only 3.3 per cent. The conclusion therefrom was that most persons acquiring meningococcal disease did so from an asymptomatic carrier, rather than from exposure to an ill patient." Detroit suffered a mortality rate of over 80 percent in the infant age group; in Indianapolis the general mortality rate was over 70 percent. This put in question the previously supposed efficacy of serum therapy in epidemic situations, but

World War II marked a milestone of progress in meningococcal disease, as it was now the age of sulfonamide therapy and prophylaxis. . . . During the five year period from 1940 to 1945, 14,504 hospital admissions of military personnel were due to this disease with a fatality rate of only 3.8 per cent. The remarkable reduction in mortality from 33 per cent to 3.8 per cent in the two World Wars largely reflected the effectiveness of sulfonamide therapy, plus more prompt diagnostic and therapeutic measures generally. During the war years from 1939 through 1945, meningococcal disease caused profound civilian public health problems, in addition to its effects on military forces. From June 1939 to June 1941, [for] 3,575 reports of meningococcal meningitis from England and Wales [involving] 45.5 per cent . . . under 15 years of age, . . . the overall mortality rate was 15.9 per cent. One of the most remarkable meningococcal epidemics occurred in Santiago, Chile, between 1941 and 1943, in which 4,464 meningitis cases were recorded . . . one case per 300 inhabitants, perhaps the highest incidence rate recorded in a large population group. The fatality rate during this epidemic was 16.5 per cent overall and 38 per cent among affected children under four years of age.[33]

The meningococci have been classified into four groups, A, B, C, and D, of which group A has caused the major epidemics, with groups B and C producing sporadic cases and small outbreaks in interepidemic periods. In 1968 Emil C. Gotschlich and his co-workers in the department of bacteriology of the Walter Reed Army Institute of Research developed a polysaccharide vaccine that proved effective against *N. meningitidis* group C. In 1971–72 a group A vaccine was proved effective in a field trial in Egypt sponsored by the World Health Organization, a conclusion that was confirmed in the Sudan in 1973 (as well as in studies in Finland and South Africa). But, in the 1971 words of William E. Bell and David L. Sibler of the University of Iowa College of Medicine,

> The available data indicate that the meningococcal polysaccharide vaccine is safe, is highly immunogenic, and will decrease the carrier state in a given population, but is group specific. Because of the group specific qualities of this material, a trivalent vaccine providing protection against A, B and C meningococci will be desired. The eventual development and utilization of such an immunizing agent should further alter the epidemiology of this illness.[34]

The issue of *Morbidity and Mortality Weekly Report* (published by the Public Health Service–U.S. Department of Health, Education and Welfare) for the week ending October 12, 1974, showed 1051 meningococcal infections in the United States for the first forty-one weeks of 1974 in contrast with 1117 for the same period of 1973, and a median of 1860 for 1969–73. The same issue, however, reported on an epidemic in progress in Brazil.

> The predominantly serogroup A epidemic has not decreased significantly since it began to increase in June 1974. A total of 13,141 suspected cases were admitted to Sao Paulo hospitals in July and August; 40–50% of these have laboratory confirmation as meningococcal disease. Based on these numbers, the overall attack rate is approximately 65 suspected cases/100,000 population/month, with 30–35 laboratory confirmed cases/100,000 population/month in the city. . . .
>
> The epidemic has spread to other Brazilian cities with increased rates of disease reported in Brasilia, Rio de Janeiro, the state of Minas Gerais, and Rio Grande do Sul.
>
> Serogroup A *Neisseria meningitidis* still accounts for 80–85% of cases in Sao Paulo with serogroup C responsible for the balance.
>
> A large-scale immunization campaign of school-age children was begun in mid-August, and approximately 700,000 doses of group A vaccine had been administered by late September. Immunization with group C vaccine began in early September. The ultimate goal is to vaccinate all school-age children with both types. The campaign was begun in sanitary districts with the highest incidence of the disease.[35]

ENCEPHALITIS

Encephalitis is *any* inflammation of the brain. Consequently there is a variety of encephalitides of which the earliest was encephalitis lethargica (Von Economo's disease) which raged in Europe and North America between 1916 and 1926 and has rarely been reported since. "This is a disease of which the name is unsatisfactory, the epidemiology little understood and the aetiology completely unknown." [36] *Lethargica* does not give a completely accurate picture of the symptoms. Since different forms of encephalitis have now generally taken the place of this disease, even the designation "epidemic" no longer really applies. There has been no proof that a virus is the cause, although the implication is strong because of the manner in which the disease was spread. Epidemiological historians, such as England's Francis Graham Crookshank,[37] have attempted to establish for epidemic encephalitis a history even dating back to Hippocrates, but MacNalty was somewhat skeptical. "It is indisputable, however, that the authentic study of the malady began in the winter of 1916–17, when [Rumanian-born Constantin] von Economo [1876–1931] and Von Wiesner in Vienna described the clinical and pathological features of 13 cases presenting the cardinal phenomena of stupor accompanied by disturbances of the ocular muscles."[38] Von Economo's observation of the thirteen cases led him to the conclusion that he was dealing with an epidemic viral disease in which *"the severity of the cerebral symptoms indicate a specific affinity for the central nervous tissue, similar but not identical to the virus of poliomyelitis (Heine-Medin)* [italics in original]."[39] When he published his findings in 1917 he believed himself to be the discoverer of the disease. "But the first cases of encephalitis, as was afterwards historically ascertained, had already appeared in some European countries a year before I recognized this disease as a new entity. Cruchet claimed to have observed several cases in the winter of 1915–16 amongst the French soldiers in Verdun, while a few cases are said to have been seen in Rumania by Urechia as early as the spring of 1915, and even though the observers failed to recognize the appearance of a hitherto unknown disease their descriptions were sufficiently accurate to identify their cases a few years later as encephalitis."[40]

Encephalitis lethargica appeared in England in February 1918 and within four months 230 cases had been reported in London and the provinces. Thereafter, England and Wales had 541 cases with 294 deaths in 1919, 890 (480) in 1920, 1470 (729) in 1921, 454 (339) in 1922, 1025 (531) in 1923, 5038 (1407) in 1924, and 2635 (1372) in 1925. The disease was not epidemic in Scotland until 1923 and does not seem to have been more than sporadic in Ireland.

"In 1924 a severe outbreak of an epidemic cerebral disease apparently resembling epidemic encephalitis was reported from Japan; the disease was widespread and virulent, the case-mortality

ranging from 50 to 60 per cent." [41] Whether MacNalty was referring to Japanese B encephalitis, one of the types that is currently
active, is hard to say. The modern types differ from lethargica and
do not seem generally to have become active until the thirties. The
basic difference was noted by Robert H. Wilkins and Irwin A.
Brody of the divisions of neurology and neurosurgery, Duke University Medical Center, when they wrote in 1968: "A large number
of individuals who contracted encephalitis lethargica subsequently
developed parkinsonism, though there was often a latent period of
many years. More recent epidemics of encephalitis have occurred,
but they probably differ from von Economo's disease since they
have not had this sequela." [42]

"The term 'arthropod-borne' was first cut to 'arborvirus,' a pleas-
ant word but tending to suggest some association with trees. The
offending letter was therefore removed to give 'arbovirus.' " [43] Almost two hundred arboviruses are known, and about eighty of
these cause disease in man. Most of these are transmitted either by
a tick or a mosquito; the diseases do not pass from man to man. As
with polio a high proportion of individuals infected by arboviruses
give no outward indication of the disease.

In the following review of the more important viruses causing
encephalitis in man, the vector is a mosquito of one type or another
unless otherwise indicated.

Western equine encephalitis (WEE), known primarily as a dis-
ease of horses, is occasionally transmitted to man (both adults and
children). Infection in man ranges from subclinical to rapidly fatal.
The virus is sustained in nature by wild birds and their arthropod
parasites. Related to WEE is the California group of viruses—
California and LaCrosse. WEE is epidemic in the western United
States and Canada, but also makes scattered appearances from
Connecticut to Florida and in South America.

Eastern equine encephalitis (EEE), like the Western variety, is
transmitted from wild birds to horses, and to man, but only when
there is a high incidence of infection among birds in the area. It
was first recognized in New Jersey where there were equine outbreaks as early as 1905, although it was not identified as EEE until

1933. This virus attacks children more often than the Western type and mortality and severe damage to the nervous system are greater. The first human cases in New Jersey were found in 1959. They were thirty-two in number and eleven of them were in the zero-to-age-four group and another eleven between five and fourteen. Mortality ran 55 percent in the first of these groups, 73 percent in the second, and 69 percent for all ages. EEE occurs in Eastern and North Central American states and adjacent parts of Canada, in some countries of Central and South America, and in the Caribbean.

St. Louis encephalitis (SLE), so named because it was first recognized as a clinical entity in St. Louis in 1933, while distinct from the Western and Eastern varieties, is found in most parts of the United States, in the Caribbean, and Central and South America. It is transmitted from birds to man. The sixties revealed two distinct forms of SLE—rural and urban. The former "is endemic to western United States, particularly to the Yakima Valley in Washington and to the central valley in California. The disease is more common in males than in females, perhaps because of occupational exposure, and shows a fairly even age distribution. In distinction to western equine encephalitis, however, infants under one year of age are spared." [44] In 1964 Houston, Texas, with a population of around one and a quarter million, experienced one of the largest epidemics of urban SLE on record. In the course of the epidemic, 712 cases of acute febrile central nervous system disease were reported of which 243 were laboratory confirmed (or presumptive) SLE, involving twenty-seven deaths. Incidence was highest in the seventy-and-over age group (108.8 per 100,000) and lowest in the zero-to-nine group (8.2 per 100,000). There were no fatalities between age zero and twenty-nine (and between forty and forty-nine), but mortality ran 27 percent in the sixty-to-sixty-nine group and 27.9 percent for seventy and over. Two years later there were epidemics in Dallas and Corpus Christi. In the summer of 1975 SLE hit many of the southern and midwestern states, with over two hundred cases in Chicago, which normally sees only one or two cases annually.

Venezuela equine encephalitis (VEE) is found in more or less contiguous areas of South and Central America and the southern United States, and in Trinidad. Prior to 1943 VEE had been detected only in horses, but the year two human fatalities occurred in Trinidad. Subsequently doubt was thrown on this diagnosis of VEE, but by the 1950s the activity of VEE in humans in the areas mentioned had been positively confirmed. "All clinical information about VEE infection in man prior to 1952 derived from accidental infections with epizootic subtypes. . . . Fully documented natural epidemic infection in man was first described in 1952 in Colombia." In 1964, by the time a Zulia, Venezuela, epidemic of 1962 had run its course, an estimated 32,000 cases had produced 190 deaths (mostly of children). In Mexico in 1971 an epidemic of 16,900 cases severely affected children. There were 42 fatal cases of which 75 percent were children under five and another 20 percent aged five to fourteen. The first United States epidemic occurred in Texas, also in 1971.[45]

The only tick-borne encephalitis present in the United States (and Canada) is Powassan. Its highest incidence occurs where man has intimate association with large numbers of infected ticks—generally in rural and forest areas but not unknown in urban areas.

Japanese B has received considerable attention because of epidemics involving American forces (and civilian populations) in Okinawa and South Korea since World War II. It has attacked western Pacific islands from Japan to the Philippines, eastern Asia from Korea to Singapore, and India. Mouse brain inactivated vaccine has been used on Japanese children and experimentally in a few other countries.

Murray Valley encephalitis is epidemic in parts of Australia and in New Guinea, tick-borne Langat in Malaysia, and relatively mild louping ill (an infection of sheep, also tick-borne) in Great Britain. Tick-borne Russian spring-summer encephalitis appears in Europe and Asia, attacking mostly persons who work in woodlands.

Vaccines have been used on a large scale to protect horses but, apart from the Japanese effort, little progress has been made against encephalitides in man. Tissue culture vaccines are under development but have not yet been licensed. Elimination of vectors is currently the best means of protecting the human population, but this is a mammoth undertaking.

No *specific* treatment for the encephalitides is available.

Bubonic Plague — from London to San Francisco

THE Great Plague of London was the last epidemic of the bubonic pestilence in the British Isles, and during the second half of the seventeenth century, Europe, with the exception of Russia and the Balkan peninsula (which bordered on the current focal points— Turkey and Syria), was essentially plague-free. "Only twice afterwards did the pestilence become at all widely diffused in the western and central regions of the Continent. . . . The first occasion was from 1707 to 1714, when it issued on the one hand from Russia to overrun Silesia, Prussia, and Pomerania, spreading thence to Holstein and Brunswick and severely attacking several places in Denmark (Elsinore and Copenhagen) and in Sweden (Karlskrona, Upsala, and Stockholm), and, on the other, from Prague in 1713, visiting Austria, Styria, and the south-east of Bavaria. The second of the two was introduced into Marseilles in 1720 by a vessel from Syria; it spread over a great part of Provence, and did not die out until 1722." [1]

As would occur in San Francisco almost two hundred years later, the authorities were loath to admit that the malignant disease had entered Marseilles, notwithstanding the fact that the local physicians who had attended the first victims were satisfied that they were dealing with bubonic plague and that it was contagious. No confidence being placed in their reports, experts were called in from Montpellier, the famous seat of medical learning located relatively nearby. "Messrs. Chycoineau and Verny, physicians of Montpellier, . . . arrived, accordingly, on the 12th of August, with Mons. Soulliers, one of the principal surgeons of the same university, . . . and every one hoped from them such a decision as should favour their own incredulity." They consulted with the local physicians, visited the sick, witnessed three postmortem examinations, and reported to the Marseilles *échevins* (aldermen)—in private.

'On the report made to the governor and échevins of the city by the physicians from Montpellier, they have thought it their duty to advertise the public, that the malady which now reigns here is not pestilential, but only a common malignant fever, the progress of which, it is hoped, will speedily be stopped, by separating those who are suspected of being diseased from those in perfect health, and by certain other regulations which will immediately be established.' [2]

Their reassuring report notwithstanding, before returning to the university the three gentlemen from Montpellier quarantined themselves in a country house near Aix. It turned out to be a useless gesture. Conditions in Marseilles grew so desperate that the king ordered them (along with additional practitioners of medicine) to proceed to Marseilles and *personally* attend the sick.

Struck with the state in which they found them, with the similarity of the disease in all the persons attacked, with its resistance to all their remedies, with the numbers that fell victims to it, with the death of their own servants, and even of some of the surgeons who had accompanied them, they spoke loudly of the contagion, and even showed that they feared it not a little. Not that they can be accused of having been sparing of their persons; on the contrary, it is but justice due to them to own, that they uniformly approached the sick with the utmost firmness, yet it was not without great precautions, and evident apprehension of danger. [But when the epidemic had somewhat abated they] began again to waver in their opinions. Emboldened by the evident diminution of the malady, which became every day more and more palpable, they as loudly denied the contagion as they had before confessed it,—nay, they even in some sort insulted the timidity of those who feared it, forgetting that they themselves had been of that number.[3]

The episode led the Anglo-Indian surgeon Patrick Russell (1727–1805), author of *A Treatise of the Plague* (London, 1791) to comment, "The conduct of several physicians in France in the years 1720 and 1721, affords remarkable instances of the power of prepossession in favour of an hypothesis." [4]

But the action of the Marseilles governor and aldermen was not typical of European reaction. Once the continent had seemingly become plague-free, since most people lived in perpetual fear that the scourge might regain a footing, elaborate quarantine measures were adopted. The extremity to which such measures were sometimes pushed was well illustrated by what happened to the body of the drowned British poet Percy Bysshe Shelley in 1822.

When Shelley's body was washed up on the shore of Tuscany, in case he should have died of plague, the corpse was quickly covered with quicklime. Edward John Trelawney, Lord Byron, and Leigh Hunt sought permission to approach the body and cremate it. This proved no light undertaking. Ultimately the secretary of the British legation and the English consul prevailed upon the governor of the province to issue an order to the officer commanding the lookout tower nearest the point where Shelley had been buried to deliver the body to Trelawney, to be cremated under the supervision of a sanitary officer. "At equal distances along the coast stood high square towers . . . for the double purpose of preventing smuggling and enforcing the quarantine laws, the latter being here severer than in any part of the world. . . . We then with instruments made for the purpose of dragging wrecked seamen out of the sea—for you are on no account allowed to touch a body—we dragged the remains out of the grave. . . . The soldiers who appeared superstitiously fearful had withdrawn themselves as far as possible." [5]

A peculiar form of quarantine grew out of an epidemic of plague in Malta in 1675–76 that took 8732 lives out of an estimated population of 60,000. This quarantine, begun in 1678, involved the disinfection of letters entering or passing through Malta, there being a current belief that the "contagion" of plague could attach itself to paper. The method then employed is unknown, but regulations issued on September 12, 1720, by the Department of Health of the Order of St. John included the following: "Dispatches brought in by ships are not to be received unless they are first perfumed. The packets and letters are to be unpacked, disinfected by a double perfume, and left exposed to the action of the latter for twenty-four hours. It is only after undergoing this process that letters are to be delivered." [6]

These regulations contained no reference to the "slitting" of letters, but this practice had clearly been adopted by 1744 when a copy of a report, now in the Royal Malta Library, was sent to the island from Sicily. The report had been prepared by a plague "expert" from Venice, Dr. Pietro Polacco, who had been called to Messina to conduct a "depuration" when the city was invaded by plague in 1743. Paul Cassar, psychiatric consultant to the Royal University of Malta's department of medicine, writing in 1967, while pointing out that the copy of the report carried no indication of the place of disinfection, added: "We know, however, that there was a direct sea route between Messina and Malta. It is therefore reasonable to suppose that this letter was disinfected at Malta, which was the receiving—and vulnerable—end." The Malta copy "bears unmistakable proof that it was disinfected by slitting and perfuming." By 1749 slitting was official. A quarantine regulation then issued read, "Letters brought by ships with a clean bill of health but hailing from suspected places are to be incised by a scalpel to ascertain that they contain no susceptible goods such as objects of wool, silk, and thread and to ensure that the perfume penetrates inside them. The letters are then to be placed in the perfuming stove." To which Cassar added: "Correspondence conveyed on ships with a foul bill of health, besides being incised, was also immersed in vinegar." [7] It is hard to say when the incising of transient letters was instituted, but there is evidence that a letter passing through Malta in 1809, en route from the Turkish port of Smyrna to Great Britain, was slit.

The belief that paper was a carrier of plague persisted and, when plague was again epidemic in Malta in 1813, the government took stringent steps to restrict its use. "In contrast to paper, wood was regarded as being incapable of conveying the 'contagion' of plague. This explains why in some instances tablets of wood were employed for writing wills, receipts, and other documents. . . . On one of these boards the Rev. Filippo Calleja, of Zebbug village, one of the most severely hit localities, wrote his last will and testament before he died on September 9, 1813. . . . The writing fills both surfaces, but is no longer legible; however, a transcript on paper was made some six months after the testator's death. The original tablet and the transcript are to-day preserved at the Government Notorial Archives at Valetta." [8] About half a dozen such tablets are in existence.

The Napoleonic campaigns in Egypt and Syria (1798–1801) were responsible for two (unrelated) outbreaks of plague in the British navy.

In April 1796 Captain William Sidney Smith (1764–1840) of the Royal Navy was captured during an encounter with the French off Le Havre and was imprisoned in Paris. Two years later, Antoine le Picard de Phélippeaux (d. 1799), an aristocrat and a graduate of the Military School of Paris (where a strong mutual dislike had developed between him and a fellow student named Napoleon Bonaparte), who had remained loyal to the French monarchy, effected Smith's escape.

In November 1798 Smith, with the rank of commodore, was posted to the eastern Mediterranean. His now close friend Phélippeaux accompanied him as a volunteer. On March 3, 1799, Smith took command of the squadron blockading Alexandria. News came the same day that Napoleon had stormed Jaffa. Smith sent Phélippeaux aboard the *Theseus* to organize the defense of the port by the Turks. The siege of Acre followed. The Turkish empire was in the toils of a major epidemic of plague and the land forces of Turkey and France were hard hit by the infection. "On the other hand, officers and men of the British squadron patrolling off the town escaped. Colonel Phélippeaux, however, being the officer mainly responsible for organizing and conducting the defence of Acre, although his living quarters were on the *Theseus* was very much at risk, for most of his time was spent on shore with the Turks. On

May 2 he died of a fever in the captain's cabin, which had been put at his disposal. He was buried at sea, all his clothes and belongings being thrown overboard, and the captain's cabin was fumigated." Subsequently there were some cases of plague on the *Theseus*, contracted from French army stragglers picked up from small boats near Jaffa. The interesting thing about the whole episode is that the fear inspired by the very word "plague" prompted Smith, in his official report, to describe his friend's death in these words: "Colonel Phélippeaux of the Engineers, who projected and superintended the execution, has fallen a sacrifice to his zeal for the service; want of rest and exposure to the sun having given him a fever of which he died this morning; our grief for his loss is excessive on every account." It is unbelievable that he did not know the true cause of his friend's death, especially since plague was rampant on the Syrian coast.[9]

In the spring of 1801 a British force under Sir Ralph Abercromby (1734–1801) landed on the Mediterranean coast and routed the French, who had been occupying Egypt, at the battle of Abukir. On August 30 the French capitulated and a month later peace was signed between Britain and France.

"To the list of the three contending powers in Egypt, France, Britain and Turkey, must be added a fourth, bubonic plague, perhaps the most masterful belligerent of all. The Pest could cripple an army by reducing manpower but the greatest danger was fear. In the healthy terror could produce symptoms simulating acute illness; in an infected person it might so influence the course of the disease that death was the inevitable outcome; in the mass, even among disciplined troops, it could bring about a general and profound demoralisation."[10] Bubonic plague, long endemic in Egypt, had run rampant among the French and Turkish troops, and it was quick to ravish Abercromby's troops who passed through plague-infected villages on their way to Cairo. In the meantime, an advance party of eight thousand European and Indian troops, sent from Bombay to reinforce Abercromby, had landed in Suez. Finding the port abandoned by the French, the troops made their way across the desert to the Nile to join up with the British forces. Subsequently the main body followed suit. What is notable is that

254 *EPIDEMICS*

an official account of the plague "as it prevailed on board H.M. Ship *Leopard* May, 1801" was prepared by Thomas Robertson (1774–1852), surgeon of the *Leopard*. Here are excerpts from his quite lengthy report:

> The squadron of ships of war and transports under the command of Rear-Admiral Blankett arrived at Suez on the 21st April 1801. The French left it eight days before. They had lost several men to plague. The body of one in a putrid state was lying uncovered in the ditch of the town and report said that they had thrown some dead bodies into a well.
>
> On the 22nd a small detachment of troops were landed and Suez taken possession of. In the evening they returned on board. On the 23rd a considerable body of the 86th regiment was landed as a garrison. Finding flour might be procured three bakers and two carpenters were sent from the *Leopard*. . . .
>
> For some time they continued baking bread and supplying the ships [before] a report existed that some of them were ill of the plague. That was not entirely credited. On the 30th two men who had been a short time on shore died on board the *Fox* frigate of a dubious complaint. . . .
>
> The *7th of May*. On a report of Mr. Ballas, Assistant Surgeon 86th, with the party on shore, I was ordered by the Admiral with him to examine and report our opinion of the disease already strongly suspected to be plague. . . .
>
> Proceeding on board [the *Adam Smith*] we found three men with fever, buboes forming in their arm-pits and groins and complaining particularly of a load at chest. Great prostration of strength, the pulse sunk; despondency and tremor with delirium. On shore five or six more were similarly affected, one belonging to the *Leopard*, . . . Three Maltese and five more Europeans with the fever of some days' standing, some with buboes. Several had already died. They generally were delirious. The recovery of any of them seemed very improbable.
>
> Taking all circumstances into consideration, the particular symptoms of the fever, there remained no doubt with respect to its nature.
>
> . . . Before this period free communication had been allowed to take place between sick and well. . . . All of [the sick] were [now] removed to tents pitched without the garrison, those on board the

Adam Smith sent on shore. On the 9th the three Maltese and one of the Europeans died. . . .

On the 10th in the night two of our officers and a marine on board were attacked with fever . . . On the 11th some men had died on shore. . . . At this time the alarm was pretty general. On the 15th all the troops except the surgeon and a subaltern with the sick re-embarked on the smaller vessels and were not allowed to communicate with the rest of the squadron. This prohibition continued until the 29th when all the sick etc., were embarked with a number of articles from the shore on board one particular vessel.

On the 30th May H.M.S. *Babelmandeb* sailed with all of them for Tor but the disease seemed now to have entirely abated—none lately taken ill. The number lost altogether not exceeding 13 or 14 . . .[11]

Thirteen or fourteen deaths may not signify an epidemic, but it must be remembered that, while army surgeons were only too well acquainted with plague, navy surgeons rarely encountered the disease. Or, as Thomas Trotter (1760–1832), an authority on naval medicine and a great admirer of Lind, wrote in 1803: "British ships of war, disciplined as they now are, are capable of preserving themselves free from pestilential contagion on those very shores that are said to give it birth. . . . The perfect health of the fleet on the coast of Egypt is therefore great matter of triumph to the naval interests of the country." [12]

The third great pandemic of bubonic plague had its beginnings in the Yunnan province of China in 1892 but did not attract widespread interest until it reached Canton in the spring of 1894. From there it was a short step to Hong Kong, the largest and most important European possession in the area, eighty miles downstream with steamers and junks plying daily between the two cities. Hong Kong then possessed one of the busiest harbors in the world, its trade connections extending beyond the southern ports of China and islands in the Pacific to India, Australia, Japan, and America. The pandemic reached India in 1896, and its story is told by the deaths from plague that occurred over fifty years (1898–1948)—12,597,789—this despite the fact that the plague bacillus had been discovered in 1894 and vaccine inoculation introduced into India in 1897. (It should be noted that the 1898–1948

deaths were not evenly distributed over the fifty years; rather for
the first decade annual deaths averaged 548,427, for the second decade, 422,153, and by 1939–48 average annual deaths had dropped
to 21,797. For the 1898–1908 period, plague deaths represented
47.88 percent of all deaths in India; for 1939–48, 1.73 percent.)
    Beyond India, the disease was ship-borne.

As early as September, 1896, two cases of plague were discovered at
the London Docks in a vessel that left India before the plague became epidemic in that country. This experience of plague-infected
vessels coming from infected ports has happened to most maritime
countries within the past eight years [i.e., since 1896]. Fortunately,
whether it be from precautions taken at the port, or from conditions
in the port unfavourable to the lodgement of plague, or from the rar-
ity with which ships carry infection on them, or from ships being
generally unfavourable to the propagation of plague, the majority of
the ports subjected to the risk have escaped. But although there has
not been a general infection of the ports, yet the infection has been
carried to many parts of the world. They include ports in Asia,
North and South America, Australia, Africa, and Europe. It is a
distribution, as far as is known, dissimilar to that of any former epidemic of plague, its main feature being that the course followed is a
maritime one, which is most readily explained by the change in
trade routes which has taken place since the former great epidemics
of plague. . . . It is a wide diffusion so far as distance is concerned,
and is wider in this respect than that which characterised previous
pandemics, for it has reached America, Australia, and South Africa,
none of which had been ever known to have had plague imported
into them before. With the exception of Africa, the infection appears
mainly to limit itself to the ports, or to localities near these. It is also
to be noted that, notwithstanding the extensive sowing of the seed or
germ of plague which has taken place, there has hitherto been no
disposition for the disease to become severely epidemic except in
India, China, the Mauritius, and in the year 1900 in Cape Town.
How long this fortunate condition of affairs will continue it is impossible to say. Plague is slow in its progress and development, and
evidently has difficulty in adapting itself to new conditions; it remains not infrequently for years in a more or less quiescent state,
and then bursts out in a destructive and expanding epidemic. While,
therefore, the ports of a country are infected or liable to infection

from communication with infected ports, that country is never free from the danger of suffering from a plague epidemic which may assume large proportions. [13]

SAN FRANCISCO

In May 1897 Victor C. Vaughan (1851–1929), then professor of hygiene at the University of Michigan, posed the question, Are we in danger from the plague? His answer: "Yes, there is danger; but this, being foreseen, may be easily avoided. Thorough inspection of persons and disinfection of things from infected districts will keep the disease out of Europe and America. Only by the most gross carelessness could the plague be permitted to enter either of these continents." Two years later he returned to the question, giving the same answer but adding: "In my opinion, our most vulnerable point is along the Pacific coast. With the plague at Hong Kong, it is possible that it may be transferred to Manila, and the transports bringing soldiers to this country may also bring the infection. However, I think the chances of this happening are small. The length of time required to make the voyage from Manila to San Francisco is so great that, with the infection on board, it would be almost certain to manifest itself before reaching our shores, and, knowing its presence on board a ship reaching San Francisco or any other port on the western coast, thorough inspection and disinfection will keep the disease out of this country." [14]

On March 5, 1900, the body of Wing Chut King was found in the basement of the Globe Hotel. Plague had come to San Francisco.

Chinese who died in San Francisco and who had not been under the care of a white physician were examined by a young assistant city physician, Frank P. Wilson. Alerted by enlarged inguinal lymph nodes, he advised city health officer A. P. O'Brien and city bacteriologist Wilfred H. Kellogg. The latter took smears and discovered organisms with the characteristics of *P. pestis*. He notified Joseph J. Kinyoun (1860–1919), chief quarantine officer of the United States Marine Hospital in San Francisco. (Kinyoun, a noted bacteriologist who had studied under several of the great bacteriologists of his day, had, in 1887, opened what may well have been the first bacteriological laboratory in America, the forerunner of the National Institutes of Health.) Kinyoun inoculated a monkey, a rat, and two guinea pigs with infected lymph tissue to assure himself that he was dealing with plague. He also ordered antipest serum from Washington. On O'Brien's recommendation the Board of Health, headed by Dr. John M. Williamson, cordoned off twelve blocks of Chinatown. Streetcars were fumigated and no longer stopped in the restricted area and a search was instituted for more cases of plague.

What was different about the San Francisco epidemic was that the governor, Henry T. Gage, prompted by big-business interests, flatly denied that plague existed in the area. In response to a demand for information from U.S. Secretary of State John Hay (1838–1905) he stated: "No case in San Francisco or California has been diagnosed as bubonic plague by any attending physician while patient was alive, nor by attending physician after death. The examinations made . . . since the alleged discovery of the disease more than three months ago fail to establish satisfactory proof of the plague." [15]

Furthermore, from the very beginning the San Francisco newspapers (with the exception of Hearst's *Examiner*) had reacted violently to the suggestion that plague could come to California, launching a bitter campaign to discredit Kinyoun and the Board of Health. So great was the pressure, in fact, that on March 9 the Chinatown quarantine had to be lifted, sixty hours after it had been imposed. Even the two leading medical journals, the *Occidental Medical Times* and the *Pacific Medical and Surgical Journal*, took opposite sides on the issue.

To complicate the situation, the Chinese refused to cooperate in steps proposed by the Board of Health and those associated with it to eradicate plague from Chinatown and restrict its spread. When on May 22 President William McKinley (1843–1901) allowed Surgeon-General Walter Wyman to limit the travel of Orientals on public transportation, Chinese officials brought suit in circuit court on the grounds that the Federal Government had exceeded its authority. Judge W. W. Morrow ruled that McKinley's order was class legislation and that only the San Francisco Board of Supervisors had the power to restrict movement in the city. When the Board of Health attempted to clean up Chinatown by transferring its inhabitants to detention camps, the same judge ruled the action illegal and ordered Kinyoun to show cause why he should not be held in contempt of court for refusing Orientals freedom of movement in and out of California. Kinyoun's trial opened on June 25 with the defendant anything but sanguine about the outcome, but on July 3 the judge found him not guilty of contempt. In the meantime, Kinyoun reported attempts to bribe him and threats to run down his official launches in the bay.

Things continued to be rough until the beginning of 1903 when George C. Pardee replaced Gage as governor. He immediately promised that "whatever the Marine Hospital Service desires me to do in the way of public health preservation shall be done. . . . The medical authorities have emphatically declared that plague has existed and does exist in San Francisco, and that settles it so far as I am concerned. . . ." [16]

An encomium has been provided by bacteriologist Kellogg who, when the *Bulletin* declared of Williamson and the members of his Board of Health "These men are marked!" answered,

> These men are indeed marked; marked as men of sterling integrity, as men who had the courage of their convictions and who stood steadfast against the most virulent combination of falsehood and personal attack that probably ever was endured by any Board of Health before or since. They were attacked by editors, supervisors, mayors, governors, judges of the Federal courts and by their fellow citizens. They served without pay and suffered loss of practice and prestige. They were overwhelmed temporarily with a cloud of suspicion, distrust and positive hate that was almost universal in the community, but they withstood both threats and bribes. Their names should be indelible in the annals of public health and to these should be added that of Dr. Kinyoun, . . . [17]

By the end of February 1904 the epidemic was suppressed. It had claimed by various counts 119, 120, or 121 victims, only 8 of whom recovered. Bubonic plague again appeared in San Francisco in May 1907. This may have been the result of reinfection but seems to have been a recrudescence of the Chinatown outbreak. This second epidemic was not confined to Chinatown. In fact, very few Orientals were affected, almost all of the 160 cases (involving 77 deaths) "being white persons, many of them of a good condition of life, subsisting on generous diet and dwelling in houses that would commonly be called 'sanitary.' The difference in mortality was probably due . . . to early discovery and prompt treatment, . . ." [18]

On January 28, 1908, Mayor Edward Robeson Taylor appointed a Citizens' Health Committee. Its twenty-five members were a cross section representing public health, medicine, the legal profession, business, and labor. Its work was essentially social in character. Its purpose was to acquaint the public with the activities of the sanitary authorities and gain its cooperation, especially in the elimination of rats. On March 31, 1909, the committee reported to the mayor: "To-day there is no plague in San Francisco, and no plague-infected rats are to be found here." [19]

AFTER SAN FRANCISCO

The next ten years saw about 150 cases of plague in the United States, all in port cities where the occasional infected rat slipped by an unusually efficient quarantine service. In the first quarter of the century 50 percent of ships entering American ports were rat-infested, but by the late thirties the danger of infected shipborne rats as a source of plague was significantly reduced and today shipborne plague is virtually nonexistent. However, 1908 to 1968 saw 120 cases attributable to wild rodent, rabbit, squirrel, and dog sources occurring in California, New Mexico, Arizona, Utah, Colorado, Idaho, Oregon, and Nevada.

On October 29, 1924, a physician requested an ambulance from the Los Angeles County General Hospital for two Mexican patients critically ill of a malady which he could not definitely diagnose, but which he knew to be highly contagious since several others in the neighborhood were also affected with similar symptoms of very high fever and pains in the back and chest. The following day 13 other cases displaying the same symptoms were detected and subsequently admitted to the hospital, where they all developed signs of severe pneumonia, with bloody expectoration and marked cyanosis. It was during this day, after three of the 15 patients who had been admitted had died, that the diagnosis of pneumonic plague was first suggested. The diagnosis was confirmed the following morning, but not made public, when the staff pathologist performed an autopsy and reported the presence of gram-negative bipolar staining bacilli characteristic of plague in the lungs of one of the deceased patients.[20]

This "epidemic" ran for only two weeks and it was not until it appeared to have run its course that the Los Angeles newspapers admitted that what they had referred to as a "strange malady," "pneumonia," "virulent pneumonia," or "malignant pneumonia" was indeed pneumonic plague. Twenty-eight Mexicans and two Caucasians succumbed to the disease.

In 1971, 965 cases of plague (47 deaths) were reported to the World Health Organization; in 1972, 677 (35 deaths); in 1973, 384 (15 deaths). The decline is encouraging and, in contrast with the picture in India alone a quarter of a century ago, the figures have become almost negligible, the more so when one realizes that of 1973's 384 cases, 135 occurred in Brazil and 130 in Indonesia. (It should be further noted that cases in the Republic of Vietnam dropped from 518 in 1971 to 42 in 1973.)

Rat control, health education, and malaria eradication programs using insecticides that kill bacillus-carrying fleas have helped to bring plague to its current low level throughout the world. In those relatively rare instances where infection has occurred, early diagnosis, and treatment with antibiotics (such as tetracycline and streptomycin) have significantly reduced the mortality from this cause.[21]

The Rickettsial Diseases

RICKETTSIA is the generic name applied to a group of microorganisms which occupy a position intermediate between viruses and bacteria. With one exception (Q fever) rickettsial diseases are transmitted to man by an arthropod vector. Louse-borne are epidemic typhus, Brill-Zinsser disease (recrudescent epidemic typhus), and trench fever. Murine (or endemic) typhus is flea-borne. Rocky Mountain spotted fever is tick-borne. Mite-borne are tsutsugamushi fever (scrub typhus) and rickettsialpox.

The order derives its name from Howard Taylor Ricketts (1871–1910) of Findlay, Ohio. Graduating from Northwestern University Medical School in 1897, after an internship at Cook County Hospital in Chicago, Ricketts turned to pathology, and in 1906 his interest became centered upon Rocky Mountain spotted fever which each summer decimated the Nez Perce and Flat Head Indians in Bitterroot Valley, Montana. He identified the causative agent and established the tick as vector. In December 1909 Ricketts went to Mexico to investigate an apparently similar fever, epidemic typhus. "As the investigations were progressing in the typically brilliant manner of Ricketts' work, an awareness of the potential dangers gradually became apparent. Despite Ricketts' meticulous care he was bitten toward the end of April while transferring lice in his laboratory and came down with a fatal attack." He died on May 3.[1] In 1916 the famous Brazilian scientist Henrique da Rocha-Lima (1879–1956), who had himself contracted epidemic typhus but recovered, gave the organism the designation *Rickettsia prowazekii.*

Other rickettsiae followed. It in no way detracts from Ricketts' martyrdom or his claim to fame that, as early as 1606, the German physician Tobias Cober (d. 1625) noted the relationship between typhus and lice infestation.

EPIDEMIC TYPHUS

Of the rickettsial diseases, epidemic typhus (also known as classic typhus and European typhus) can alone lay claim to antiquity, and some of its appearances through the middle of the seventeenth century have already been noted.

Hans Zinsser (1878–1940) of New York, who became professor of bacteriology at Columbia University in 1913, wrote, in addition to several first-rate textbooks, a popular work on typhus fever that was published in 1935. By his own description—"we hesitate to call so rambling a performance a book"—it was "written at odd moments as a relaxation from studies of typhus in the laboratory and in the field." In developing the history of typhus epidemics, he observed that to recount every outbreak

> would be dull with constant repetition. The circumstances of occurrence, sequence of events, and manner of spread were always the same in principle. Typhus had come to be the inevitable and expected companion of war and revolution; no encampment, no campaigning army, and no besieged city escaped it. It added to the terror of famines and floods; it stalked stealthily through the wretched quarters of the poor in cities and villages; it flourished in prisons and even went to sea in ships. And whenever circumstances were favorable it spread through countries and across national boundaries. If there were any significant differences between the eighteenth-century manifestations of typhus and those of preceding periods, they consisted in the fact that, in addition to the major epidemics that regularly accompanied human strife and misfortune, there were now numerous smaller group outbreaks, . . .
>
> As a matter of fact, until the last decade of the nineteenth century mankind changed very little as concerns those customs and personal habits which determine its relationship with typhus fever. The extraordinary political, philosophical, and scientific awakenings which

shed so much lustre over the eighteenth century found no reflection in that fastidiousness of physical living which alone can curtail the homicidal aggressiveness of our disease. Elegance of manners and dress was never more assiduously cultivated, but cleanliness did not keep pace. . . .

The new freedom which was preached by Voltaire and Rousseau did not include freedom from vermin. . . . Cities and villages stank to heaven. The streets were the receptacles of refuse, human and otherwise. The triangular intervals which one sees between adjacent mediæval houses in streets still inhabited are apertures through which waste, *pots de chambre*, and so forth, could be conveniently disposed of from the upper stories. . . . Baths were therapeutic procedures not to be recklessly prescribed after October. The first bathtubs did not reach America—we believe—until about 1840. And public bath houses lacking sanitary laundry arrangements were as likely to spread disease as to arrest it. Schools, prisons, and public meeting places of all kinds were utterly without provisions which might have limited the transmission of infection. . . .

Considering these circumstances, it is not surprising that typhus fever ran riot through Europe and, occasionally, reached America during the period of which we write. The turbulent events of the eighteenth century had carried the infection into the remotest corners of the civilized world. . . .[2]

Zinsser's description of typhus as "the inevitable and expected companion of war" certainly fitted Napoleon's invasion of Russia in 1812. On the way to Moscow, thanks to the scorched earth policy of the fleeing peasants, the French troops suffered severely from dysentery and diarrhea, but typhus was rare until after the battle of Smolensk (August 14–18). During the occupation of Moscow (September 14–October 19) typhus became the most common affliction, and "when Napoleon's army withdrew from the city it left behind several thousand typhus-fever patients, almost all of whom died—only the stronger patients were taken along on wagons." The pursuing Russians lost about sixty-two thousand men to disease, mostly to typhus. Hotly pressed remnants of the French army passed through Vilna (Lithuania) on December 8, dropping off thirty thousand soldiers who could go no farther. Most of them died of typhus. From soldiers, typhus spread to civilians and the disease became rampant through much of what is now the USSR lying west of a line running north-south through Moscow. After crossing the Neman River, the surviving French troops fanned out, bringing typhus wherever they went. In a short time it spread over a large part of Germany. Outbreaks in France, Switzerland, and Austria followed.[3]

In July 1914 Serbia (now part of Yugoslavia) had barely recovered from a two-year war between Turkey and the Balkan states when, following the grand duke's assassination at Sarajevo, Austria declared war on the little nation. Typhus began to show itself in the Serbian army in November. "During the heights of the epidemic the number of new fever cases entering the military hospitals alone reached as high as 2500 per day, and the number of reported cases among the civilian population was approximately three times this." [4] In less than six months some hundred and fifty thousand individuals died of typhus, including about thirty thousand Austrian prisoners.

> During all this time Serbia was practically helpless. Yet Austria did not attack. . . . Austrian strategists knew better than to enter Serbia at this time. . . . Typhus—while scouring the Serbian population—was holding the border. The Central Powers lost six months during the most critical time of the war. It is anybody's guess as to the effect this delay may have had on the early Russian and even the Western campaigns. It is at least not unreasonable to believe that a quick thrust through Serbia at this time,—with its reactions on Turkey, Bulgaria, and Greece,—the closing of Salonika, and the establishment of a Southwestern front against Russia might have tipped the balance in favor of the then very vigorous Central Powers. Typhus may not have won the war—but it certainly helped. . . . Among the most remarkable phenomena of the war is the total absence of typhus from the Western front. No completely satisfactory explanation for this can be offered. Soldiers in the trenches on this front were as universally lousy as soldiers have always been. And a louse-borne disease, Trench fever, closely allied to typhus, was common. We can attribute it only to the fact that the armies were—on both sides—more afraid of typhus than they were of shot and shell. The Central Powers, realizing that a typhus epidemic, introduced with troops transferred from the East, would lose them the war,

took the utmost precautions to avoid this. And army sanitary organizations, in all forces, were ever conscious of the possible peril, alert for suspicious cases, and unusually quick to resort to wholesale delousing. The mortality of lice in this war must have been the greatest in the history of the world.[5]

By the outbreak of World War II immunization, delousing, and hospitalization methods had been developed to a point where the impact of epidemic typhus on the U.S. army in all theaters was negligible. The only epidemic that might have caused havoc occurred in Naples from July 1943 to May 1944 (2009 civilian cases—429 deaths) but it was promptly controlled, the first time in history, in fact, that a typhus epidemic was brought under control.

Typhus sometimes returns to its victims years after the initial attack. It is then known as Brill-Zinsser disease. (Nathan Brill [1860–1925], a New York physician, reported the first cases in 1898.) This recrudescence does not involve lice and is usually milder, having fewer complications and lower fatality.

Trench fever, caused by *R. quintana*, has already been mentioned in connection with World War I (when there were over one million cases in the Allied and German armies). It reappeared early in World War II on the Russo-German front.

Murine typhus (also known as endemic typhus) is caused by *R. typhi* which is flea-borne from natural rodent hosts to man. It occurs sporadically in Mexico and the southern United States where infected rodents are plentiful and is an occupational disease of workers in granaries and warehouses which are likely to be rat-infested.

ROCKY MOUNTAIN SPOTTED FEVER

While Rocky Mountain spotted fever was first observed in Idaho and was described by Edward Ernest Maxey (1867–1934) in 1899, and while Ricketts' investigations centered on Montana, activity of the tick-borne *R. rickettsiae* is not limited to the northern Rocky

Mountains. It has, in fact, been reported in almost every state of the union, in Canada, and in many parts of South America. In the western United States the rabbit tick is said to be the natural host of the microorganism but it does not feed on man. Rather, man is the victim of other ticks, notably the wood tick, that have become infected by feeding on infected animals. In the Eastern states the dog tick is the major culprit. Rickettsial infections of the spotted fever type have occurred in Australia, India, Siberia, and particularly Africa where *R. conorii* causes South African tick-bite fever and, in the Mediterranean area, *boutonneuse fever*.

Vaccination against Rocky Mountain spotted fever is recommended for persons who work outdoors in tick-infested areas. However, special clothing and high boots will generally prevent ticks from attaching themselves. But if one does become attached, immediate removal should avoid infection which does not occur until the tick has fed for several hours. (It is to be noted that, apart from tick bite, *R. rickettsiae* may enter man through the skin from tick feces or blood from crushed ticks.)

Precautions notwithstanding, however, Rocky Mountain spotted fever cases in the United States have been on an upswing since 1968. In 1973 there were 668 cases and, as 1974 drew to a close, close to 800 cases were anticipated for that year. It is true that the mortality rate has dropped to one-third of what it was thirty or forty years ago but it still runs at about 6 percent.

MITE-BORNE RICKETTSIAE

The scientific investigations on tsutsugamushi disease or scrub typhus and its vector "tsutsugamushi" (disease bug) or trombiculid mites in Japan were initiated near the end of the last century, in endemic areas of the disease in northern Honshu, and have been expanded to one of the most prosperous research fields in the biomedical sciences of Japan during the past seventy years. The disease which was described and named first from Japan is now known to be distributed widely in southern Asia and western Pacific regions. The fact was established also by these early investigators that the disease be transmitted to man by larval mites of tsutsugamushi, and its

causative agent was isolated first by a group of Japanese scientists
from cases in these endemic areas.[6]

Irwin Bälz (1845–1913), in conjunction with Kawakami, is generally credited with the earliest scientific account (1879) of tsutsugamushi fever, but while this German bacteriologist, who did
much to advance parasitology in Japan, seems undoubtedly to have
produced the first report in European literature, he had been anticipated by Nagino (1878) and Kawakami (1878–79) in *Tokyo Ijishinshi*.
After graduating from the Imperial University of Tokyo Medical
School, Keisuke Tanaka spent his life as a country physician near
an endemic area. "It is said that he was never associated with
research laboratories, nor attended in any scientific meetings.
However, he frequently sent manuscripts to Japanese and German
medical journals for publication of information accumulated while
examining patients and the areas. The first unambiguous evidence
that the causative agent of tsutsugamushi (or his Kedani Krankheit)
be transmitted to man by the bite of the bug (Kedani) was demonstrated through careful observations of large numbers of cases by
TANAKA (1899). He stated that the bug was closely related to the
harvest mite of *Leptus autumnalis* in Europe but did not give scientific name to it." [7]
    In 1917 *R. tsutsugamushi* was isolated by Norio Ogata.
    Since World War II information on the disease and the vector
mites has been greatly expanded through Japanese research. Before
the war "mites in Japan were represented only by seven species
found in the classic endemic areas . . . but are now known to
occur in all over Japan, and the number of species so far described
from her territory reached over seventy. At least several species
among them are considered to act as the vectors to man, and to
cause various types of the disease corresponding to ecological characteristics of each vector species." [8]
    Of relatively recent vintage is rickettsialpox, found to be en-
demic in New York City and Boston but probably existing elsewhere. A species of mite fostered by the house mouse carries the *R.
akari* to man. The resulting mild disease is clinically similar to

chickenpox. Steps to reduce mouse population quickly eliminate the disease.

Q FEVER

"Investigations of an outbreak of fever of unknown origin [with symptoms similar to those of pneumonia] among a large number of workers in a meat plant in Brisbane, Australia in 1935, by Dr. E[dward] H[olbrook] Derrick, Director of the Laboratory Section of the Queensland Health Department, led to the first knowledge of the clinical entity known as 'Q fever'." [9] Derrick gave the causative agent, which he isolated in guinea pigs, the name of *R. burnetii* (in honor of a contemporary Australian researcher in the field, Frank Macfarlane Burnet), but in 1948 it was changed to *Coxiella burnetii* after it had been determined that the organism, in contrast with other rickettsiae, was filterable, was resistant to physical and chemical agents, and did not typically produce the rash seen in other rickettsial diseases.

Until 1944, Q fever was regarded as belonging almost exclusively to Australia, but in the winter of 1944–45 and the following spring there were eight outbreaks among U.S. troops in the Mediterranean area that were diagnosed as atypical pneumonia but turned out to be Q fever. Most of the outbreaks occurred in Italy, in the region between Florence and Bologna, but there was one in Corsica and another originated in Greece. The attack rate was between 20 and 30 percent of the units involved.

March 1946 saw the first naturally occurring outbreak of Q fever in the United States. It involved stock handlers and slaughterhouse workers in Amarillo, Texas. There were 55 cases among 136 employees. There were two deaths, but at the other extreme some of the victims experienced only a mild influenza-like attack. A few months later there was an explosive outbreak in a Chicago packing plant. In 1948 Dr. F. W. Young, practicing in Artesia, California, connected outbreaks of what turned out to be Q fever with severe windstorms that blew through the surrounding dairyland. In 1949

Pennsylvania reported the first case in an Eastern state. In 1950 there was an epidemic (175 cases) in Stuttgart, Germany, and the disease appears to be endemic in England, Italy, Turkey, North Africa, the Balkans, and Panama.

Most human cases in the United States are the result of contact with infected animals or their products, inhalation of dust from contaminated barns, or the drinking of raw milk. (Pasteurization will, however, destroy the Q fever rickettsiae.) Vaccination has proved very effective in protecting laboratory workers and it is increasingly used to immunize persons whose occupations expose them to the disease.

CHAPTER 17

Influenza—Modern Style

THE third of the three most devastating epidemics to hit mankind struck in 1918. It involved so-called Spanish influenza. The fact that World War I was in full vigor has obscured the time and place of the pandemic's origin—even the origin of the disease's name. It has been suggested that it was called Spanish influenza because the original North American epidemic in 1647 came from Valencia, Spain, but what seems more likely is that, when influenza manifested itself in Europe in 1918, more information was forthcoming from neutral Spain than from her warring neighbors. Furthermore, while Spanish influenza was the name adopted by Americans, in Germany it was called *Blitz Katarrh*, in England, *Flanders grippe*, in Japan, *wrestler's fever*. [1]

The pandemic's place of origin has been a matter of question because there were in fact two outbreaks of influenza in 1918. "The first wave . . . received special prominence in Spain, where it was said to have been sudden in its appearance and brief in its course. During April an illness similar to the Spanish epidemic occurred in American, British, and French troops in France, as well as in the civilian population. In England the first wave appeared in June and was composed for the most part of mild cases. . . . An influenza epidemic occurred also in Japan and China in the spring of 1918. It was mild and was variously called '3-day fever' or 'wrestler's fever,' in addition to influenza. The spring wave of influenza was not highly diffusible; it reached only limited areas of Africa, largely missed South America, and affected Canada only slightly." [2] But influenza had appeared in the United States as early as it had hit Spain. On March 11 at Camp Funston (part of Fort Riley), Kansas, Albert Gitchell, a company cook, reported sick. His symptoms: fever, sore throat, headache, and muscular pains. "Hardly had a corpsman put a thermometer in the soldier's mouth when Corporal Lee W. Drake from First Battalion, Headquarters Transportation Detachment, reported to the same admitting desk in Building 91. His symptoms, even to a 103° fever, were identical with Gitchell's." The similarity of these two cases could have been coincidental, but by noon 107 cases had been admitted to the hospital. Colonel Edward R. Schreiner had no doubt that he was dealing with influenza. By the week's end he had 522 cases and reports of outbreaks were coming in from camps in California, Florida, Virginia, Alabama, South Carolina, and Georgia, from naval ships berthed on the East Coast, and even from San Quentin. But by "no stretch of the imagination, except on the part of those morbidly apprehensive, could the March infection at Army camps be interpreted as the forerunner of a plague." [3] Nevertheless these outbreaks fostered a belief in some that the spring epidemic had originated in America and had been carried by U.S. troops to Europe. Actually the "first relatively mild wave of influenza would have passed unnoticed had it not been followed by a lethal second wave." [4] This lethal second wave (that was in Chungking in July, in Persia (Iran) early in August, and reached France in the middle of August) "killed 22,000,000 people, almost twice as many as the war itself. More were dead in India in a few months than in twenty years of cholera. In the United States half a million died. . . . In two months it covered the globe." [5] "Only tiny Tristan da Cunha [in the extreme South Atlantic] . . . escaped totally untouched. No one ever quite figured out how the flu traveled such great distances in so short a space of time. Coast Guard searching parties, for example, discovered Eskimo villages in remote, inaccessible Alaskan regions wiped out to the last adult and child. . . . Had the epidemic continued its mathematical rate of acceleration, . . . Civilization could have disappeared within a few more weeks." [6]

If the pandemic did not originate in America, where did it come from? Throughout history epidemics had generally run from east to west.

> Traditionally Asia had been the matrix of disease, as if there were a permanent focus of infection that existed in the vastness of Mongolia from where it would erupt periodically into the rest of the world. Some doctors maintained that the influenza was introduced into Europe by Chinese labor battalions that landed on the coast of France. Some attributed it to Russian soldiers arriving from Vladivostok. Others thought it might have developed among the troops from an earlier bronchitis so prevalent in Spain in the spring that it gave the name Spanish to the autumn influenza. There was even one tenuous theory that the disease sprang into being in an isolated Georgia training camp during the winter of 1917 and that from there it migrated westward until it had circumnavigated the earth.[7]

On August 28, 1918, the pandemic entered the United States at Boston. "A sailor, on a transport being tied up to a Boston dock that day, had symptoms of influenza. It infected New England like a forest fire. In Massachusetts alone it killed 15,000 civilians in four months, plus an unknown number of others whose deaths were erroneously classed as 'pneumonia,' 'encephalitis,' 'meningitis' or masked under other rubrics. The invasion struck along two prongs: civilian and military. Some of the sailors on the first Boston shipment were transferred to Michigan and Illinois and became nuclei for the spread of influenza in the midwest." [8] Within a matter of days influenza spread rapidly down the East Coast. At the height of the scourge total death rate per 1000 population was Philadelphia, 158; Baltimore, 148; Washington, 109; Boston, 100; New York, 60. Inviting targets throughout the country were crowded army camps in which 24,000 died (in contrast with 34,000 killed in battle). In September–October one out of every five soldiers stationed in the United States was stricken with the illness. The problem of caring for the sick (both military and civilian) was enlarged by a lack of facilities and of medical and nursing personnel, a large number of whom were serving overseas. Makeshift emergency hospitals, volunteers, and nursing in homes somewhat reduced the gap. Fortunately, while the pandemic struck hard, it did not linger but quickly resumed its race around the world. "The pattern was the same in nearly every major city: one or two weeks of rapid spread followed by two or three weeks of high morbidity and mortality, whereafter the epidemic rapidly subsided. A peak period of mortality for many of the nation's urban areas, and especially New York, New Orleans, and San Francisco, occurred in the third week of October, attesting to the extraordinary contagiousness of the disease." [9]

Among large populations reliable morbidity rates are hard to come by. A house-to-house survey, covering 130,033 individuals, conducted in various parts of the United States immediately after the September–November wave, revealed an overall influenza attack rate of 28 percent. "This corresponded closely to attack rates in the United States Army camps and fairly well to morbidity reports from Scandinavia as well as population surveys in England." [10]

Of the worldwide deaths in excess of twenty million, already referred to, it has been estimated that an unbelievable twelve million occurred in India alone. "Mortality rates for the epidemic period ranged from 120 per 100,000 population in Argentina, 527/100,000 in the United States, 680/100,000 in England and Wales to 4,000/100,000 in India and 2,280/100,000 in South Africa. In certain of the Pacific Islands, mortality reached as high as 20% of the entire population." [11]

"In the lonely islands of the South Pacific, where respiratory diseases were uncommon, if not almost unknown, natives and whites alike 'died like flies,' according to one correspondent. . . . From Rewa, in the Fiji Islands, Alick Rea, a representative of the Colonial Sugar Refining Company of Sydney, wrote: 'For a full week I was the only person moving about in this particular district.' . . . More than a thousand children were orphaned in Samoa, and the native chieftains were attempting to place them under the care of the New Zealand Government. Some placed the total Samoan dead already at eight thousand, two thirds of the number being men. Describing the ravages in the Samoan group . . . the *Sydney Daily Telegraph* correspondent wrote: 'As at one time

80 or 90 per cent of the people were lying helpless, many died from starvation who might probably have recovered, for even when rice, milk, and other items were sent out and delivered, the survivors were too weak to prepare and apportion the food.' . . . New Zealand recorded an estimated six thousand influenza deaths. . . .

"Few countries the world over—few island kingdoms, or even outposts of civilization astride the tundra or in the jungles—did not share in this tragedy. The microbes had struck dispassionately over vast terrestrial distances, without fear, or favor—or mercy." [12]

CAUSE AND PREVENTION

Influenza is caused by a filterable virus. The discovery that an ultramicroscopic organism could produce disease was made by the German bacteriologist Friedrich Löffler (1852–1915) of Frankfort on the Oder in 1898 in course of investigations of foot-and-mouth disease. A year later he introduced the concept of preventive inoculation against this disease.

From this beginning it might be assumed that twenty years later the virus that causes influenza would have been discovered and a vaccine developed. After all, it was not as if the disease had first appeared in the twentieth century. It had been a periodic visitor, sometimes in epidemic proportions, since antiquity and had been pandemic in 1889–90 when an outbreak at Bukhara in Turkestan spread through most of Siberia and European Russia to Europe, England, and the United States. Nevertheless the virus was not isolated (by the English team of Wilson Smith, Christopher H. Andrewes, and Patrick P. Laidlaw [1881–1940]) until 1933. Subsequent investigations have shown that the influenza virus is mutational and no one can be certain that the "type A" virus isolated in 1933 had prevailed in 1918. In 1940 the Americans Thomas Francis, Jr., and T. P. Magill, working independently (although they had collaborated earlier in influenza research), isolated "type B." (In 1949 "type C" was isolated but was found seldom to cause human illness.)

In 1952 Australian microbiologist Burnet wrote:

Of all virus diseases influenza is probably that in which mutational changes in the virus are of great human importance. We can
only guess what type of virus was responsible in 1918–19 and what
changes took place during the course of the pandemic. But even in
the period since the human virus was first isolated in 1933 there have
been striking changes in the immunological character of both influenza A and B viruses. Some of us believe that the influenza virus'
chief means of survival is its capacity for constant mutation to new
serological patterns, and those of us who have had anything to do
with the production of influenza vaccines know very well how that
capacity can nullify the most painstaking work.[13]

To complicate matters, there are strains within the types, and
immunity developed by a bout of influenza only operates to protect
the subject from the same strain and type. The same restriction
applies to vaccines.

"New" viruses, exhibiting antigenic variation, occur at intervals
of roughly twelve years. The original "type AO" (1934) gave place
to "type A1" in 1947. The Asian flu pandemic of 1957 involved
type A2; the pandemic of 1968 introduced the A2/Hong Kong
strain.

In March 1970 Charles H. Stuart-Harris of the University of
Sheffield (England) delivered the Gudakunst Lecture at the University of Michigan. He began:

> The turbulent history of the twentieth century has been marked al-
> ready by the two greatest wars that mankind has known and by the
> most lethal epidemic of influenza from which it has ever suffered. It
> has also witnessed the emergence of man from the straitjacket of his
> earthbound state. Brave men have hazarded their lives in space and
> have taken the first steps on the moon. Extraterrestrial radiation has
> proved a lesser hazard than skin sensitivity and the common cold.
> Those who have spent their lives in attempts to further the conquest
> of infectious disease are humiliated by the contrast between the suc-
> cess of the astronauts and the failure to control respiratory disease. It
> is true that in the laboratory much success has been achieved in
> recovering viruses from the human respiratory tract and in studying
> their properties. Yet the multiplicity of species thus found has actu-
> ally increased the complexity of the problem of specific prophylaxis.

The cynical might well regard the task of prevention as beyond realization and yet in one sector—that of influenza—success, albeit of limited character, has been obtained.

Individuals, groups, and whole military cadres have been protected by specific influenza vaccines whose composition has been varied to coincide with the shifts in antigenic composition of the viruses in nature and that have been applied assiduously. This limited control has not been extended to the whole population, nor has it succeeded uniformly in the face of pandemic influenza. Indeed, as each major antigenic change of the influenza A viruses has occurred, the puny character of the preventive effort that has been mustered has only emphasized our present impotence.[14]

To check an epidemic, the appropriate vaccine must be available in quantities sufficient for population inoculation at least two or three weeks ahead of the outbreak. When a new strain emerges there is seldom enough time to develop and administer a vaccine. Vaccines are useless once the disease has taken hold and there is no specific treatment for influenza. But relief may be on its way:

In August 1972 scientists of the National Institute of Allergy and Infectious Diseases announced the preliminary success of a new vaccine that uses a combination of live viruses (in contrast with the customary killed virus) and can be produced quickly enough to meet an influenza threat. Live viruses can be used because the vaccine is extremely sensitive to heat and cannot survive in the temperature of the lungs, where flu viruses ordinarily settle to bring on illness. Field trials had to be conducted before the new vaccine could be employed extensively, but there was cautious confidence that the vaccine would be licensed before the next flu epidemic. It was not. The London flu of 1972 swept through America late that year and early in 1973.[15]

The Continuing Scene

TIME, until the middle of the nineteenth century, was often reckoned in terms of the epidemics that spread across regions, countries, and continents with discouraging frequency. Epidemics are far from unknown today, but their character has changed in many cases and public reaction is more one of surprise than anticipation. Furthermore, man is now less often oppressed by the "old" epidemics than by new ones, some of which he has either directly or indirectly brought on himself.

In 1958 the chairman of a regional hospital board in England replied to a request for funds to reconstruct a venereal disease clinic with the statement, "We don't want to spend money on these dying diseases." [1] The premature writing off of syphilis and gonorrhea is tragic and not untypical. There are other epidemic diseases that might flare up at any time. Increasing ease and speed of transportation, political unrest, carelessness, and indifference have complicated the picture.

In Brazil in 1930 an alert investigator tracked down a specimen of the *Anopheles gambiae*. Unfortunately this African import had already gained a foothold and by 1938 the scene was set for a six-month epidemic of malaria that caused more than a hundred thousand cases and fourteen thousand deaths. However, after a concerted effort against the mosquito, rather than the disease, the area was cleared and South America has been free of epidemic malaria since that time. [2]

"Imported diseases" is the term often used for such epidemic

sparks. The danger is twofold: many American and European physicians would neither think of nor recognize a number of the diseases still predominantly found in tropical areas; their patients,
lacking built-up immunity, would be largely defenseless. And the
reverse, of course, is true. For example, west Africa had been
cholera-free since before 1900. Then in August 1970 a devastating
epidemic struck with 150,000 cases and 20,000 deaths. The explo-
siveness of this epidemic served notice on physicians in other
cholera-free regions that they should familiarize themselves with
the appearance, spread, and treatment of this terrible disease.[3]

Political unrest can create tinderbox conditions for epidemics.
Java had just about wiped out smallpox by its vaccination program
in the 1940s. However, the political and social confusion toward
the end of the decade and in the years that followed made it possible for the disease to reestablish itself there on an endemic basis
and to raise the possibility of an epidemic.[4] Smallpox epidemics
have recently swept over major areas of Bangladesh, Pakistan, and
India. In the Indian state of Bihar in early 1974 over ten thousand
deaths resulted from smallpox.

Measles is another epidemic disease that still maintains a sub-
stantial foothold. Carelessness demonstrated by the failure to pro-
mote vaccination and a presumption by the federal and state governments that the "other one" was responsible for funding such
programs have created a problem in the United States today.[5]
While the number of cases of measles in the United States had
fallen to 22,000 in 1968, it climbed to 75,000 in 1971. There was a
decline the following year, but since then the level has been rising
and epidemics have occurred in several cities in the United States
and Canada. Since approximately one in each group of fifteen
measles-victims develops a potentially serious complication, it can
readily be seen that the disease is not just a mild sickness.[6]

A major epidemic of dysentery struck Central America and Mexico in 1970 causing almost 200,000 cases and 11,500 deaths before
it subsided. The bacillus *Shigella dysenteriae*, type 1, that produced
this epidemic had almost vanished forty years earlier.

Other epidemic diseases keep popping up despite known
methods for control. In the first six months of 1972 typhoid in

Mexico produced thousands of cases and led to a vaccination program that reached nearly five million people.

Lassa fever (named for the village in northeast Nigeria where it was first reported in 1969) is typical of the new diseases that can spring up unexpectedly. The diagnosis of this viral infection can only be positive when serum antibodies are present. Since their development requires several weeks, an individual with Lassa fever can travel a considerable distance and expose many people before his condition is identifiable.[7] The first outbreaks of this disease were so "atrociously virulent" that the Nigerian Ministry of Health petitioned the World Health Organization to change the name to remove any relationship with their country, an interesting echo of the national arguments over the names for syphilis four hundred years earlier.

While the dancing mania disappeared in the eighteenth century, other forms of psychosomatic epidemics have appeared from time to time. These can be quite confusing until the cause is identified. At about 9:30 A.M. on Monday May 13, 1974, an eleven-year-old girl in the fifth grade of the Bay Harbor Elementary School near Miami, Florida, became ill while singing in a music class. After being taken to the clinic she fainted. The rescue unit from the local fire department arrived while the corridors were filled with children changing classes; after this commotion, additional children began to suffer from the same symptoms of dizziness, headache, and fainting.

A gas leak was rumored to be the cause, but no fumes were located, nor was any clinical evidence found to indicate a physical illness. The local health department suggested that this was an outbreak of "mass hysteria" with hyperventilation. Ultimately seventy-three students were affected. A similar outbreak had occurred in an Alabama elementary school the previous year, and others are noted in the literature. The epidemiological account of the Bay Harbor event concludes with the statement, "It is likely that the prompt recognition of the hysterical basis of the Florida outbreak prevented further problems." [8]

The term epidemic is currently used loosely in such statements as "we are faced with an epidemic of heart disease (or drug abuse or alcoholism)." While the writer or speaker is frequently counting on the shock value of the word to assist him or her in arousing the public to support his or her program, its use has a certain justification as a means of alerting the scientific community to areas that require rethinking or positive action, often with beneficial results.

Diseases of Medical Progress: A Study of Iatrogenic Disease is the title of a book [9] that has gone through three editions and includes in its "contemporary analysis of illness produced by drugs and other therapeutic procedures" more than a few situations that might bear the title epidemic in the sense employed in the previous paragraph. Some indication of the growth of the problem and its increasing recognition is shown by reviewing the number of pages in the successive editions: 1959, 131 pages; 1964, 543; 1969, 925.

The classic example in modern times of a man-made epidemic is retrolental fibroplasia which was first reported in 1942.[10] The identification of prolonged exposure to a high concentration of oxygen as the causative factor in blindness of premature infants was the result of major medical detective work.[11] Unfortunately, many infants suffered from this epidemic before it was recognized.

There is, of course, more to medicine than the work of white-coated figures to be seen in the aseptic surroundings of research institutions. Two "epidemics" provide bridges between the very necessary but seemingly remote research that goes on in these institutions and events that appear more immediate in our everyday lives. The first example is that of the lead content of the cheap paint that has often been used in slum areas of modern cities. This paint chips off and these chips are often eaten by young children who then develop the cumulative symptoms of lead poisoning. Here is a man-made epidemic that involves several aspects of modern society.

The second bridging epidemic formed the title of a recent paper in a medical journal, "Dog Bites—An Unrecognized Epidemic." [12] In it, the authors show that, while the number of dog bites each year in New York City remained approximately the same between 1945 and 1964, it began to rise in 1965 and by 1972 the annual total stood at 37,896, an increase of 37 percent in seven years. An analysis of data from New York City and elsewhere revealed that increases had also occurred in Baltimore and in Norfolk, Virginia. As to "probable causes," they included: increased proportions of low-income inhabitants who resent and resist payment for a dog-license fee and the prerequisite shots, changes in the types of dogs owned with a trend toward larger and more aggressive breeds to protect their owners and property from criminal assault, the fact that such dogs become irritable and frustrated when penned up in restricted city locations. The authors concluded that these dogs running loose (not strays) caused most of the trouble.

The dog-bite "epidemic" is just another illustration of how closely the many aspects of our modern society are woven together. The fact that medical scientists are deeply involved in helping to eradicate such problems is a further indication of the widespread role of medicine in modern society, as old epidemics are supplanted by new ones.

REFERENCE NOTES

SELECTED BIBLIOGRAPHY

ILLUSTRATION CREDITS

INDEX

REFERENCE NOTES

1. FROM ANCIENT TO CLASSICAL TIMES

1. Manetho, [*Works*], trans. W. G. Waddell (London: Heinemann, 1940), p. 35.
2. Arthur Weigall, *A History of the Pharaohs* (New York: Dutton, 1925), I:122–23.
3. Cornelius Walford, *A Statistical Chronology of Plagues and Pestilences as affecting Human Life* (London: Harrison and Sons, 1884), p. 56.
4. Alexander Hamilton Howe, *A Theoretical Inquiry into the Physical Cause of Epidemic Diseases* (London: John Churchill & Sons, 1865), p. 30.
5. Exod., 7–12.
6. Edward Bascombe, *A History of Epidemic Pestilences from the Earliest Ages* (London: John Churchill, 1851), p. 1.
7. Exod., 7:20–21.
8. *Ibid.*, 8:13.
9. *Ibid.*, 12:31–32.
10. *Ibid.*, 12:33, 35–36.
11. Num., 11:1, 3.
12. *Ibid.*, 11:31–33.
13. *Ibid.*, 16.
14. *The Iliad of Homer*, trans. Mr. [Alexander] Pope (London: Bernard Lintott, 1715), Book I.
15. 1 Sam., 5:6, 8–11; 6:3, 5.
16. *See* R. Pollitzer, *Plague* (Geneva: World Health Organization, 1954), pp. 11–12.
17. S. H. Blondheim of the Hadassah Medical School, Jerusalem, writing three years after MacArthur, was even more positive. He said that "the word *achbar* signifies not only 'mouse' but 'rat' as well." "The First Recorded Epidemic of Bubonic Plague: The Bible, 1 Sam. vi," *Bulletin of the History of Medicine* XXIX (1955):337.
18. W. P. MacArthur, "The Occurrence of the Rat in Early Europe. The Plague of the Philistines (1 Sam., 5, 6)," *Transactions of the Royal Society of Tropical Medicine and Hygiene* XLVI (1952):210–11.
19. W. P. MacArthur, "Plague of the Philistines," *Transactions of the Royal Society of Tropical Medicine and Hygiene* XLVI (1952):464.
20. 1 Sam., 6:4, 10, 12.
21. *Ibid.*, 6:13, 15.
22. *Ibid.*, 6:19. Blondheim, on technical textual grounds, questions the

loss of 50,070 men, suggesting that for "as small a town as Beth-Shemesh must have been, the death of only 70 men would have been a severe blow." One explanation offered is that "70 men died, whose worth was that of 50,000, which would imply that among the victims were the elders and important men of the community." Blondheim, *op. cit.*, p. 339.

23. Blondheim, *op. cit.*, pp. 339–41.
24. 2 Sam., 24:1.
25. 1 Chron., 21:1.
26. 2 Sam., 24:10; 1 Chron., 21:8.
27. Samuel states seven years rather than three.
28. George Gordon Byron, *The Destruction of Sennacherib*, Stanza 1.
29. Isa., 37:36. Like accounts occur in 2 Kings, 19, and 2 Chron., 32.
30. 2 Chron., 32:21.
31. Sethos does not appear in Manetho's lists of kings of Egypt. Herodotus may have conferred the title of king on a priest of Pthah.
32. Herodotus, *The Persian Wars*, trans. George Rawlinson, II:141, in *The Greek Historians*, ed. Francis R. B. Godolphin (New York: Random House, 1942), I:148–49.
33. *Plutarch's Lives*. Tr. from the original Greek with Notes, Critical and Historical and a Life of Plutarch by John Langhome and William Langhome. A new edition (New York: Harper & Bros., 1870), p. 24.
34. *Ibid.*, p. 51.
35. *Livy*, with an English translation by B. O. Foster, 13 vols. (London: William Heinemann Ltd., 1939), I:111, 113.
36. B. G. Niebuhr, *The History of Rome*, second volume, trans. Julius Charles Hare and Cannop Thirlwall (London: Walton and Maberly, 1855), p. 272.
37. *The Roman Antiquities of Dionysius of Halicarnassus with an English translation by Earnest Cary on the basis of the version of Edward Spelman*, 7 vols. (Cambridge, Mass.: Harvard University Press, 1947), VI:341, 343, 345.
38. Livy, *op. cit.*, II:107.
39. Niebuhr, *op. cit.*, II:278–79.
40. Herodotus, *op. cit.*, VIII:113, 115, 117 (I:505–6).

2. THE PLAGUE OF THUCYDIDES AND THE EPIDEMICS OF HIPPOCRATES

1. Thucydides, *The Peloponnesian War*, trans. Benjamin Jowett, I:1, in *The Greek Historians*, I:567.
2. *Ibid.*, I:23 (I:576–77).
3. *Ibid.*, II:47–53 (I:653–56).

4. *Ibid.*, III:87 (I:723).
5. D. L. Page, "Thucydides' Description of the Great Plague at Athens," *Classical Quarterly*, n.s. III (1953):98–109.
6. *Ibid.*, pp. 111–13.
7. J. F. D. Shrewsbury, "The Plague of Athens," *Bulletin of the History of Medicine* XXIV (1950):1–25.
8. Page, *op. cit.*, pp. 113–18.
9. W. P. MacArthur, "The Athenian Plague: A Medical Note," *Classical Quarterly*, n.s. IV (1954):171–73.
10. D. L. P[age], "The Plague: A Lay Comment on a Medical Note" (letter), *Classical Quarterly*, n.s. IV (1954):174.
11. P. Salway and W. Dell, "Plague at Athens," *Greece and Rome* (continuous series vol. XXIII), 2nd. ser. I (1954):66–70.
12. Page, *supra*, note 5, p. 116n.
13. *Ibid.*, p. 113.
14. W. H. S. Jones, *Hippocrates*, 4 vols. (London: Heinemann, 1923), I:141.
15. Francis Clifton, Hippocrates *upon Air, Water*, and *Situations; upon Epidemical Diseases; and upon* Prognostics In *Acute Cases* especially (London: Printed for J. Watts, 1734), pp. iv–v.
16. *Ibid.*, pp. 52–53.
17. Rudolph E. Siegel, "Epidemics and Infectious Diseases at the Time of Hippocrates. Their Relation to Modern Accounts," *Gesnerus* XVII (1960):79–80.
18. Clifton, *op. cit.*, p. 53.
19. *Ibid.*, pp. 55–60, 68.
20. *Ibid.*, pp. 61–62, 64.
21. Siegel, *op. cit.*, p. 81.
22. Clifton, *op. cit.*, pp. 89, 91; Thucydides, *op. cit.*, II:49 (I:654); *see* Francis Adams, *The Genuine Works of Hippocrates*, 2 vols. in 1 (New York: William Wood & Company, 1929), I:334.

3. FROM ATHENS TO CONSTANTINOPLE

1. *Diodorus of Sicily*, trans. G. H. Oldfather, 12 vols. (Cambridge, Mass.: Harvard University Press, 1950), V:445, 445n.
2. Niebuhr, *The History of Rome*, second volume, pp. 509, 509n.
3. Alfred J. Church, *The Story of Carthage* (New York: G. P. Putnam's Sons, 1886), pp. 38, 44–45, 56–57.
4. Paulus Orosius, *The Seven Books of History Against the Pagans*, trans. Roy J. Deferrari (Washington, D.C.: The Catholic University of America Press, Inc., 1964), p. 85. In *The Fathers of the Church: A New Translation*. Founded by Ludwig Schopp, vol. L.

5. C. Kerényi, *Asklepios*, trans. Ralph Mannheim (New York: Pantheon Books for Bollingen Foundation, 1959), pp. 3–4.
6. *Livy* (Foster translation), IV:541, 543, 547.
7. Ovid, *Metamorphoses*, trans. Frank Justus Miller, 2 vols. (Cambridge, Mass.: Harvard University Press, 1946), II:409, 411, 413, 415, 417.
8. William K. Beatty, "Medical and Numismatic Notes, XV: Medical Aspects of Greek and Roman Coins," *Bulletin of the New York Academy of Medicine*, 2nd ser. L (1974):89–90.
9. J. F. Gilliam, "The Plague Under Marcus Aurelius," *American Journal of Philology* LXXXII (1961):227.
10. Arthur E. R. Boak, *A History of Rome to 565 A.D.*, 3rd ed. (New York: The Macmillan Company, 1947), p. 325.
11. *Ibid.*, p. 418.
12. Eusebius Pamphili, *Ecclesiastical History* (Books 6–10), trans. Roy J. Deferrari (New York: Fathers of the Church, Inc., 1955), p. 123. In *The Fathers of the Church*, vol. XXIX.
13. Boak, *loc. cit.*
14. Eusebius, *op. cit.*, p. 220. In *The Fathers of the Church*, vol. XXIX.
15. *Ibid.*, pp. 221–23.
16. The Venerable Bede, *The Ecclesiastical History of the English Nation* (London: J. M. Dent & Sons Ltd., 1910), p. 21.
17. J. F. D. Shrewsbury, "The Saints and Epidemic Disease," *Birmingham Medical Review* XIX (1956):214–15.

4. THE PLAGUE OF JUSTINIAN

1. Edward Gibbon, *The History of the Decline and Fall of the Roman Empire*, a new edition in 12 vols. (London: Printed by T. Miller, 1820), VII:423.
2. *Procopius*, trans. H. B. Dewing, 6 vols. (London: Heinemann, 1914), I:451, 453, 455, 457, 459, 461, 463, 465.
3. Gibbon, *op. cit.*, VII:419, 423.
4. Paul the Deacon, *History of the Langobards*, trans. William Dudley Foulke (Philadelphia: University of Pennsylvania, 1907), pp. 56–58, 126–28, 160, 200.
5. Gregory of Tours, *The History of the Franks*, trans. O. H. Dalton, 2 vols. (Oxford: The Clarendon Press, 1927), II:119, 140–41, 394–96, 459, 461, 526, 555.
6. Procopius, *op. cit.*, I:465.
7. Josiah C. Russell, "That Earlier Plague," *Demography* V (1968):184.

5. THE MIDDLE AGES

1. Richard Mead, *A Discourse on the Small Pox and Measles* . . . (London: Printed for John Brindley, 1748), p. 99.
2. Fielding H. Garrison, *An Introduction to the History of Medicine*, 4th ed. (Philadelphia: W. B. Saunders Company, 1929), p. 129.
3. Rhazes' *Treatise on the Small Pox and Measles*, trans. Thomas Stack, in Mead, *op. cit.*, pp. 121–23, 127–31.
4. James Moore, *The History of Small Pox* (London: Printed for Longman, Hurst, Rees, Orme, and Brown, 1815), p. 22.
5. *Ibid.*, pp. 38–39.
6. *Ibid.*, p. 40.
7. *Ibid.*, pp. 41–43.
8. *Ibid.*, pp. 43–45.
9. *Ibid.*, pp. 46–54.
10. *Ibid.*, pp. 56–57, 63–64, 74–75.
11. *Ibid.*, pp. 76–77.
12. *Ibid.*, pp. 81, 94, 106.
13. Rudolph Marx, "The Fifth Column at the Battle of Gettysburg," *Surgery, Gynecology, and Obstetrics* CVI (1958):375.
14. August Hirsch, *Handbook of Geographical and Historical Pathology*, trans. Charles Creighton, 3 vols. (London: The New Sydenham Society, 1883–86), III:284.
15. Gregory, *The History of the Franks*, II:204–7, 467–68, 546, 600.
16. The Venerable Bede's *Ecclesiastical History of England also the Anglo-Saxon Chronicle*, ed. J. A. Gil, 5th ed. (London: Bell & Daldy, 1871) (Bohn's Antiquarian Library), p. 162.
17. William MacArthur, "The Medical Identification of Some Pestilences of the Past," *Transactions of the Royal Society of Tropical Medicine and Hygiene* LIII (1959):432, 435.
18. Charles Creighton, *A History of Epidemics in Britain*, 2 vols. (Cambridge: The University Press, 1891, 1894. Reprinted with additions, New York: Barnes & Noble, Inc., 1965), I:v, 4, 8.
19. MacArthur, *op. cit.*, pp. 430–32.
20. Creighton, *op. cit.*, II:272.
21. Marx, *loc. cit.*
22. Friedrich Prinzing, *Epidemics Resulting from Wars*, ed. Harald Westergaard (Oxford: The Clarendon Press, 1916), pp. 13–15.
23. *Chronicles of the Crusades, being Contemporary Narratives of the Crusade of Richard Cœur de Lion*, by Richard of Devizes and Geoffrey de Vinsauf; *and of the Crusade of Saint Louis*, by Lord John de Joinville (London: Henry G. Bohn, 1848), pp. 431–32, 434–35.

6. THE BLACK DEATH

1. John Stewart, *Nestorian Missionary Enterprise* (Edinburgh: T. & T. Clark, 1928), pp. 198–99, 209.
2. Philip Ziegler, *The Black Death* (New York: The John Day Company, 1969), p. 15.
3. Quoted in Vincent J. Derbes, "De Mussis and the Great Plague of 1348," *Journal of the American Medical Association* CXCVI (1966):60.
4. Quoted in Christos S. Bartsocas, "Two Fourteenth Century Greek Descriptions of the 'Black Death,' " *Journal of the History of Medicine* XXI (1966):395.
5. Quoted in Johannes Nohl, *The Black Death*, trans. C. H. Clarke (London: George Allen & Unwin Ltd., 1926), pp. 18–20.
6. *Ibid.*, p. 20.
7. Giovanni Boccaccio, *The Decameron*, trans. John Payne (New York: The Modern Library, 1931), pp. 8–17.
8. *Letters from Petrarch*, selected and translated by Morris Bishop (Bloomington, Ind.: Indiana University Press, 1966), pp. 73–75.
9. Quoted in Derbes, *op. cit.*, p. 62.
10. Nohl, *op. cit.*, pp. 122–23.
11. Quoted in George Deaux, *The Black Death 1347* (New York: Weybright and Talley, 1969), p. 101.
12. *Ibid.*, p. 100.
13. Nohl, *op. cit.*, p. 129.
14. Quoted in Deaux, *op. cit.*, p. 105.
15. J. F. C. Hecker, *The Epidemics of the Middle Ages*, trans. B. G. Babington (London: The Sydenham Society, 1844), p. 50.
16. Quoted in Ziegler, *op. cit.*, pp. 80–81.
17. *Ibid.*, p. 161.
18. Quoted *ibid.*, pp. 161–62.
19. Hecker, *op. cit.*, pp. 32–34, 37–40.
20. *Ibid.*, pp. 40–42, 45–46.
21. A chronicler of Limburg quoted in Nohl, *op. cit.*, p. 260.

7. THE DANCING MANIA

1. Hecker, *The Epidemics of the Middle Ages*, p. 87.
2. Quoted in George Rosen, "Psychopathology in the Social Process, Dance Frenzies, Demonic Possession, Revival Movements and Similar so-called Psychic Epidemics. An Interpretation," *Bulletin of the History of Medicine* XXXVI (1962):15.
3. Quoted in Nohl, *The Black Death*, pp. 250–51.
4. Quoted in Rosen, *op. cit.*, p. 19.

5. Hecker, *op. cit.*, pp. 97–98.
6. Rosen, *op. cit.*, p. 20.
7. Quoted in Nohl, *op. cit.*, p. 252.
8. George Mora, "An Historical Sociopsychiatric Appraisal of Tarantism and its Importance in the Tradition of Psychotherapy of Mental Disorders," *Bulletin of the History of Medicine* XXXVII (1963):417–18.
9. Hecker, *op. cit.*, pp. 110–12.
10. *Ibid.*, p. 117.
11. Quoted in Nohl, *op. cit.*, p. 254.
12. Hecker, *op. cit.*, pp. 119–20.
13. *Ibid.*, p. 133.
14. Edward D. Andrews, *The People Called Shakers. A Search for the Perfect Society* (New York: Oxford University Press, 1953), p. 29.

8. THE SWEATING SICKNESS

1. Hecker, *The Epidemics of the Middle Ages*, p. 181.
2. Maurice B. Strauss, "A Hypothesis as to the Mechanism of Fulminant Course and Death in the Sweating Sickness," *Journal of the History of Medicine* XXVIII (1973):48.
3. Quoted in Manley Bradford Shaw, "A Short History of the Sweating Sickness," *Annals of Medical History*, n.s. V (1933):270–71.
4. *Ibid.*, pp. 252–53, 271.
5. Hecker, *op. cit.*, pp. 209–11.
6. William Roper, *The lyfe of Sir Thomas Moore, knighte*, ed. J. M. Cline (New York: Swallow, 1950), pp. 32–33.
7. Strauss, *op. cit.*, pp. 50–51.
8. Francis C. Webb, "The Sweating Sickness in England," *Sanitary Review and Journal of Public Health* III (1857):114–15.
9. Hecker, *op. cit.*, pp. 246–47.
10. *Ibid.*, pp. 335–36.
11. *Ibid.*, pp. 257–58.
12. Jhon Caius, *A boke or counseill against the disease commonly called the sweate or sweatyng sicknesse* (London: Richard Grafton, 1552), pp. 7–20 in *The Works of John Caius, M.D.*, ed. E. S. Roberts (Cambridge: The University Press, 1912), pp. 8–19.

9. THE *MORBUS GALLICUS*

1. Shrewsbury, "The Saints and Epidemic Disease," p. 221.
2. Howard N. Simpson, "The Impact of Disease on American History," *The New England Journal of Medicine* CCL (1954):680.

3. *The Medical Works of Francisco López de Villalobos*, trans. George Gaskoin (London: John Churchill and Sons, 1870), p. 76.
4. Ellis Herndon Hudson, "Villalobos and Columbus," *American Journal of Medicine* XXXII (1962):578.
5. *Supra*, note 3, p. 93.
6. Hudson, *op. cit.*, p. 579.
7. *Supra*, note 3, pp. 93–94.
8. *Ibid.*, p. 98.
9. *Ibid.*, pp. 107, 110; Hudson, *op. cit.*, p. 582.
10. Hudson, *op. cit.*, p. 585.
11. Quoted in W. A. Pusey, *The History and Epidemiology of Syphilis* (Springfield, Ill.: Charles C Thomas, 1933), p. 21.
12. Garrison, *An Introduction to the History of Medicine*, p. 190.
13. Quoted in Derek J. Cripps and Arthur C. Curtis, "Syphilis Maligna Praecox," *Archives of Internal Medicine* CXIX (1967):415.
14. Quoted *ibid.*, pp. 415–16.
15. Girolamo Fracastoro, *Syphilis or the French Disease*, trans. Heneage Wynne-Finch (London: William Heinemann Medical Books Ltd., 1935), p. 1.
16. *Ibid.*, p. 17.
17. *Ibid.*, p. 53.
18. *Ibid.*, pp. 55–57.
19. *Ibid.*, p. 135.
20. Hieronymus Fracastorius, *De Contagione et Contagiosis Morbis et Eorum Curatione, Libri III*, trans. Wilmer Cave Wright (New York: G. P. Putnam's Sons, 1930), pp. 277–83.
21. Fracastoro, *supra* note 15, pp. 63, 65, 69, 75, 77.
22. *Ibid.*, pp. 79, 81, 83, 85.
23. *Ibid.*, pp. 115, 117.
24. *Ibid.*, pp. 119, 121, 125, 129.
25. *Ibid.*, pp. 159, 161, 163.
26. *Ibid.*, p. 211.
27. R. S. Morton, "Another Look at the *Morbus Gallicus*," *British Journal of Venereal Diseases* XLIV (1968):176.
28. Hirsch, *Handbook of Geographical and Historical Pathology*, II:92, 99–100.
29. *Ibid.*, pp. 94–95.
30. *Ibid.*, p. 98.
31. Quoted in A. Fessler, "Venereal Disease Phobia in the 17th Century," *British Journal of Venereal Diseases* XXXI (1955):190.
32. Quoted *ibid.*

10. THOMAS SYDENHAM AND
THE EPIDEMIC DISEASES OF THE
SIXTEENTH AND SEVENTEENTH CENTURIES

1. Kenneth Dewhurst, *Dr. Thomas Sydenham (1624–1689), His Life and Original Writings* (Berkeley: University of California Press, 1966), pp. vii–viii.
2. *Ibid.*, p. 15.
3. *Ibid.*, p. 17.
4. Thomas Sydenham, *Tractus de Podagra et Hydrope* (London: G. Kettilby, 1683), p. 148.
5. Dewhurst, *op. cit.*, pp. 30, 60–61.
6. Barbara Gastel, "Measles, A Potentially Finite History," *Journal of the History of Medicine* XXVIII (1973):36; I. J. T. Davies, "Highlights in the history of measles," *Hospital Medicine* I (1967):810–11.
7. E. W. Goodall, *A Short History of the Epidemic Infectious Diseases* (London: John Bale, sons and Danielsson, 1934), pp. 65–66.
8. Dewhurst, *op. cit.*, pp. 102–3.
9. Robert Rosenthal, "The History and Nature of Smallpox," *The Journal-Lancet* LXXIX (1959):498; for the development of inoculation and vaccination, *see* Geoffrey Marks and William K. Beatty, *The Story of Medicine in America* (New York: Charles Scribner's Sons, 1973), pp. 217–33.
10. Dewhurst, *op. cit.*, pp. 123–24.
11. *Ibid.*, p. 55.
12. *Ibid.*, p. 10.
13. For a discussion of possible earlier usage, *see* Saul Jarcho, "A Cartographic and Literary Study of the Word *Malaria*," *Journal of the History of Medicine* XXV (1970):31–39.
14. Horace Walpole, *Private correspondence*, 4 vols. (London: Rodwell and Martin, 1820), I:68.
15. Hirsch, *Handbook of Geographical and Historical Pathology*, I:229.
16. *Ibid.*, pp. 546–47.
17. Fracastorius, *De Contagione*, pp. 101, 103.
18. Hirsch, *op. cit.*, I:548–49.
19. *Ibid.*, pp. 550–51.
20. *Ibid.*, pp. 617–18.
21. Quoted in Charles G. Roland, "Historical Aspects of Diphtheria," *The Manitoba Medical Review* XXXVIII (1958):253.
22. Garrison, *An Introduction to the History of Medicine*, p. 208.
23. *Ibid.*, p. 187; Hirsch, *op. cit.*, I:7–16, 18.
24. Charles F. Mullett, *The Bubonic Plague and England* (Lexington: University of Kentucky Press, 1956), p. 18.

25. J. F. D. Shrewsbury, *A History of Bubonic Plague in the British Isles* (Cambridge: The University Press, 1970), p. 487.
26. M. J. Howell, "The Plague at Eyam," *The Practitioner* CCIII (1969):100–1.
27. Daniel Defoe, *A Journal of the Plague Year* (London: E. Nutt, 1722).
28. Dewhurst, *op. cit.*, p. 31.
29. Nohl, *The Black Death*, pp. 87–88.
30. R. S. Roberts, "The Place of Plague in English History," *Proceedings of the Royal Society of Medicine* LIX (1966):103.
31. William Boghurst, *Loimographia—An Account of the Great Plague of London in the Year 1665*, ed. Joseph Frank Payne (London: Shaw and Sons, 1894), p. vi. (The original manuscript is in the British Museum.)
32. *Ibid.*, p. 1.
33. *Ibid.*, pp. 58–61.
34. Richard, Lord Braybrooke, ed., *Diary and Correspondence of Samuel Pepys, F.R.S.*, 4 vols. (London: Allen & Unwin Ltd., 1929), II:167, 172, 179.
35. *Ibid.*, pp. 181–82, 184, 186–88, 191–92, 195, 198–200, 203–4, 214–16, 221–23, 225, 249–50, 259, 263, 267–68, 272–73, 276, 282, 351, 372–74.

11. THE FRUITS OF EXPLORATION AND COLONIZATION

1. Noah Webster, *A brief history of epidemic and pestilential diseases* (Hartford, Conn.: Hudson & Goodwin, 1799), I:202; Claude Edwin Heaton, "Yellow Fever in New York City," *Bulletin of the Medical Library Association* XXXIV (1946):67; Simon Harcourt-Smith, "Yellow Jack," *History Today* XXIII (1973):618–19; John Duffy, *Epidemics in Colonial America* (Baton Rouge: Louisiana State University Press, 1953), p. 141.
2. Quoted in Duffy, *loc. cit.*
3. *See* Hirsch, *Handbook of Geographical and Historical Pathology*, I:319–21 for epidemics in the West Indies, North and Central America, and the northern coast of South America.
4. M. Foster Farley, "Stranger's Fever In Eighteenth Century Charleston," *Alabama Journal of Medical Science* VI (1969): 201, 203.
5. Gordon W. Jones, "Doctor John Mitchell's Yellow Fever Epidemics," *The Virginia Magazine of History and Biography* LXX (1962):44–46.
6. Duffy, *op. cit.*, p. 151.
7. Edmund Berkeley and Dorothy Smith Berkeley, *Dr. John Mitchell: The*

Man Who Made the Map of North America (Chapel Hill: University of North Carolina, 1974), pp. 72–81.

8. Mathew Carey, *A Short Account of the Malignant Fever, lately prevalent in Philadelphia:* . . . (Philadelphia: Printed by the Author, 1793), pp. 28–29; Benjamin Rush, *An Account of the Bilious remitting Yellow Fever as it appeared in the City of Philadelphia, in the Year 1793,* 2nd ed. (Philadelphia: Thomas Dobson, 1794), pp. 124–25.

9. John B. Blake, "Yellow Fever in Eighteenth Century America," *Bulletin of the New York Academy of Medicine* XLIV (1968):678.

10. Quoted in Herbert E. Klingelhofer, "Philadelphia in Distress," *Manuscripts* XVIII, 2 (1966):22.

11. Blake, *op. cit.,* pp. 678–79.

12. *A Series of Letters and Other Documents relating to the Late Epidemic of Yellow Fever,* . . . (Baltimore: Printed by William Warnen, 1820).

13. John Duffy, "Yellow Fever in the Continental United States during the Nineteenth Century," *Bulletin of the New York Academy of Medicine* XLIV (1968):688.

14. Simpson, "The Impact of Disease on American History," p. 683.

15. Joseph Ioor Waring, "The Yellow Fever Epidemic of Savannah in 1820, . . ." *Georgia Historical Quarterly* LII (1968):399, 402.

16. Gordon W. Jones, "The Year Virginia Mourned: . . ." *Bulletin of the History of Medicine* XXXV (1961):257–58.

17. Thomas H. Baker, "Yellowjack: The Yellow Fever Epidemic of 1878 Memphis, Tennessee," *Bulletin of the History of Medicine* XLII (1968):241.

18. Duffy, *supra,* note 13, p. 695.

19. *A Gazeta,* Rio de Janeiro, March 29, 1903.

20. Henry F. Dobyns, "An Outline of Andean Epidemic History to 1720," *Bulletin of the History of Medicine* XXXVII (1963):496.

21. Alfred W. Crosby, "Conquistador y Pestilencia: The First New World Pandemic and the Fall of the Great Indian Empires," *Hispanic American Historical Review* XLVII (1967):331.

22. Dobyns, *loc. cit.*

23. Crosby, *op. cit.,* pp. 332–33.

24. Dobyns, *op. cit.,* pp. 505, 508.

25. Simpson, *op. cit.,* p. 681.

26. John Duffy, "Social Impact of Disease in the Late Nineteenth Century," *Bulletin of the New York Academy of Medicine* XLVII (1971):797–98.

27. Wyndham B. Blanton, "Epidemics, Real and Imaginary, and Other Factors Influencing Seventeenth Century Virginia's Population," *Bulletin of the History of Medicine* XXXI (1957):454; for a more detailed account of epidemics in the American colonies and the United States, *see* Marks and Beatty, *The Story of Medicine in America,* passim.

28. Gordon W. Jones, "The First Epidemic in English America," *The Virginia Magazine of History and Biography* LXXI (1963): 5, 7; Blanton, *op. cit.*, p. 455; Duffy, *supra*, note 1, p. 223.
29. Jones, *op. cit.*, p. 10.
30. Theodore E. Woodward, "Typhus Verdict in American History," *Transactions of the Americal Clinical and Climatological Association* LXXXII (1970):2.
31. *Ibid.*
32. Duffy, *supra*, note 1, p. 230.
33. Woodward, *op. cit.*, p. 5.
34. Duffy, *supra*, note 1, p. 225.
35. "Latent Killer," *MD Newsmagazine* VII, no. 9 (1963):160.
36. Saul Jarcho, "Cadwallader Colden as a Student of Infectious Disease," *Bulletin of the History of Medicine* XXIX (1955):106.
37. William Osler, "Some Aspects of American Medical Bibliography," *American Medicine* IV (1902):425; Abraham Jacobi, "History of Pediatrics in New York," *Archives of Pediatrics* XXXIV (1917):2.
38. Robert Rosenthal, "An 18th Century American Classic on Diphtheria," *Bio-Medical Library Bulletin (University of Minnesota)*, November 1968, p. 6.
39. *Supra*, note 35, p. 161.
40. Duffy, *supra*, note 26, p. 798.
41. Blanton, *op. cit.*, pp. 459–60; Hirsch, *op. cit.*, I:8; Duffy, *supra*, note 1, pp. 186–89.
42. Richard E. Shope, "Influenza," *Public Health Reports (Washington)* LXXIII (1958):166.
43. Duffy, *supra*, note 1, pp. 214–21.
44. *Ibid.*, pp. 212–14.
45. Simpson, *op. cit.*, p. 683.
46. René J. Dubos, "The Evolution of Infectious Disease in the Course of History," *The Canadian Medical Association Journal* LXXIX (1958):446.
47. Richard K. C. Lee, "Public Health Contrasts in Hawaii, 1859–1953," *Public Health Reports* LXIX (1954):403, 405.
48. *Ibid.*, p. 403.
49. "Hawaiian Health," *MD* III (June 1959), 137–38.
50. R. E. Wright-St Clair, "The impact of infection on a Polynesian community," *The Canadian Medical Association Journal* CX (1974):953.
51. *Ibid.*, pp. 953–54.
52. F. S. Maclean, *Challenge for Health* (Wellington, N.Z.: R. E. Owens, Government Printer, 1964), p. 383.
53. Wright-St Clair, *op. cit.*, p. 956.
54. Hirsch, *op. cit.*, I:333–34.
55. C. J. Roberts, "The Origins of Smallpox in Central Africa," *The Central African Journal of Medicine* XIII (1967):31.

56. *Ibid.*, p. 32.
57. J. Campbell, *Travels in South Africa* (London: Black & Co., 1822), and R. F. Burton, *The Lake Regions of Central Africa* (London: Longmans Green, 1860), quoted *ibid.*, p. 33.
58. Hirsch, *op. cit.*, I:130.
59. *Ibid.*, pp. 198–99.
60. John Atkins, *The Navy-Surgeon: or a Practical System of Surgery* (London: Caesar Ward and Richard Chandler, 1734), Appendix pp. 18–22.
61. T. M. Winterbottom, *An account of the Native Africans in the Neighborhood of Sierra Leone*, 2 vols. (London: John Hatchard, 1803), II:29–30.
62. John J. McKelvey, Jr., *Man Against Tsetse—Struggle for Africa* (Ithaca, N.Y.: Cornell University Press, 1973), pp. 56–58.
63. Hirsch, *op. cit.*, I:508, 627.
64. Donald E. Carey, "Chikungunya and Dengue: A Case of Mistaken Identity?" *Journal of the History of Medicine* XXVI (1971):243–62.
65. Quoted *ibid.*, p. 244.
66. Hirsch, *op. cit.*, I:58.
67. *Ibid.*
68. Benjamin Rush, "An Account of the Bilious Remitting Fever as It Appeared in Philadelphia in the Summer and Autumn of the Year 1780," in *Medical Inquiries and Observations* (Philadelphia: Prichard & Hall, 1789), pp. 92–94, 100.
69. N. Joel Ehrenkranz et al., "Pandemic Dengue in Caribbean Countries and the Southern United States—Past, Present and Potential Problems," *The New England Journal of Medicine* CCLXXXV (1971):1462.
70. Samuel H. Dickson, "Account of dengue as it appeared in Charleston, S.C., during the summer of 1828," *American Journal of the Medical Sciences* III (1828):3–14.
71. Ehrenkranz, *op. cit.*, p. 1467.
72. Albert Sabin, "Research on dengue during World War II," *American Journal of Tropical Medicine and Hygiene* I (1952):40–41.
73. *See* Harald Frederikson, "Historical Evidence for Interference between Dengue and Yellow Fever," *American Journal of Tropical Medicine and Hygiene* IV (1955):484–90.
74. R. N. Chaudhuri, "Tropical Medicine—Past, Present, and Future," *British Medical Journal* II (1954):429.

12. THE TERROR OF CHOLERA

1. L. M. Bhattacharji et al., "Changing Phases of Cholera in India," *Indian Journal of Medical Research* LII (1964):751.
2. *Weekly Epidemiological Record (WHO, Geneva)* XLIX (1974):309.

3. John Parkin, *Are Epidemics Contagious?* (London: Samson Low et al., 1887), p. 97; Hirsch, *Handbook of Geographical and Historical Pathology*, I:394.
4. Bhattacharji, *loc. cit.;* Hirsch, *op. cit.*, I:432–33; Richard Pankhurst, "The History of Cholera in Ethiopia," *Medical History* XII (1968):262.
5. Hirsch, *op. cit.*, I:396.
6. R. E. McGrew, "The First Russian Cholera Epidemic: . . ." *Bulletin of the History of Medicine* XXXVI (1962):221.
7. Phyllis Allen Richmond, "Cholera—Its Impact on Continental Europe," *Bulletin of the Cleveland Medical Library Association* VI (1959):76; George Polgar, "Notes on the History of Medicine in Hungary," *Transactions & Studies of the College of Physicians of Philadelphia*, fourth series, XXXVII (1969):137.
8. Richmond, *op. cit.*, pp. 76–77.
9. Garrison, *An Introduction to the History of Medicine*, pp. 774–75.
10. Hirsch, *op. cit.*, I:398.
11. Quoted in Fraser Brockington, "Public Health at the Privy Council 1831–34," *Journal of the History of Medicine* XVI (April 1961):163–64.
12. *The Cholera Gazette*, . . . (London: S. Higley, 1832), pp. 127–33.
13. Francis Sheppard, *London 1808–1870: The Infernal Wen* (London: Secker & Warburg, 1971), p. 249.
14. Nellie J. Kerling, "St. Bartholomew's and Epidemics in the City of London," *St. Bartholomew's Hospital Journal* LXXV (1971):120–21.
15. Duffy, "Social Impact of Disease in the Late Nineteenth Century," pp. 802–3.
16. *The Cholera Gazette (Philadelphia)* I (1832):64, 189.
17. Charles E. Rosenberg, *The Cholera Years—The United States in 1832, 1849, and 1866* (Chicago: The University of Chicago Press, 1962), pp. 25–26, 25n.
18. *Supra*, note 16, I:32.
19. *Evening Post* (New York), July 3, 1832.
20. Stuart Galishof, "Cholera in Newark, New Jersey," *Journal of the History of Medicine* XXV (1970):441–42.
21. *Supra*, note 16, I:15–16, 31, 47, 80, 94–96, 112, 128, 176, 191.
22. C. A. Hutchinson, "The Asiatic Cholera Epidemic of 1833 in Mexico," *Bulletin of the History of Medicine* XXXII (1958):16–17.
23. Quoted *ibid.*, p. 153.
24. *Ibid.*, p. 160.
25. Norbert Hirschhorn and William B. Greenough III, "Cholera," *Scientific American* CCXXV (1971):15.
26. Quoted in Patrick E. McLear, "The St. Louis Cholera Epidemic of 1849," *Missouri Historical Review* LXIII (1969):181.
27. Abraham M. Gordon, "Cholera in the New World," *Pagina di Storia Della Medicina* XIV, 3 (1970):62.

28. Hirsch, *op. cit.*, I:412.
29. Duffy, *op. cit.*, p. 803.
30. A. M. Kamal, "The Seventh Pandemic of Cholera," in *Cholera*, Dhiman Barua and William Burrows, eds. (Philadelphia: W. B. Saunders Company, 1974), p. 6.
31. Eugene J. Gangarosa and William H. Barker, "Cholera—Implications for the United States," *Journal of the American Medical Association* CCXXVII, no. 2 (January 14, 1974):170–71.

13. HOSPITAL-RELATED EPIDEMICS

1. James Robert Goodall, *Puerperal Infection* (Montreal: Murray Printing Co., 1932), pp. 2–3; *see also* Garrison, *An Introduction to the History of Medicine*, p. 400.
2. Goodall, *op. cit.*, p. 3.
3. Alexander Gordon, *A Treatise on the Epidemic Puerperal Fever of Aberdeen* (London: Printed for G. G. and J. Robinson, 1795), pp. 1–3, 17–21, 55–56, 62–63, 98–99.
4. Leonard Colebrook, "The Story of Puerperal Fever—1800–1950," *British Medical Journal* I (1956):247.
5. Oliver Wendell Holmes, "On the contagiousness of puerperal fever," *New England Quarterly Journal of Medicine and Surgery* I (1842–43): 503–30, reprinted in *Medical Classics* I (1936–37):242–43.
6. Quoted in Herbert Thoms, *Chapters in American Obstetrics* (Springfield, Ill.: Charles C Thomas, 1933), p. 60.
7. William J. Sinclair, *Semmelweis—His Life and his Doctrines* (Manchester, England: The University Press, 1909), pp. 48–49.
8. *Ibid.*, p. 50.
9. *Ibid.*, p. 61.
10. James Y. Simpson, "On the communicability and propagation of puerperal fever," *Monthly Journal of Medical Science, London & Edinburgh* XIII (1851):72–81.
11. S. Selwyn, "Sir James Simpson and Hospital Cross-Infection," *Medical History* IX (1965):241–42.
12. Colebrook, *op. cit.*, p. 248.
13. *Ibid.*, pp. 251–52.
14. Mary Barber, "Hospital Infection yesterday and today," *Journal of Clinical Pathology* XIV (1961):2.
15. Sydney Selwyn, "Changing Patterns in Hospital Infection," *Nursing Times* LXVIII (May 25, 1972):643.
16. H. Taylor Caswell, " 'Typhus of Surgical Wounds' in the War Between the States," *Transactions & Studies of the College of Physicians of Philadelphia*, fourth series, XXX (1962):36–37.

17. Barber, *loc. cit.*
18. James Y. Simpson, "On the analogy between puerperal and surgical fever," *Monthly Journal of Medical Science, London & Edinburgh* XI (1850):414–29.
19. Quotations from Selwyn, *supra*, note 11, p. 242.
20. Barber, *op. cit.*, pp. 2, 9.

14. POLIOMYELITIS AND OTHER EPIDEMIC DISEASES OF THE CENTRAL NERVOUS SYSTEM

1. Arthur Salusbury MacNalty, *Epidemic Diseases of the Central Nervous System* (London: Faber & Gwyer, 1927), p. 1.
2. John R. Paul, *A History of Poliomyelitis* (New Haven, Conn.: Yale University Press, 1971), p. 12.
3. Amin Rida, "A Dissertation from the Early Eighteenth Century, Probably the First Description of Poliomyelitis," *The Journal of Bone and Joint Surgery* XLIVB (1962):735–36.
4. MacArthur, "The Medical Identification of Some Pestilences of the Past," pp. 437–38.
5. For Scott's personal account of his illness (based on what had been told him by his family), *see* John Gibson Lockhart, *Memoirs of the Life of Sir Walter Scott, Bart.* (Boston and New York: Houghton Mifflin, 1901), I:12–17.
6. Quoted in Paul, *op. cit.*, p. 22.
7. Quoted in Stig Cronberg and Ebbe Cronberg, "First Description of a Small Epidemic of Poliomyelitis (1808)," *Journal of the History of Medicine* XX (1965):33.
8. MacNalty, *op. cit.*, p. 101.
9. Paul, *op. cit.*, p. 43.
10. *Ibid.*, p. 32.
11. *Ibid.*, p. 76.
12. James J. Putnam and Edward Wyllys Taylor, "Is Acute Poliomyelitis Unusually Prevalent this Season?" *Boston Medical and Surgical Journal* CXXIX (1893):509–10.
13. Paul, *op. cit.*, p. 79.
14. *Ibid.*, p. 81.
15. MacNalty, *op. cit.*, p. 43.
16. Paul, *op. cit.*, p. 98.
17. A. B. Christie, *Infectious Diseases: Epidemiology and Clinical Practice* (Edinburgh and London: Livingstone, 1969), p. 533.
18. Paul, *op. cit.*, p. 132.
19. *Ibid.*, p. 208n.

20. M. F. Bigler and J. M. Neilson, "Poliomyelitis in Los Angeles in 1934; neurologic characteristics of the disease in adults," *Bulletin of the Los Angeles Neurological Society* II (1937):47–58.
21. For a short account of this development *see* Marks and Beatty, *The Story of Medicine in America*, pp. 286–91.
22. Hirsch, *Handbook of Geographical and Historical Pathology* III:547.
23. *Ibid.*
24. MacNalty, *op. cit.*, p. 36.
25. L. Danielson and E. Mann, "The History of a singular and very mortal Disease, which lately made its appearance in Medfield," *Medical and Agricultural Register* I (1806):65–66, 68–69.
26. Nathan Strong, *An Inaugural Dissertation on the Disease Termed Petechial or Spotted Fever* (Hartford, Conn.: Peter B. Gleason, 1810), p. iv.
27. Reprinted in Elisha North, *A Treatise on a Malignant Epidemic commonly called Spotted Fever* (New York: T. & F. Swords, 1811), p. 139.
28. Frank J. Grady, "Some Early American Reports on Meningitis . . ." *Journal of the History of Medicine* XX (1965):29–30.
29. North, *op. cit.*, p. 10.
30. Hirsch, *op. cit.*, III:562.
31. *Ibid.*, pp. 565–67.
32. William E. Bell and David L. Silber, "Meningococcal Meningitis: Past and Present Concepts," *Military Medicine* CXXXVI (1971):601.
33. *Ibid.*, pp. 601–2.
34. *Ibid.*, p. 609.
35. "Follow-up on Meningococcal Meningitis," *Morbidity and Mortality Weekly Report* XXIII (1974):349–50.
36. Christie, *op. cit.*, p. 604.
37. F. G. Crookshank, "A Note on the History of Epidemic Encephalomyelitis," *Proceedings of the Royal Society of Medicine* XII, 5 (March 1919):1–21.
38. MacNalty, *op. cit.*, p. 143.
39. Quoted in Robert H. Wilkins and Irwin A. Brody, "Encephalitis Lethargica," *Archives of Neurology (Chicago)* XVIII (1968):328.
40. C. von Economo, *Encephalitis Lethargica, its Sequelae and Treatment*, trans. K. O. Newman (London: Oxford University Press, 1931), p. 3.
41. MacNalty, *op. cit.*, p. 149.
42. Wilkins and Brody, *op. cit.*, p. 324.
43. Christie, *op. cit.*, p. 584.
44. C. Alan Phillips and Joseph L. Melnick, "Urban Epidemic Encephalitis in Houston Caused by a Group B Arbovirus (SLE)," *Progress in Medical Virology* IX (1967):162.
45. N. Joel Ehrenkranz and Arnold K. Ventura, "Venezuelan Equine Encephalitis Virus Infection in Man," *Annual Review of Medicine* XXV (1974):11–12.

15. BUBONIC PLAGUE—FROM LONDON TO SAN FRANCISCO

1. Hirsch, *Handbook of Geographical and Historical Pathology*, I:500–2.
2. Jean-Baptiste Bertrand, *A Historical Relation of the Plague at Marseilles in the year 1720*, trans. Anne Plumptre (London: Joseph Mawman, 1805), pp. 97–99.
3. *Ibid.*, p. 247.
4. Patrick Russell, *A Treatise of the Plague* (London: G. G. and J. Robinson, 1791), 79n[5].
5. H. Burton Forman, ed., *Letters of Edward John Trelawney* (Oxford: Oxford University Press, 1910), p. 4.
6. Quoted in Paul Cassar, "Slitting of Letters for Disinfection in the Eighteenth Century in Malta," *British Medical Journal* I (1967):106.
7. *Ibid.*
8. Paul Cassar, "Documents Written on Wood during the Plague of 1813 in Malta," *British Medical Journal* II (1961):377.
9. William N. Boog Watson, "The Plague of HMS 'Theseus,' Jaffa, 1799," *Journal of the Royal Naval Medical Service* LVI (1970):261, 264.
10. William N. Boog Watson, "A Naval Surgeon's Encounter with the Plague Suez 1801," *Journal of the Royal Naval Medical Service* LII (1966):158.
11. Quoted *ibid.*, pp. 161–63.
12. Quoted in Watson, *supra*, note 9, p. 261n.
13. W. J. Simpson, *A Treatise on Plague* (Cambridge: The University Press, 1905), Part I:74–75.
14. Victor C. Vaughan, "Are we in Danger from the Plague?" *Appletons' Popular Science Monthly* LV (1899):577, 591.
15. Quoted in Silvio J. Onesti, Jr., "Plague, Press, and Politics," *Stanford Medical Bulletin* XIII (1955):7.
16. Quoted in Loren George Lipson, "Plague in San Francisco in 1900," *Annals of Internal Medicine* LXXVII (1971):309.
17. W. H. Kellogg, "Present Status of Plague, with Historical Review," *American Journal of Public Health* X (1920):842.
18. Frank Morton Todd, ed., *Eradicating Plague from San Francisco* (San Francisco: Citizens' Health Committee, 1909), p. 9.
19. *Ibid.*, p. 10.
20. Arthur J. Viseltear, "The Pneumonic Plague Epidemic of 1924 in Los Angeles," *Yale Journal of Biology and Medicine* XLVII (1974):41.
21. *Statistical Bulletin, Metropolitan Life* LV (August 1974):6–8.

16. THE RICKETTSIAL DISEASES

1. William K. Beatty and Virginia Beatty, "Northwestern's Medical Martyr—Howard Taylor Ricketts," *Northwestern University Medical School Magazine* XI (Winter 1973):13.
2. Hans Zinsser, *Rats, Lice and History* (Boston: Little, Brown and Company, 1935 [reprinted 1940]), pp. vii, 282–86.
3. Prinzing, *Epidemics Resulting from Wars*, pp. 116–64.
4. Richard P. Strong, *Typhus Fever with Particular Reference to the Serbian Epidemic* (Cambridge, Mass.: Harvard, 1920), p. 3.
5. Zinsser, *op. cit.*, pp. 298–99.
6. Manabu Sasa, "A Historical Review of the Progress in Studies of Tsutsugamushi in Japan," *Acta Medica et Biologica (Niigata)* XV Suppl. (1967):9.
7. *Ibid.*, p. 10.
8. *Ibid.*, p. 9.
9. Bettina B. Wentworth, "Historical Review of the Literature of Q Fever," *Bacteriological Reviews* XIX (1955):129.

17. INFLUENZA—MODERN STYLE

1. A. A. Hoehling, *The Great Epidemic* (Boston: Little, Brown and Company, 1961), p. 5; Fred B. Rogers, "The Influenza Pandemic of 1918–1919 in the Perspective of a Half Century," *American Journal of Public Health* LVIII (1968):2192; "Medicine's Living History (Flu Pandemic)," *Medical World News* XV (March 8, 1974):43.
2. Shope, "Influenza," pp. 168–69.
3. Hoehling, *op. cit.*, pp. 13–16.
4. Rogers, *loc. cit.*
5. Francis Russell, "A Journal of the Plague: The 1918 Influenza," *Yale Review* XLVII (1958):219.
6. Hoehling, *op. cit.*, pp. 8–9.
7. Russell, *loc. cit.*
8. Henry A. Davidson, "New Jersey and the Great Pandemic," *The Journal of the Medical Society of New Jersey* LIV (1957):391.
9. Stuart Galishoff, "Newark and the Great Influenza Pandemic of 1918," *Bulletin of the History of Medicine* XLIII (1969):249.
10. Robert N. Philip and John E. Gordon, "The Impact of Influenza on Human Populations," *Indian Journal of Child Health* III (1954):533.
11. *Ibid.*
12. Hoehling, *op. cit.*, pp. 109–11.
13. Frank MacFarlane Burnet, *The Virus and the Cell* (Washington: Govern-

ment Printing Office, 1952—Public Health Service Publication No. 328), p. 20.
14. Charles H. Stuart-Harris, "Pandemic Influenza: An Unresolved Problem in Prevention," *The Journal of Infectious Diseases* CXXII (1970):108.
15. Marks and Beatty, *The Story of Medicine in America*, p. 255.

18. THE CONTINUING SCENE

1. Ambrose King, " 'These Dying Diseases'—Venereology in Decline?" *Lancet* I (1958):651.
2. Walter Modell, "Malaria and Victory in Vietnam," *Science* CLXII (1968):1347.
3. Richard W. Goodgame and William B. Greenough, "Cholera in Africa: A Message for the West," *Annals of Internal Medicine* LXXXII (1975):101–6.
4. M. F. Polak, "Smallpox Control in Indonesia During the Second Quarter of the Century and Re-establishment of Endemic Smallpox from 1947," *Tropical and Geographical Medicine* XX (1968):243–50.
5. Herbert A. Schreier, "On the Failure to Eradicate Measles," *The New England Journal of Medicine* CCXC (1974):803–4.
6. "Measles in the United States," *Statistical Bulletin, Metropolitan Life* LV (1974):6–10.
7. A. M. Geddes, "Undiagnosed Fever—Rickettsial, Viral, and Helminth," *British Medical Journal* IV (1974):455; Bernard Dixon, "Lassa—what are the lessons?" *New Scientist* LXV (1975):250.
8. "An Outbreak of Psychosomatic Illness in an Elementary School," *Morbidity and Mortality Weekly Report* XXIII (1974):186, 191.
9. Robert H. Moser, ed., *Diseases of Medical Progress: A Study of Iatrogenic Disease*, 3rd ed. (Springfield, Ill.: Charles C Thomas, 1969).
10. T. L. Terry, "Extreme and fibroblastic overgrowth of persistent vascular sheath behind each crystalline lens. I. Preliminary report," *American Journal of Ophthalmology* XXV (1942):203–4.
11. V. Everett Kinsey and Leona Zacharias, "Retrolental Fibroplasia," *Journal of the American Medical Association* CXXXIX (1949):572–78; Arnall Patz, Leroy E. Hoeck, and Edgar De La Cruz, "Studies on Effects of High Oxygen Administration in Retrolental Fibroplasia," *American Journal of Ophthalmology* XXXV (1952):1248–53; V. Everett Kinsey, "Retrolental Fibroplasia," *A.M.A. Archives of Ophthalmology* LVI (1958):482–529.
12. David Harris, Pascal James Imperato, and Barry Oken, "Dog Bites—An Unrecognized Epidemic," *Bulletin of the New York Academy of Medicine* L (1974):981–1000.

SELECTED BIBLIOGRAPHY

Adams, Francis. *The Genuine Works of Hippocrates.* 2 vols. in 1. New York: William Wood & Company, 1929.

Bascombe, Edward. *A History of Epidemic Pestilences.* London: John Churchill, 1851.

Beatty, William K., and Beatty, Virginia. "Northwestern's Medical Martyr—Howard Taylor Ricketts," *Northwestern University Medical School Magazine* XI (Winter 1973):10–13.

Blake, John B. "Yellow Fever in Eighteenth Century America," *Bulletin of the New York Academy of Medicine* XLIV (1968):673–86.

Boak, Arthur E. R. *A History of Rome to 565 A.D.* 3rd ed. New York: The Macmillan Company, 1947.

Carey, Mathew. *A Short Account of the Malignant Fever, lately prevalent in Philadelphia: . . .* Philadelphia: Printed by the Author, 1793.

Caulfield, Ernest. "A History of the Terrible Epidemic, Vulgarly Called the Throat Distemper, As It Occurred in His Majesty's New England Colonies Between 1735 and 1740," *Yale Journal of Biology and Medicine* XI (1938–39):219–72, 277–335.

Collier, Richard. *The Plague of the Spanish Lady.* New York: Atheneum, 1974.

Creighton, Charles. *A History of Epidemics in Britain.* Cambridge: At the University Press, 1891, 1894. (Reprinted with additions, New York: Barnes & Noble, Inc., 1965.)

Crosby, Alfred W. "Conquistador y Pestilencia: The First New World Pandemic and the Fall of the Great Indian Empires," *Hispanic American Historical Review* XLVII (1967):321–37.

Deaux, George. *The Black Death 1347.* New York: Weybright and Talley, 1969.

Defoe, Daniel. *A Journal of the Plague Year.* London: E. Nutt, 1722.

Derbes, Vincent J. "De Mussis and the Great Plague of 1348," *Journal of the American Medical Association* CXCVI (1966):59–62.

Dewhurst, Kenneth. *Dr. Thomas Sydenham (1624–1689), His Life and Original Writings.* Berkeley: University of California Press, 1966.

Dobyns, Henry F. "An Outline of Andean Epidemic History to 1720," *Bulletin of the History of Medicine* XXXVII (1963):493–515.

Duffy, John. *Epidemics in Colonial America.* Baton Rouge: Louisiana State University Press, 1953.

———. *Sword of Pestilence; The New Orleans Yellow Fever Epidemic of 1853.* Baton Rouge: Louisiana State University Press, 1966.

Ehrenkranz, N. Joel et al. "Pandemic Dengue in Caribbean Countries and the Southern United States—Past, Present and Potential Problems," *The New England Journal of Medicine* CCLXXXV (1971):1460–69.

Fleming, William L. "Syphilis Through the Ages," *Medical Clinics of North America* XVIII (1964):587–612.

Hecker, J. F. C. *The Epidemics of the Middle Ages.* Translated by B. G. Babington. London: The Sydenham Society, 1844.

Helmuth, J. Henry C. *A Short Account of the Yellow Fever in Philadelphia for the Reflecting Christian.* Translated from the German by Charles Erdmann. Philadelphia: Printed by Jones, Hoff & Derrick, 1794.

Hirsch, August. *Handbook of Geographical and Historical Pathology.* Translated by Charles Creighton. 3 vols. London: The New Sydenham Society, 1883–86.

Hoehling, A. A. *The Great Epidemic.* Boston: Little, Brown and Company, 1961.

Howe, Alexander Hamilton. *A Theoretical Inquiry into the Physical Cause of Epidemic Diseases.* London: John Churchill & Sons, 1865.

Hudson, Ellis Herndon. "Christopher Columbus and the History of Syphilis," *Acta Tropica (Basel)* XXV (1968):1–15.

Jones, William Henry Samuel. *Malaria, a Neglected Factor in the History of Greece and Rome.* Cambridge: Macmillan & Bowes, 1907.

MacArthur, William. "The Medical Identification of Some Pestilences of the Past," *Transactions of the Royal Society of Tropical Medicine and Hygiene* LIII (1959):423–39.

McGrew, Roderick E. *Russia and the Cholera, 1823–1832.* Madison: University of Wisconsin Press, 1965.

McKelvey, John J., Jr. *Man Against Tsetse—Struggle for Africa.* Ithaca, N.Y.: Cornell University Press, 1973.

MacNalty, Arthur Salusbury. *Epidemic Diseases of the Central Nervous System.* London: Faber & Gwyer, 1927.

Marks, Geoffrey. *The Medieval Plague.* New York: Doubleday & Company Inc., 1971.

Marks, Geoffrey, and Beatty, William K. *The Story of Medicine in America.* New York: Charles Scribner's Sons, 1973.

Mead, Richard. *A Discourse on the Small Pox and Measles, To which is annexed A Treatise on the same Diseases, by the celebrated* Arabian *Physician* Abubeker Rhazes. London: Printed for John Brindley, 1748.

Moore, James. *The History of Small Pox.* London: Printed for Longman, Hurst, Rees, Orme, and Brown, 1815.

Mullett, Charles F. *The Bubonic Plague and England.* Lexington: University of Kentucky Press, 1958.

Nohl, Johannes. *The Black Death.* Translated by C. H. Clarke. London: George Allen & Unwin Ltd., 1926.

Paul, John R. *A History of Poliomyelitis.* New Haven, Conn.: Yale University Press, 1971.

Prinzing, Friedrich. *Epidemics Resulting from Wars.* Edited by Harald Westergaard. Oxford: The Clarendon Press, 1916.

Rosenberg, Charles E. *The Cholera Years—The United States in 1832, 1849, and 1866.* Chicago: The University of Chicago Press, 1962.

Rush, Benjamin. *An Account of the Bilious remitting Yellow Fever as it appeared in the City of Philadelphia, in the Year 1793,* 2nd ed. Philadelphia: Thomas Dobson, 1794.

Russell, Josiah C. "That Earlier Plague," *Demography* V (1968):179–84.

Shaw, Manley Bradford. "A Short History of the Sweating Sickness," *Annals of Medical History,* n.s. V (1933):246–74.

Shope, Richard E. "Influenza," *Public Health Reports (Washington)* LXXIII (1958):165–78.

Shrewsbury, J. F. D. "The Saints and Epidemic Disease," *Birmingham Medical Review* XIX (1956):209–24.

Siegel, Rudolph E. "Epidemics and Infectious Diseases at the Time of Hippocrates. Their Relation to Modern Accounts," *Gesnerus* XVII (1960):77–98.

Sigerist, Henry E. *Civilization and Disease.* Ithaca, N.Y.: Cornell University Press, 1943.

Sinclair, William J. *Semmelweis—His Life and his Doctrines.* Manchester, England: The University Press, 1909.

Stevenson, Lloyd. " 'New Diseases' in the Seventeenth Century," *Bulletin of the History of Medicine* XXXIX (1965):1–21.

Walford, Cornelius. *A Statistical Chronology of Plagues and Pestilences as affecting Human Life.* London: Harrison and Sons, 1884.

Webster, Noah. *A brief history of epidemic and pestilential diseases.* Hartford, Conn.: Hudson & Goodwin, 1799.

Winslow, Charles-Edward Amory. *Man and Epidemics.* Princeton, N.J.: Princeton University Press, 1952.

————. *The Conquest of Epidemic Disease.* Princeton, N.J.: Princeton University Press, 1943.

Ziegler, Philip. *The Black Death.* New York: The John Day Company, 1969.

Zinsser, Hans. *Rats, Lice and History.* Boston: Little, Brown and Company, 1935 (reprinted 1940).

ILLUSTRATION CREDITS

1. Sutherland, C. H. V. *Art in Coinage: The Aesthetics of Money from Greece to the Present Day.* New York, Philosophical Library, 1956. Figure 54.
2. Badt, Kurt. *Die Kunst des Nicolas Poussin.* Cologne, Verlag M. DuMont Schauberg, 1969. Plate 86.
3. Dumesnil, Rene. *Histoire Illustree de la Medecine.* Paris, Librairie Plon, 1935. Page 133.
4. Sigerist, Henry E. *Civilization and Disease.* Ithaca, New York, Cornell University Press, 1944. Plate 16.
5. Sigerist, Henry E. *Civilization and Disease.* Ithaca, New York, Cornell University Press, 1944. Plate 36.
6. Grünpeck, Joseph. "Tractatus de Pestilentiali Scorra." 1496. In: Sudhoff, Karl, ed. *Zehn Syphilis-Drucke aus den Jahren 1495–1498.* Mailand, R. Lier, 1924. Page xxii.
7. Dumesnil, Rene. *Histoire Illustree de la Medecine.* Paris, Librairie Plon, 1935. Illustration facing page 126.
8. Northwestern University Medical School Library Portrait File.
9. Northwestern University Medical School Library Portrait File.
10. *Thomae Bartholini Historiarum Anatomicarum & Medicarum Rariorum, Centuria V. & VI.* Hafniae, Petri Hauboldi, 1661. Illustration facing page 143.
11. Rida, Amin. "A Dissertation from the Early Eighteenth Century, Probably the First Description of Poliomyelitis." *Journal of Bone and Joint Surgery* 44B:735, 1962.
12. *The Laboratory* (Fisher) 19 (1):6, (1949).
13. Northwestern University Medical School Library Portrait File.
14. Holländer, Eugen. *Die Karikatur und Satire in der Medizin.* Second edition. Stuttgart, Enke, 1921. Figure 85.
15. Williams, Ralph Chester. *The United States Public Health Service, 1798–1950.* Washington, Commissioned Officers Association of the U.S. Public Health Service, 1951. Illustration facing page 129.
16. Kellogg, W. H. "Present Status of Plague, With Historical Review." *American Journal of Public Health* 10:836, 1920.

INDEX

Aachen, 92
Aaron, 4-6
Aaron of Alexandria, 54
Aberdeen, 215
Abiram, 6
Abrahah, 59-60
Abydos, 18
Achilles, 7
Acre, 68, 252
Aesculapius, 34-36, 81
Aëtius of Amida, 138
Afghanistan, 194, 209-210
Africa, 44, 48, 61, 67, 115, 149, 178-183, 187, 191, 193, 209, 211, 241, 256, 267, 270-271, 274, 279
Agamemnon, 7
Agrigentum, 33
Aix-la-Chapelle, 94, 249
Alabama, 234, 239, 272, 280
Alaric the Visigoth, 132-133
Albany, N.Y., 171, 201
Albert, Duke of Austria, 90
Alexander VI, 112-113
Alexander (the Great), 58, 132
Alexandria, 38, 45, 59-60, 148, 196, 252
Algiers, 209
Alviano, 115
America, 109, 123, 156, 193, 255, 257-258, 264, 272, 277; Central, 67, 116, 149-150, 162, 181, 187, 208-209, 245-246, 279; North, 67, 150, 152, 166-167, 170-171, 173, 200, 242, 256, 271; South, 67, 149, 160, 162, 166, 170, 181, 209, 244-246, 256, 267, 271, 278
amnesia, 26
Amsterdam, 105

Ancona, 135
Andrewes, Christopher H., 275
Androis, Enrique, 205-206
Annapolis, 166
Antalya, 68
Antilles, Lesser, 188
Antioch, 68
Antonius Puis, 36
Antwerp, 105
Apollo, 7-8, 120-121
Apulia, 96
Arabia (Arabians), 12, 59-61, 148, 193, 196
Archidamus, 20
arc of God, 8, 10
Arcot, 192
Aredius, 64
Aretaeus, 137-138
Argentina, 159, 274
Arles, 51
Armstadt, 94
Asclepiades of Bithynia, 138
Ashdod, 8
Asia, 72, 74, 115, 174, 187, 191-192, 209-210, 246, 256, 267, 273
Astrakan, 193, 211
Athens (Athenians), 19-20, 23-24, 26-27, 32
Atkins, John, 181
Attica, 20
Augsburg, 104
Augusta, 187
Austin, 188
Australia, 176-178, 189, 233, 236, 246, 255-256, 267, 269
Austrechild, 64
Austria (Austrians), 75, 115, 135, 195, 236, 248, 265